The New York Times
Expect the World®

BRIDGE

W9-DAI-761

Catalog No. Q207

Published by Pomegranate Communications, Inc.
Box 808022, Petaluma, California 94975

© 2004 The New York Times Company

Available in Canada from Canadian Manda Group
One Atlantic Avenue #105, Toronto, Ontario M6K 3E7

Available in the U.K. and mainland Europe from Pomegranate Europe Ltd.
Unit 1, Heathcote Business Centre, Hurlbutt Road, Warwick, Warwickshire CV34 6TD, U.K.

Available in Australia from Hardie Grant Books, 12 Claremont Street, South Yarra, Victoria 3141

Available in New Zealand from Southern Publishers Group, P.O. Box 8360, Symonds Street, Auckland

Available in Asia (including the Middle East), Africa, and Latin America from
Pomegranate International Sales, 113 Babcombe Drive, Thornhill, Ontario L3T 1M9, Canada

Pomegranate also publishes the 2005 calendars *New York City: Photographs, History and Headlines from The New York Times*; *The New York Times Crossword Puzzles*; and *The New York Times Sunday Crossword Puzzles*, as well as a book of postcards, *New York City: Photographs from The New York Times*, and three decks of *Headlines from The New York Times Knowledge Cards™, Sports, World War II*, and *World Events of the 20th Century*. Our products and publications include many other calendars in several formats, books, posters, postcards, notecards and boxed notecard sets, magnets, mousepads, birthday books, journals, address books, screen savers, stationery ensembles, and bookmarks. For more information or to place an order, please contact Pomegranate Communications, Inc.: 800-227-1428; www.pomegranate.com.

For other *New York Times* products, visit www.nytstore.com.
The New York Times® is a registered trademark of The New York Times Company.

Designed by Mariah Lander

Dates in color indicate federal holidays.

All astronomical data supplied in this calendar are expressed in Greenwich Mean Time (GMT). Moon phases and American, Canadian, and U.K. holidays are noted.

● NEW MOON   ◐ FIRST QUARTER   ○ FULL MOON   ◑ LAST QUARTER

2005 ENGAGEMENT CALENDAR

THE PLAYER OF THE YEAR MAKES A SLAM

Alan Truscott 01/5/02

NORTH
- ♠ A 8 7 3
- ♥ A 4 2
- ♦ K 6 4
- ♣ J 5 3

WEST
- ♠ 10 6 2
- ♥ Q J 10 8 7 5
- ♦ 7
- ♣ 10 6 4

EAST
- ♠ K J 9 4
- ♥ K 9 6
- ♦ Q J 8 5 2
- ♣ 2

SOUTH (D)
- ♠ Q 5
- ♥ 3
- ♦ A 10 9 3
- ♣ A K Q 9 8 7

Both sides were vulnerable. The bidding:

South	West	North	East
1 ♣	Pass	1 ♠	Pass
2 ♦	Pass	3 ♣	Pass
3 ♦	Pass	3 ♥	Pass
3 ♠	Pass	4 ♦	Pass
4 ♥	Pass	4 ♠	Pass
5 ♣	Pass	6 ♣	Pass
Pass	Pass	Pass	

West led the heart queen.

The calendar year in New York City always begins with the nomination of the Player of the Year for the previous 12 months. The 2002 title went to Chris Willenken, who at 26 was the youngest-ever winner. Contributing to that success was the diagramed deal, in which he and his teammates produced one of the greatest come-from-behind victories in New York bridge history: A half-time deficit of 52 imps in a Grand National Teams match was erased.

Willenken was South, playing with Sam Lev. Both players fell in love with the location of their high cards, and the result was an optimistic six-club contract in which the opening lead was highly significant. As West, what would you have led?

West decided that a diamond lead was unlikely to generate a ruff, and he did not wish to risk damaging the defense by leading the opener's side-suit. He therefore chose the safe heart queen, and South won with dummy's ace.

Willenken drew trumps ending in dummy and led a low spade. East took his king and returned a heart, as good as anything. South ruffed, cashed the spade queen, and played his remaining trumps. This squeezed East in spades and diamonds, so the slam was made.

Curiously, the diamond lead that West rejected would have given the declarer a lot of trouble. It would not, indeed, have produced a ruff, but it would have attacked South's communications.

Suppose that South wins an opening diamond lead with dummy's king, draws trumps as before, and leads a low spade. East takes his king and returns a heart — preferably the king to guard against a singleton queen in the closed hand. South is then cut off from the dummy and cannot even score two spade tricks.

Suppose, however, that South wins a diamond lead with the ace over East's jack. Drawing trumps, ending in dummy, and leading a low spade will now fail. The declarer must instead play five trump winners. East is forced to throw hearts and the position is:

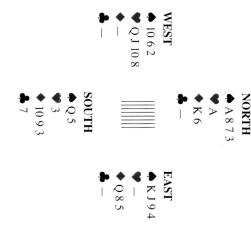

NORTH
- ♠ A 8 7 3
- ♥ A
- ♦ K 6
- ♣ —

WEST
- ♠ 10 6 2
- ♥ Q J 10 8
- ♦ —
- ♣ —

EAST
- ♠ K J 9 4
- ♥ —
- ♦ Q 8 5
- ♣ —

SOUTH
- ♠ Q 5
- ♥ 3
- ♦ 10 9 3
- ♣ 7

DEC ♠ JAN

monday
27
₃₆₂

tuesday
28
₃₆₃

wednesday
29
₃₆₄

thursday
30
₃₆₅

friday
31
₃₆₆

saturday
1
₁

NEW YEAR'S DAY

sunday
2
₂

The New York Times

Leading the last trump at this point squeezes the dummy fatally, but a heart to the ace ruins East. Whatever suit he discards South will play with decisive effect. It is not certain, of course, that Willenken would have found this line if put to the test, but in his role as Player of the Year he must be given the benefit of the doubt.

s	m	t	w	t	f	s
						1
2	3	4	5	6	7	8
9	10	11	12	13	14	15
16	17	18	19	20	21	22
23	24	25	26	27	28	29
30	31					

JANUARY

♠ ROMANIA WINS WORLD TITLES, UNEXPECTEDLY

Alan Truscott 1/10/02

```
                    NORTH
                    ♠ —
                    ♥ A Q 8 7 3
                    ♦ A Q 10 8 3
                    ♣ 6 5 4
WEST (D)                                    EAST
♠ A J 7 2        ▦▦▦▦▦                     ♠ 10 9
♥ 4 2                                       ♥ 10 9 6 5
♦ K 9                                       ♦ 7 6 5 4
♣ A Q 10 8 3                                ♣ J 9 7
                    SOUTH
                    ♠ K Q 8 6 5 4 3
                    ♥ K J
                    ♦ J 2
                    ♣ K 2
```

Neither side was vulnerable. The bidding:

West	North	East	South
1 N.T.	2 ♥	Pass	3 ♠
Pass	4 ♠	Pass	Pass
Pass			

West led the heart four.

Some countries have little opportunity to win major international titles because economic circumstances make it difficult for their players to travel. One of these is Romania, which has, however, taken full advantage of the opportunity to play on the Internet. Three years ago, four of its players, Dorin Petra Musat, Serban Criscota, Alexandre Feber and Catalin Popescu, calling themselves Romanian Beauty, won the third OKbridge Internet World Championship without moving outside their homes. A year earlier they had captured the same title, but on that occasion they had to travel to Birmingham, Ala., to contest the final. On both occasions, the Romanians overcame strong American opposition to take the title.

On the diagramed deal from the 2002 final, Popescu opened the West hand with one no-trump and North overcalled two hearts, promising hearts and a minor.

South indicated a very strong suit and a strong hand by jumping to three spades with the South hand. Showing great faith, North continued to four spades. A bid of four diamonds would have allowed South to try four hearts, reaching an unbeatable game.

Against four spades, West opened a heart and South won with the king. The diamond jack was led, and covered with the king and ace. The diamond winners were played, for a club discard, but West was able to ruff the third round. The club ace was cashed, and the queen was continued. South ruffed and tried a low spade, allowing for the possibility that West had begun with a doubleton ace. East won with the nine, and the play of a diamond would now have promoted an extra trump trick for West. But East led a club, and South escaped for down one.

Notice that South's trumps were not strong enough, by a hair, Trade South's six for West's seven, and the game could have been made by leading a top spade at the second trick. The declarer would lose two trump tricks and one club, but nothing more.

In the replay the Romanian South, Criscota, was highly cautious. He bid just three hearts after an opening bid of one one club and an overcall of two no-trump, showing the red suits, by Musat. Again a heart was opened, and South won. He led the spade king and allowed West to win with the ace, discarding a club from the dummy.

Another trump lead was won in the closed hand, and the spade queen was cashed, for a second club discard. Now South led the diamond jack, covered with the king and won with the ace. Trumps were drawn and 11 tricks were made, thanks to the fall of the diamond nine from West.

So Romania gained 6 imps en route to victory. The moral seems to be that with a choice of trump suits, internal solidity is often the vital factor.

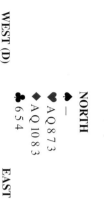

JANUARY

monday 3	BANK HOLIDAY (U.K.)
tuesday 4	BANK HOLIDAY (SCOTLAND)
wednesday 5	
thursday 6	
friday 7	
saturday 8	
sunday 9	

◆ LIGHTNER BACKFIRES AGAIN, 70 YEARS LATER

Alan Truscott 1/12/02

NORTH
♠ A 8 3
♥ A J 9
♦ 9 8 6
♣ A 10 7 4

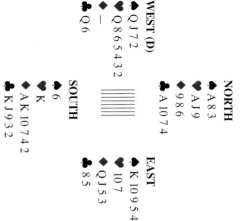

WEST (D)
♠ Q J 7 2
♥ Q 8 6 5 4 3 2
♦ —
♣ Q 6

EAST
♠ K 10 9 5 4
♥ 10 7
♦ Q J 5 3
♣ 8 5

SOUTH
♠ 6
♥ K
♦ A K 10 7 4 2
♣ K J 9 3 2

Both sides were vulnerable. The bidding:

West	North	East	South
Pass	1♣	Pass	1♦
Dbl.	Redbl.	3♠	4♣
4♥	4♠	Pass	4 N.T.
Pass	5♦	Pass	5♥
Pass	6♣	Pass	7♣
Dbl.	7♦	Pass	7 N.T.
Pass	Pass	Pass	

West led the spade queen.

At the dawn of contract bridge, some seven decades ago, a great player had a great idea. Theodore Lightner suggested that a double of a slam should ask partner to make a non-obvious lead. This often helps the defenders uncover a crucial ruff. Unfortunately for Lightner, the first time he used it a disaster ensued and his partner, Ely Culbertson, indignantly refused to have anything more to do with this sensible suggestion.

The international bridge community soon adopted the Lightner double, but deals that support Culbertson's view occur occasionally. Consider what happened to East-West on the diagramed deal played in a match in the Von Zedwitz Double Knockout Championship.

North and South were Linda Gordon and Sylvia Moss, a new partnership. They had not specifically agreed the meaning of a redouble when a one-diamond response to one club is doubled. Traditionally, this simply shows a strong hand, but the modern interpretation is three-card support for responder's suit.

The result was some confusion. North made an aggressive cue-bid of four spades, causing her partner to expect a strong hand. South charged on with Blackwood, received a response of five diamonds showing three key cards, and eventually bid a grand slam.

Seven clubs is highly optimistic, needing good fortune in both minor suits. It was about to fail, barring double-dummy play in diamonds after a non-diamond lead, but West came to the rescue with a Lightner double. He knew that a diamond lead would defeat seven clubs and wanted his partner to be aware of this. Unfortunately for him, South decoded the message and retreated to seven no-trump.

This contract would have been no bargain in normal circumstances, but South now knew the diamond position—the double had given away West's void. So, after winning the opening spade lead in dummy, South led the diamond nine and finessed. When this won, and West discarded, it was an easy matter to continue that suit and neutralize East's honors. It was still necessary to locate the club queen and South succeeded, making her improbable grand slam.

In the replay, the contract was a more rational six clubs by North. Since West had bid hearts, the declarer misguessed the trumps and lost a trick to the queen. With no clue to the diamonds, he later made the normal play of the ace and had to lose a trick in that suit too for down one.

This was a gain of 20 imps for Moss and Gordon, a very rare number. One could play a bridge lifetime without recording such a score.

JANUARY

monday
10
○ 10

tuesday
11
11

wednesday
12
12

thursday
13
13

friday
14
14

saturday
15
15

MARTIN LUTHER KING JR.'S BIRTHDAY

sunday
16
16

The New York Times

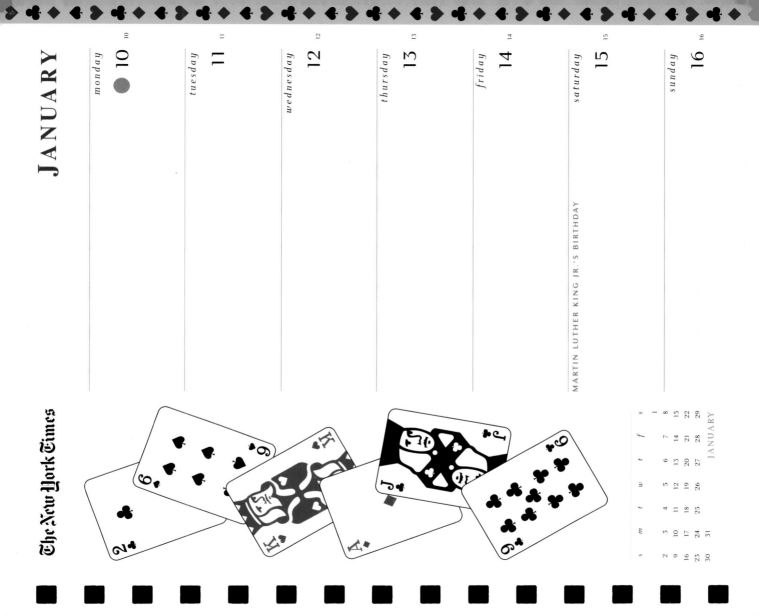

s	m	t	w	t	f	s
						1
2	3	4	5	6	7	8
9	10	11	12	13	14	15
16	17	18	19	20	21	22
23	24	25	26	27	28	29
30	31					

JANUARY

THE WORLD AUTHORITY ON SUIT COMBINATIONS
Alan Truscott 1/17/02

Three years ago, Jean-Marc Roudinesco, the world authority on suit combinations, died in France, the country he represented with distinction on many occasions. His master work, "The Dictionary of Suit Combinations," published in 1995, gave detailed analyses of every significant possibility, with percentage calculations that took into account the information available about lengths in other suits. He was twice a European Champion, and was a runner-up in the Bermuda Bowl world championship in 1971. In the diagramed deal, played in a French selection match in 1969, he sat South.

His six-heart contract would have been a strong favorite to make with a normal division of dummy's club suit. But West led the club four, a bird of ill omen.

Both sides were vulnerable. The bidding:

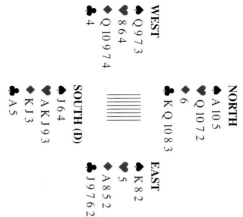

NORTH
♠ A 10 5
♥ Q 10 7 2
♦ 6
♣ K Q 10 8 3

WEST
♠ Q 9 7 3
♥ 8 6 4
♦ Q 10 9 7 4
♣ 4

EAST
♠ K 8 2
♥ 5
♦ A 8 5 2
♣ J 9 7 6 2

SOUTH (D)
♠ J 6 4
♥ A K J 9 3
♦ K J 3
♣ A 5

South	West	North	East
1 ♥	Pass	2 ♣	Pass
3 ♥	Pass	3 ♠	Pass
3 N.T.	Pass	4 N.T.	Pass
5 ♥	Pass	6 ♥	Pass
Pass	Pass		

West led the club four.

Now South needed a little help and got it. He won with the club ace and drew trumps ending in dummy. He then led the singleton diamond from dummy, and East would have prevailed if he had snatched his ace: There would have been no way for South to avoid a spade loser.

But East played low smoothly, which is often the right move in this situation. It prevents the declarer from making two tricks with a holding headed by the K-Q, and may induce a misguess with K-Q-10 or K-J-x. Here it was fatal, because East had parted with a spade and a diamond on the earlier heart plays.

South put up the king, realizing that this was his best chance: Playing the jack and forcing the ace would still leave him with a diamond loser. Now the position was this:

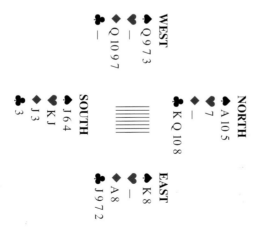

NORTH
♠ A 10 5
♥ —
♦ 7
♣ K Q 10 8

WEST
♠ Q 9 7 3
♥ —
♦ Q 10 9 7
♣ —

EAST
♠ K 8
♥ —
♦ A 8
♣ J 9 7 2

SOUTH
♠ J 6 4
♥ —
♦ K J
♣ 3

South judged that West held spade length and did not have a king-queen combination, which he would have led. Roudinesco played a club to dummy's queen, and was not surprised when West discarded. He led a low spade from the dummy, and East put up the king.

South now made his slam by taking a spade finesse later. If East had played low on the spade lead, Roudinesco would have played the ace later to drop the king.

JANUARY

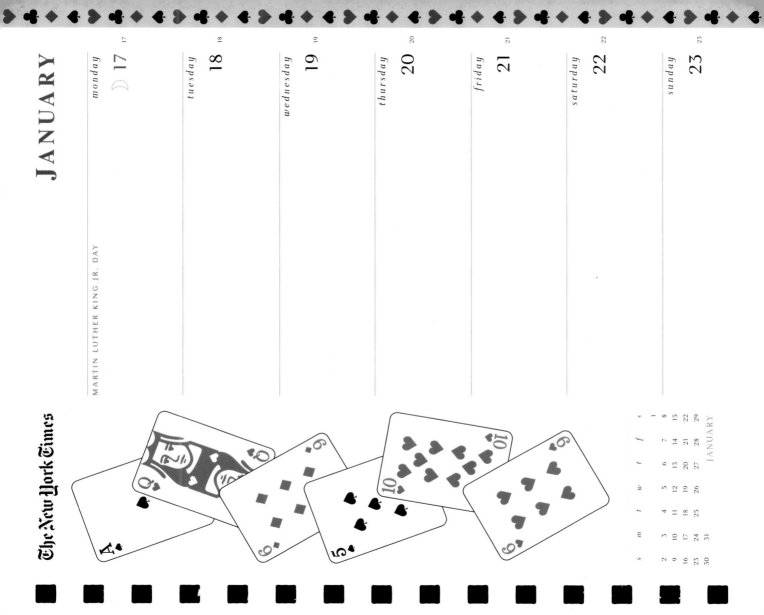

monday ☽ 17

MARTIN LUTHER KING JR. DAY

tuesday 18

wednesday 19

thursday 20

friday 21

saturday 22

sunday 23

The New York Times

JANUARY

s	m	t	w	t	f	s
						1
2	3	4	5	6	7	8
9	10	11	12	13	14	15
16	17	18	19	20	21	22
23	24	25	26	27	28	29
30	31					

RECALLING NORMAN KAY, A PAINSTAKING GENTLEMAN

Alan Truscott 1/19/02

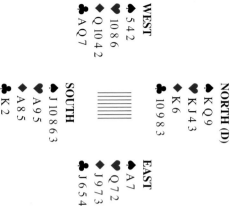

NORTH (D)
♠ K Q 9
♥ K J 4 3
♦ K 6
♣ 10 9 8 3

WEST
♠ 5 4 2
♥ 10 8 6
♦ Q 10 4 2
♣ A Q 7

EAST
♠ A 7
♥ Q 7 2
♦ J 9 7 3
♣ J 6 5 4

SOUTH
♠ J 10 8 6 3
♥ A 9 5
♦ A 8 5
♣ K 2

Neither side was vulnerable. The bidding:

North	East	South	West
1 N.T.	Pass	3 ♠	Pass
4 ♠	Pass	Pass	Pass

West led the diamond two.

The world of bridge lost an all-time great three years ago when Norman Kay died, aged 74. Those who played against him in a career lasting half a century considered him at the top of the tree as a player and as a human being. He bent over backwards to avoid criticizing his partner, or his opponents, blaming himself for any misfortune if he possibly could.

He never quite managed to win a world title, although he came close on three occasions. But he did amass a remarkable collection of major national titles. He won the Vanderbilt Knockout Teams seven times, a record in the modern era, and five of these were with the late Edgar Kaplan, his favorite partner for four decades. The last two victories were with Bill Root and Richard Pavlicek in 1985 and 1986, when they disproved the popular belief that a four-man team, playing without relief, cannot expect to win on a major occasion.

Kay believed in thorough analysis at the table, and never played a card until he had examined every angle. This leisurely approach occasionally caused problems. When he completed play in the 1986 Vanderbilt, one of his team-

mates had already departed to catch a plane and would have had to return in a hurry in the unlikely event that a tied score necessitated the play of extra deals.

On that occasion, the diagramed deal gave plenty of scope for Kay's skill as declarer. Sitting South, he arrived in four spades by a traditional route after a weak no-trump opening by Kaplan. Looking at all four hands, would you wish to play or defend?

A diamond was led and won with the king in dummy. South led the spade king, reaching the moment of truth. It is far from obvious, but for the defense to prevail East must allow the king to win. (The same ducking play would be necessary had West led a trump originally.)

When East returned a diamond, South won with the ace and ruffed his remaining diamond with the spade queen. Then he made the fine play of finessing the heart nine. Since he was protected from a club lead, he now had multiple chances. West won with the ten, and Kay eventually made his game by scoring dummy's last heart.

The analysts thought that the game would have failed if East had shifted to a club after taking his spade ace, with West winning the queen and returning a trump at the fourth trick. This is true in practice, but Kay would have had a double-dummy way to survive. After taking his diamond ruff, he would have had to lead the heart jack from dummy. This would have forced the queen from East, and Kay could have won and played two more trump winners to reach this ending:

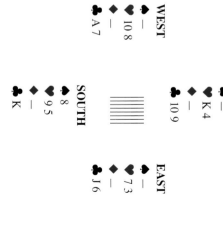

NORTH
♠ —
♥ K 4
♦ —
♣ 10 9

WEST
♠ —
♥ 10 8
♦ —
♣ 10 9

EAST
♠ —
♥ 7 3
♦ —
♣ J 6

SOUTH
♠ 8
♥ 9 5
♦ —
♣ K

JANUARY

monday	**24**
tuesday	○ **25**
wednesday	**26**
thursday	**27**
friday	**28**
saturday	**29**
sunday	**30**

The New York Times

South needs three more tricks and must get them when he leads his last trump. If West throws the club seven, he is end-played by a club lead.

s	m	t	w	t	f	s
						1
2	3	4	5	6	7	8
9	10	11	12	13	14	15
16	17	18	19	20	21	22
23	24	25	26	27	28	29
30	31					

JANUARY

TOPSY-TURVY: NORMAL PLAYS ARE WRONG

Alan Truscott 1/28/02

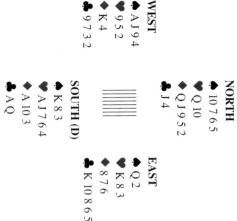

```
              NORTH
              ♠ 10 7 6 5
              ♥ Q 10
              ♦ Q J 9 5 2
              ♣ J 4

WEST                              EAST
♠ A J 9 4                        ♠ Q 2
♥ 9 5 2                          ♥ K 8 3
♦ K 4                            ♦ 8 7 6
♣ 9 7 3 2                        ♣ K 10 8 6 5

              SOUTH (D)
              ♠ K 8 3
              ♥ A J 7 6 4
              ♦ A 10 3
              ♣ A Q
```

North and South were vulnerable. The bidding:

South	West	North	East
1 ♥	Pass	1 ♠	Pass
2 N.T.	Pass	3 N.T.	Pass
Pass	Pass		

West led the club seven.

Some bridge deals have a topsy-turvy quality, with an aspect that is counterintuitive, and the one shown in the diagram has no less than three such features. It was played three year ago in a regional team tournament, and helped Elliot Sternlicht and Robert Kuhnreich, sitting East and West, to win the title.

The first topsy-turvy is that South, playing in an optimistic three no-trump after a club lead, is in danger of running out of entries to his hand. One might think that two entries in clubs, one in each red suit, and a possible in spades would be sufficient.

When Sternlicht and Kuhnreich were East and West, the opening club lead was won with the queen, and the declarer made the obvious play of cashing the diamond ace and continuing the suit. He may have wished that the defense would win the second round of diamonds, and they did. But getting one's wish sometimes proves to be a disappointment.

After winning with the diamond king, West continued clubs. South won and cashed diamonds, discarding a spade and a heart. He now had six tricks, and the lead was in dummy in this position:

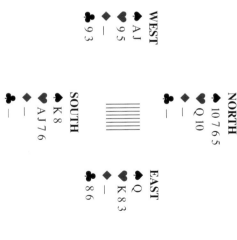

```
              NORTH
              ♠ 10 7 6 5
              ♥ Q 10
              ♦ —
              ♣ —

WEST                              EAST
♠ A J                            ♠ Q
♥ 9 5                            ♥ K 8 3
♦ —                             ♦ —
♣ 9 3                            ♣ 8 6

              SOUTH
              ♠ K 8
              ♥ A J 7 6
              ♦ —
              ♣ —
```

South led the heart queen from dummy, which was covered with the king. The declarer won with the ace, led to the ten, and had run out of entries to his hand. He lost the last four tricks for down one.

If South had looked ahead at the start, he could have seen the danger. He was going to need heart tricks, so he should have made the topsy-turvy play of a low diamond at the second trick. Whether the defense won this or not, he would have been able to play hearts from dummy, with the diamond ace as an eventual entry back to his hand. In the actual position, West would win the diamond king and play a club. Then South would enter dummy with a diamond lead, deliberately blocking the suit, in order to start the hearts.

Finally, consider the situation that would have arisen if West had held K x x of diamonds instead of a doubleton. When the ace and another were led, he would have had to make the topsy-turvy play of the king, allowing South to score the diamonds but defeating the contract.

In the replay, North-South came to rest accurately in two no-trump. Their team gained 7 imps, but would have lost 10 if three no-trump had succeeded.

monday 31   31

tuesday 1   32

wednesday ☾ 2   33

thursday 3   34

friday 4   35

saturday 5   36

sunday 6   37

The New York Times

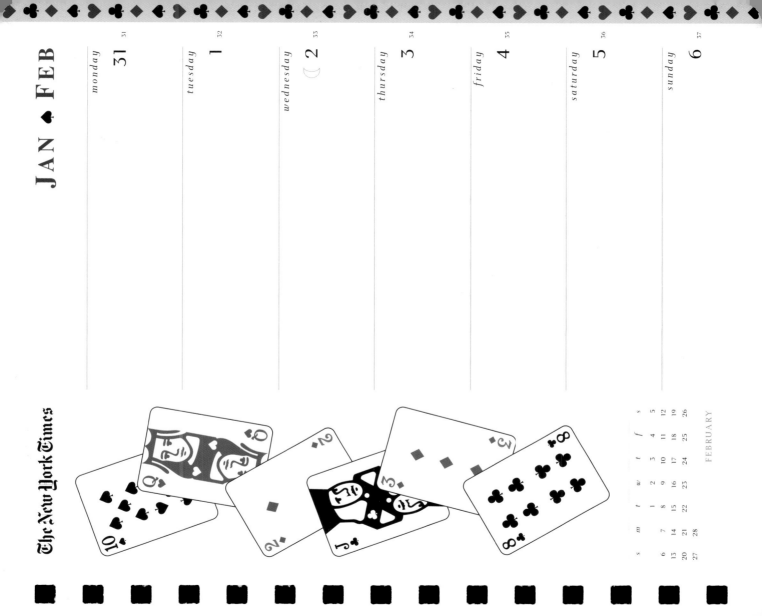

s	m	t	w	t	f	s
		1	2	3	4	5
6	7	8	9	10	11	12
13	14	15	16	17	18	19
20	21	22	23	24	25	26
27	28					

FEBRUARY

FIRST BIG WIN FOR CANADA

Alan Truscott 2/9/02

NORTH
- ♠ 7 6 5 3
- ♥ 5
- ♦ K 9 8 3
- ♣ K Q 10 4

WEST
- ♠ A 10
- ♥ K J 10 7 2
- ♦ 7 6 4
- ♣ 6 3 2

EAST
- ♠ 9 8 4
- ♥ Q 9 8 4
- ♦ Q J 5
- ♣ A J 7

SOUTH (D)
- ♠ K Q J 2
- ♥ A 6 3
- ♦ A 10 2
- ♣ 9 8 5

North and South were vulnerable. The bidding:

South	West	North	East
1 ♣	2 ♥	Dbl.	Pass
2 ♠	Pass	3 ♠	Pass
4 ♠	Pass	Pass	Pass

West led the diamond six.

Canada won its first-ever major international title three years ago. Playing in the fourth I.O.C. Grand Prix in Salt Lake City, Keith Balcombe, Gordon Campbell, Nicholas Gartaganis and Peter Jones, all newcomers at this level of competition, together with Fred Gitelman and Joseph Silver, surprised the pundits by taking the title. En route to victory they defeated strong teams from the United States, Italy and Poland.

Gitelman celebrated his 37th birthday by bringing home four spades on the diagrammed deal from the final. His partner, Silver, followed his negative double of an eccentric weak jump overall with an aggressive raise to three spades, and the result was a borderline game contract.

West led a diamond, and South captured East's jack with the ace. The declarer then cashed the heart ace and ruffed a heart. When he played a spade to his king, West won with the ace and returned the ten. South correctly inferred from this that West did not have a doubleton diamond, which would have represented an obvious second lead.

South could afford to lose two minor-suit tricks but not three. After winning the trump lead, he ruffed his remaining heart with dummy's last trump and had several options. As it happens, most of them were due to work.

Gitelman's choice was to lead a low diamond, and East was helpless after winning with the queen. He led his last heart, and South ruffed. The last trump was drawn with the spade jack, and the contract was safe. Dummy was reduced to two diamond winners and the king-queen of clubs. West had no entry, so the club ace was the third and last trick for the defense.

In the replay, the Canadian West played in three hearts doubled. With the clubs lying favorably, he escaped for down one and his team gained 11 imps.

monday **7** 38

tuesday **8** 39

wednesday **9** 40

ASH WEDNESDAY

thursday **10** 41

friday **11** 42

saturday **12** 43

LINCOLN'S BIRTHDAY

sunday **13** 44

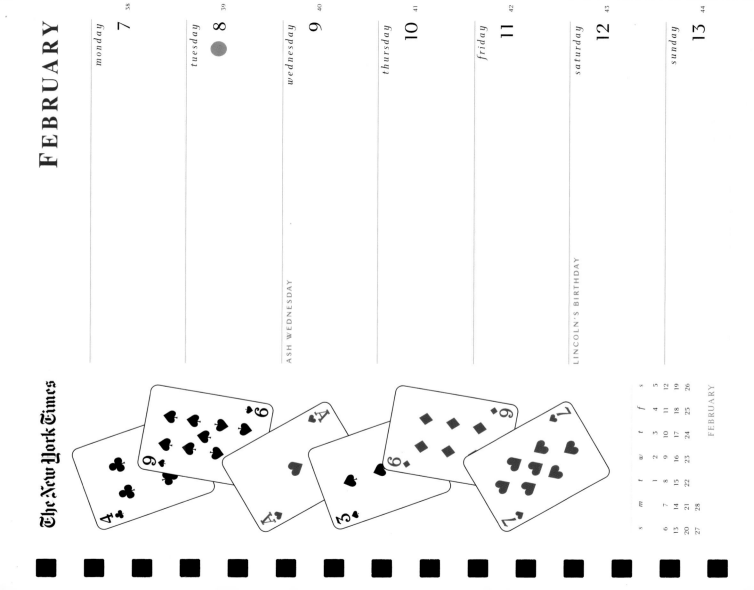

The New York Times

s	m	t	w	t	f	s
		1	2	3	4	5
6	7	8	9	10	11	12
13	14	15	16	17	18	19
20	21	22	23	24	25	26
27	28					

FEBRUARY

♣ LIFE MASTER RANK—QUICKLY AND SLOWLY

Alan Truscott 2/11/02

In 1936 there were ten. In 2002 there are 74,741. A smart bridge player–a life master, say–should know what these statistics refer to: the number of life masters.

At first, the rank was hard to come by. In the first decade the average annual number of new life masters was four. Thanks to lowering of masterpoint standards, making the rank easier to achieve, the annual increase is now averaging 2,500.

Nevertheless, life master rank is still a significant target for players of various levels. The speed record is held by a visiting Icelander, Jakob Kristinsson, who in 1996 became a life master in 43 days.

At the other end of the spectrum are players below the expert category who battle for many years, gathering a gold point here, a silver point there, hoping for the

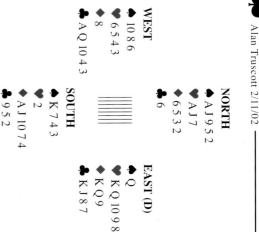

```
                    NORTH
                    ♠ A J 9 5 2
                    ♥ A J 7
                    ♦ 6 5 3 2
                    ♣ 6
WEST                                    EAST (D)
♠ 10 8 6                                ♠ Q
♥ 6 5 4 3                               ♥ K Q 10 9 8
♦ 8                                     ♦ K Q 9
♣ A Q 10 4 3                            ♣ K J 8 7
                    SOUTH
                    ♠ K 7 4 3
                    ♥ 2
                    ♦ A J 10 7 4
                    ♣ 9 5 2
```

Both sides were vulnerable. The bidding:

East	South	West	North
1♥	Pass	2♥	Dbl.
Pass	2♠	3♥	3♠
4♣	4♠	Pass	Pass
Pass			

West led the diamond eight.

appropriate collection totalling 300. One of the longest such odysseys, lasting 30 years, was undertaken by Estelle Rubenstein of Manhattan, an octogenarian who achieved her goal three years ago. She fulfilled the requirement at the Town Club with Abid Merchant as her partner, and scored 63.48% to win a citywide game.

They were aided by the diagramed deal, which at first sight appears to break the Law of Total Tricks as stated by its chief proponent, Larry Cohen. The total number of trumps for the two partnerships in their best fit is 18, in spades or diamonds for North-South and in hearts or clubs for East-West. This ought to equal the total number of tricks available, but that is 19, 20 or 21, depending on the defense.

North-South will always make five spades, assuming the declarer makes the percentage play in diamonds. If they play a diamond contract, which is not likely, the defense can make an inspired spade lead and score a ruff in that suit.

East-West will sometimes make 10 tricks, but can be held to nine or even eight. In hearts, an unlikely opening club lead allows North to score two ruffs, since South has two entries. More plausible is a spade lead and a club shift, allowing one ruff. Against an improbable club contract South can score two ruffs by leading a heart or by shifting to that suit after cashing the diamond ace.

However, Cohen points out in his book that the Law does not quite work when there is a double fit. In such situations, as exists here, the total tricks will be one or two more than the total trumps.

In actual play, with Rubenstein and Merchant sitting North and South, the bidding could have been accelerated. With a known 9-card fit, and the likelihood that the opponents would enter the bidding and find a fit, West should have responded four hearts. That would probably have silenced North: A four-spade intervention would have been tempting but risky.

North should have overcalled in spades at the two-level rather than make a take-out double, but when she did double, South should have considered jumping to three spades. West's three-club bid might have helped his partner, but in fact encouraged South to continue

FEBRUARY

The New York Times

eventually to game with the expectation of a double fit.

Four spades, with very limited high-card strength, was unbeatable. When West led his single-ton diamond, Merchant did not have to work for his overtrick. After another lead he could have demonstrated his knowledge of suit combinations by taking a first-round diamond finesse after drawing trump, with perhaps another finesse to follow.

s	m	t	w	t	f	s
		1	2	3	4	5
6	7	8	9	10	11	12
13	14	15	16	17	18	19
20	21	22	23	24	25	26
27	28					

FEBRUARY

monday 14   45

VALENTINE'S DAY

tuesday 15   46

wednesday ☽ 16   47

thursday 17   48

friday 18   49

saturday 19   50

sunday 20   51

♠ ONE MAN WITH FOUR LIVES, THREE CONNECTED BY A GAME

Alan Truscott 2/14/02

NORTH
- ♠ Q 9 8 7 3
- ♥ K J 9 5
- ♦ 8
- ♣ A 4 3

WEST
- ♠ 5 4
- ♥ 10 3
- ♦ A 10 7 4 2
- ♣ Q 8 7 2

EAST (D)
- ♠ K J 10 6 2
- ♥ 8 4
- ♦ Q J 5
- ♣ 9 6 5

SOUTH
- ♠ A
- ♥ A Q 7 6 2
- ♦ K 9 8 3
- ♣ K J 10

North and South were vulnerable. The bidding:

East	South	West	North
Pass	1 ♥	Pass	Pass
Pass	3 ♦	Pass	Pass
Dbl.	4 N.T.	Pass	5 ♦
Pass	6 ♥	Pass	Pass
Pass			

West led the spade five.

Few men can claim to have had four distinct lives in four different countries. David Berah, who died three years ago in Manhattan at the age of 81, was one of this rare breed. From a childhood in Serbia he went to England and joined the Royal Air Force, serving as a navigator-bombardier in North Africa against General Rommel. He then spent 30 years as a successful businessman in Venezuela, and 25 more as a retiree in Manhattan.

The connecting link between the last three of these lives was bridge. He learned the game as a flier, and went on to represent Venezuela, winning three South American team titles and playing in six world championships. In retirement he rarely played in tournaments, preferring the comfort of a club. The diagramed deal was played in 1984 in the Cavendish Club, seven years before the decease of that celebrated institution.

There was some confusion in the auction, but it turned out to be profitable. Berah's three-spade bid as South was a cue-bid, showing a control in the suit, but his partner thought the bid was natural and raised. East seized the opportunity to double, which proved to be a fatal error.

South persevered with Blackwood and reached six hearts. When a spade was led Berah had the pleasure of knowing that all the significant spades were on his right. He carefully played low from the dummy, saving all the valuable intermediate spot cards, and won with the ace when East contributed the deuce.

Dummy was entered with a trump to the jack, and the singleton diamond was led. East was permitted to win with the queen, and that player returned a trump. Berah won in dummy and led the spade queen, forcing a cover with the king. After South ruffed the position was:

NORTH
- ♠ 9 8 7
- ♥ 9 5
- ♦ —
- ♣ A 4 3

WEST
- ♠ —
- ♥ —
- ♦ A 10 7 4
- ♣ Q 8 7 2

EAST
- ♠ J 10 6
- ♥ —
- ♦ J 5
- ♣ 9 6 5

SOUTH
- ♠ —
- ♥ A Q
- ♦ K 9 8
- ♣ K J 10

With spade length marked on his right, the club queen was more likely than not to be on his left. Berah led the club jack and finessed successfully. The rest was easy. He crossed to the club ace, and led a spade. This was covered and he ruffed. There were just enough entries to ruff out East's remaining spade honor, so a spade winner in dummy provided the 12th trick.

Berah had his slam, and East was left to reflect that in this case silence would have been golden.

FEBRUARY

monday **21** 52

PRESIDENTS' DAY

tuesday **22** 53

WASHINGTON'S BIRTHDAY

wednesday **23** 54

thursday ○ **24** 55

friday **25** 56

saturday **26** 57

sunday **27** 58

The New York Times

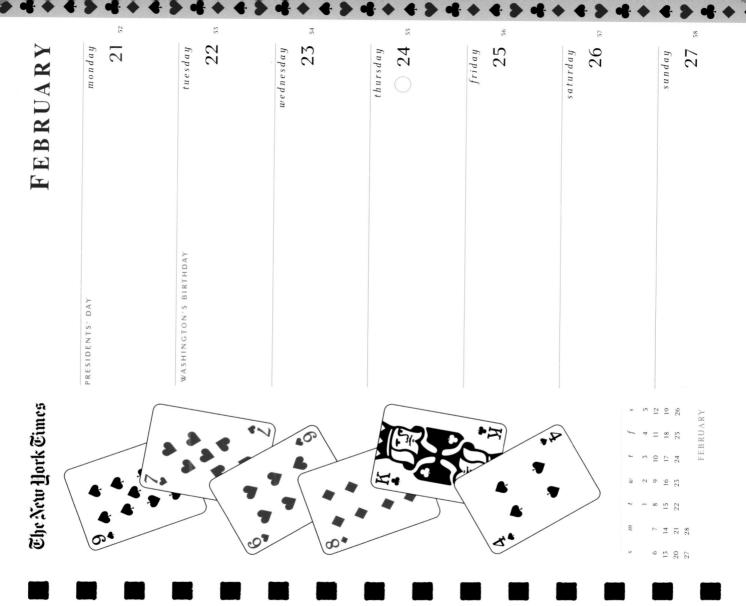

s	m	t	w	t	f	s
		1	2	3	4	5
6	7	8	9	10	11	12
13	14	15	16	17	18	19
20	21	22	23	24	25	26
27	28					

FEBRUARY

♥ A JUMP TO THREE OVER ONE NO-TRUMP HAS MANY MEANINGS

Alan Truscott 3/2/02

Most of the earliest authorities on contract bridge had begun with auction and then converted to the new game. One of them was Sidney Lenz, who had many talents including magic. He was not, however, a magician in bidding theory, for, with one exception, he did not believe in forcing bids. This confused his partners, particularly in the celebrated Culbertson-Lenz match.

His one exception was a response of three of a major to a one no-trump opening. For three decades this was a simple bid, showing a five-card suit and requesting opener to choose an appropriate game. Since the introduction of transfer bids in the 1950s, a jump response to three hearts or three spades became a mystery: A responder with a five-card major would normally use a transfer sequence.

A possible meaning is a strong suit with slam interest. Another is a five-five distribution in the major suits, with three hearts invitational and three spades forcing.

Some use it as a splinter: a short suit with no major. Others employ it to show a three-suiter short in the other major. And a few make use of the anti-lemming device by this columnist: a three-card suit with a weak doubleton in the other major.

In the diagramed deal, played in New York Regional Championships three years ago, the agreement was that the three-heart bid allowed North to use his discretion. South took veteran star Ivar Stakgold, whose opening one no-trump bid showed 12-14 points. With flat distribution he might have chosen three no-trump, but raised to four hearts. This left his partner, Adam Wildavsky, to face difficult problems.

A diamond was led to the ace and the suit was returned. South took his king, fearing that a finesse of the jack would lead to a third-round ruff by East. The king and ace of hearts were cashed, and the diamond jack was led. When West won with the queen he was in some difficulty and did the best he could by shifting to the spade jack. This rode around to the king, and South continued by playing a spade to dummy's seven.

East returned the heart ten, and dummy won, reaching this position:

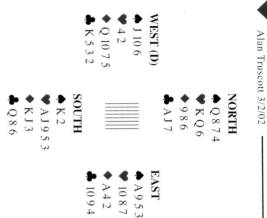

```
               NORTH
               ♠ Q 8 7 4
               ♥ K Q 6
               ♦ 9 8 6
               ♣ A J 7
WEST (D)                      EAST
♠ J 10 6                      ♠ A 9 5 3
♥ 4 2                         ♥ 10 8 7
♦ Q 10 7 5                    ♦ A 4 2
♣ K 5 3 2                     ♣ 10 9 4
               SOUTH
               ♠ K 2
               ♥ A J 9 5 3
               ♦ K J 3
               ♣ Q 8 6
```

North and South were vulnerable. The bidding:

West	North	East	South
Pass	1 N.T.	Pass	3♥
Pass	4♥	Pass	Pass
Pass			

West led the diamond five.

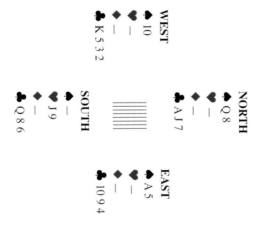

```
               NORTH
               ♠ Q 8
               ♥ —
               ♦ —
               ♣ A J 7
WEST                          EAST
♠ 10                          ♠ A 5
♥ —                           ♥ —
♦ —                           ♦ —
♣ K 5 3 2                     ♣ 10 9 4
               SOUTH
               ♠ —
               ♥ J 9
               ♦ —
               ♣ Q 8 6
```

The New York Times

Wildavsky knew that the spade ace was on his right, and was confident that the ten was on his left. Barring the faint possibility that West had led the spade jack lacking the ten, declarer was now sure of success if, as seemed likely, West held the club king. Wildavsky led the spade queen from dummy and ruffed when East covered with the ace. When the ten appeared dummy's eight was established and the club finesse sufficed to make the game. If the spade ten had not appeared, Wildavsky would have led his last trump to squeeze West.

s	m	t	w	t	f	s
		1	2	3	4	5
6	7	8	9	10	11	12
13	14	15	16	17	18	19
20	21	22	23	24	25	26
27	28	29	30	31		

MARCH

monday **28** 59

tuesday **1** 60

wednesday **2** 61

thursday **3** 62

friday **4** 63

saturday **5** 64

sunday **6** 65

MOTHERING SUNDAY (U.K.)

♦ AN ELECTRIFYING GRAND SLAM BID

Alan Truscott 3/16/02

NORTH
♠ A K 10 8 7 5 3
♥ A K Q 10 4 2
♦ —
♣ —

WEST
♠ Q J 9 2
♥ 8 6 5
♦ 9 3
♣ A 9 6 5

EAST (D)
♠ 6
♥ J 3
♦ A Q 10 8 5 4
♣ J 10 7 2

SOUTH
♠ 4
♥ 9 7
♦ K J 7 6 2
♣ K Q 8 4 3

Both sides were vulnerable. The bidding:

East	South	West	North
Pass	Pass	Pass	2 ♠
2 ◆	Pass	Pass	7 ◆
Pass	7 ♥	Pass	Pass
Pass			

West led the heart five.

Perhaps the most sensational bid in the 72-year history of the Vanderbilt Cup was made on the diagramed deal from the 2002 event, played in Houston. In fourth position, Steve Landen of Rochester Hills, Minn., opened the North hand with two clubs, strong and artificial. When he heard an overcall of two diamonds on his left, he electrified the table with a bid of seven diamonds. His partner, Pratap Rajadhyaksha of Powell, Ohio, realized that this was a command to choose between the major suits, and had to bid seven hearts. The pass of two diamonds had promised some high-card strength in the partnership style, and it was somewhat unlucky that South held only three major-suit cards without any honors.

The grand slam was a slightly inferior contract, which required good breaks in both major suits. West led a trump, which could have been crucial with a slightly different lay-out. South won in dummy, cashed the spade ace, and attempted to ruff a spade with his remaining trump. If both opponents had followed suit, and the trumps had split normally, he would have made his grand slam.

Success would have given North-South and their teammates a considerable victory: They would have beaten the formidable Nickell team which has won many titles. In the replay, Paul Soloway and Bob Hamman, North-South for the Nickell squad, played accurately and successfully in six hearts. They gained 17, but would have lost 13 if the grand slam had succeeded.

Landen and Rajadhyaksha have recovered from this blow. In 2003 they were members of the team that won the United States Team Championships, thereby qualifying to play in the world championships in Monte Carlo, later in that year.

monday 7 · 66

tuesday 8 · 67

wednesday 9 · 68

thursday ● 10 · 69

friday 11 · 70

saturday 12 · 71

sunday 13 · 72

INTERNATIONAL WOMEN'S DAY

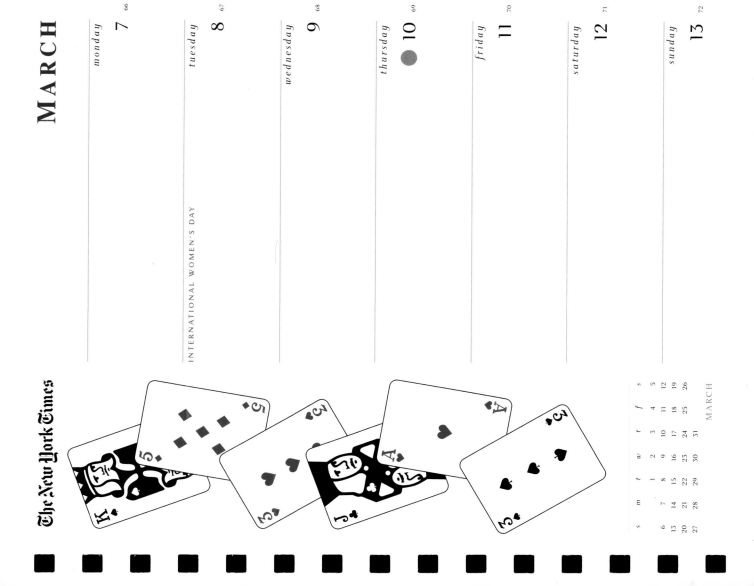

The New York Times

s	m	t	w	t	f	s
		1	2	3	4	5
6	7	8	9	10	11	12
13	14	15	16	17	18	19
20	21	22	23	24	25	26
27	28	29	30	31		

MARCH

♣ A BID TO STARTLE EVERYONE. WAS IT A MISTAKE?

Alan Truscott 3/14/02

```
                    NORTH
                    ♠ 6
                    ♥ Q 5 3
                    ♦ 10 4 2
                    ♣ A Q 10 8 6 5

WEST (D)                              EAST
♠ A K                                 ♠ 10 4 3 2
♥ J 9 8 2                             ♥ K 10 7 6
♦ A K 9 8 7 3                         ♦ Q J 6 5
♣ 3                                   ♣ J

                    SOUTH
                    ♠ Q J 9 8 7 5
                    ♥ A 4
                    ♦ —
                    ♣ K 9 7 4 2
```

East and West were vulnerable. The bidding:

West	North	East	South
1 ♣	2 ♣	Dbl.	3 ♠
3 ♦	Pass	4 ♦	5 ♣
Pass	6 ♣	Dbl.	Pass
Pass	Pass		

West led the spade ace.

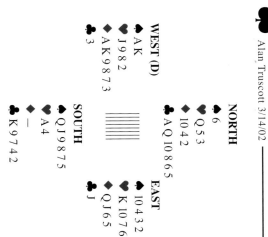

Some bridge deals are tragedies or comedies, depending on which direction you are sitting. The diagramed deal comes under this heading. North and South, playing in the 2002 Vanderbilt Cup in Houston, were Grant Baze and Michael Whitman.

West's one-club opening was strong and artificial, nominally showing 16 high-card points. The jump to two spades was "suction," a tricky convention now popular in tournament play. It showed either the next-higher suit, clubs, or the other two suits, in this case diamonds and hearts. East doubled to show some modest high-card values.

Looking at his hand, South thought it probable that the deal was a misfit, with his partner holding the red suits. He changed his mind when his opponents bid and raised diamonds, and now knew that his partnership held a massive club fit. He could have bid a simple five clubs, but electrified the table with a bid of five diamonds. This was so surprising that the other players suspected that he had pulled out the wrong bidding card. He now landed in six clubs doubled, and West naturally led a top spade.

"What sort of a bid was five diamonds?" demanded North aggressively as he put down his dummy. But he forgave the bid when Whitman made his doubled slam. He was able to draw one round of trump, establish his spades by ruffing, and discard two hearts from dummy on spade winners.

It was now apparent that North-South were playing the slam from the wrong side. Six clubs by North would have been unbeatable, since a heart lead would not have helped the defense.

East and West were in shock. They realized that they should have saved in six diamonds, down one, since West could hardly be expected to hit on the killing heart lead against six clubs.

In the replay, East-West played in four hearts. This could have been defeated by two tricks, since the defense can maneuver three ruffs, but the game succeeded and the Baze team gained 17 imps en route to victory in the match.

monday
14
73

tuesday
15
74

wednesday
16
75

thursday
☽ 17
76
ST. PATRICK'S DAY

friday
18
77

saturday
19
78

sunday
20
79
PALM SUNDAY
VERNAL EQUINOX 12:33 P.M. (GMT)

The New York Times

s	m	t	w	t	f	s
		1	2	3	4	5
6	7	8	9	10	11	12
13	14	15	16	17	18	19
20	21	22	23	24	25	26
27	28	29	30	31		

MARCH

NEVER PLAY IN A THREE-THREE FIT. WHAT, NEVER? WELL, HARDLY EVER.

Alan Truscott 3/4/02

NORTH (D)
♠ K 9 4
♥ A
♦ A J 10 8 7 3
♣ 5 4 2

WEST
♠ Q 10 6 3
♥ 5 3
♦ 5 4 2
♣ J 10 9 7

EAST
♠ 7 5 2
♥ K J 9 8
♦ K Q 9 6
♣ K 8

SOUTH
♠ A J 8
♥ Q 10 7 6 4 2
♦ —
♣ A Q 6 3

Both sides were vulnerable. The bidding:

North	East	South	West
2 ♦	Pass	2 N.T.	Pass
3 ♦	Pass	3 ♣	Pass
4 ♥	Pass	Pass	Pass

West led the club jack.

A basic principle of bidding is to search for a trump suit in which the combined hands have at least eight cards, with the proviso that a seven-card fit is acceptable on occasion.

On some rare deals, very difficult to diagnose in the bidding, it is right to play in a six-card fit divided 6-0, 5-1 or even 4-2. When the fit is 3-3 it is almost invariably due to a misunderstanding, but the diagramed deal is an exception. It was played 33 years ago, and the South cards were held by the late Merle Tom, who was one of the country's top players when he lived in the New York metropolitan area.

Two diamonds was a natural opening bid, systemically promising a six card diamond suit, 11–15 high-card points, and no side-suit. The two no-trump response asked North to show a singleton if he had one, and he duly bid three hearts.

South thought this over carefully. He knew that his partner's distribution was 3-1-6-3, and that there was therefore no fit. The obvious action was to pass three hearts, allowing his partner to play "upside-down" in a 1-6 fit. That contract would probably have made exactly nine tricks. Only an improbable lead of a diamond, into North's known length, or of an equally improbable heart honor would have permitted an overtrick.

Instead Tom made an imaginative bid of three spades, deliberately selecting a 3-3 fit in which he would score several red-suit ruffs. Since he was in charge of the auction, he expected his partner to pass. But North carried on to game, liking his two aces and a king and not suspecting the truth about South's spade length.

West did not suspect the truth either, and it did not occur to him to lead a trump with the likely sacrifice of a trick. But that was the only way in which the contract could have been defeated.

In practice the lead was the club jack, which left South in control. He began by taking two club tricks, the heart ace and the diamond ace, and therefore needed to collect six trump tricks. A diamond ruff, a heart ruff and a second diamond ruff led to this ending:

NORTH
♠ K 9
♥ —
♦ J 10 8
♣ 5

WEST
♠ Q 10 6 3
♥ —
♦ —
♣ 5

EAST
♠ 7 5 2
♥ K J
♦ K
♣ —

SOUTH
♠ A
♥ Q 10 7
♦ —
♣ 6 3

MARCH

monday 21 [80]

tuesday 22 [81]

wednesday 23 [82]

thursday 24 [83]

PURIM (BEGINS AT SUNSET)

friday 25 [84] ○

GOOD FRIDAY

saturday 26 [85]

sunday 27 [86]

EASTER SUNDAY

SUMMER TIME BEGINS (U.K.)

The New York Times

A heart was led, and West did his best by inserting the spade 10. South overruffed with dummy's king, ruffed a diamond with the spade ace, and led another heart. He could not be prevented from scoring the spade nine in dummy en passant and making his game.

Tom's remarkable decision to play in a three-three fit was therefore vindicated.

	s	m	t	w	t	f	s
			1	2	3	4	5
	6	7	8	9	10	11	12
	13	14	15	16	17	18	19
	20	21	22	23	24	25	26
	27	28	29	30	31		

MARCH

♠ LIKE A LEOPARD, MAKE THE MOST OF YOUR SPOTS

Alan Truscott 4/1/02

```
                NORTH (D)
                ♠ 9 8
                ♥ 9 7 6 3
                ♦ J 10 7 5
                ♣ A 3 2
WEST                            EAST
♠ A Q J 5 4                     ♠ —
♥ K Q J 2        ▦▦▦▦           ♥ A 10 8 5
♦ Q 6                           ♦ A K 9 4 3
♣ 7 6                           ♣ Q J 10 4
                SOUTH
                ♠ K 10 9 7 6 3 2
                ♥ 4
                ♦ 8 2
                ♣ K 9 8 5
```

Neither side was vulnerable. The bidding:

North	East	South	West
Pass	1♦	2♠	Pass
Pass	Dbl.	Pass	Pass
Pass			

West led the heart king.

Rudyard Kipling explained, in one of his Just So stories, how the leopard got his spots. They were superb camouflage, and the bridge expert sometimes uses his spots for that purpose. However, they may have a more direct purpose, depending on circumstances, and they may affect the bidding.

Nines, eights and sevens are likely to be irrelevant if a player has a long strong suit or a long weak suit. They are quite likely to be valuable in a long, broken suit, with some high-card strength, and that is particularly true if an opponent is known to have length in the same suit.

Consider the diagramed deal played in the final of the North American Open Pairs in Houston three years ago. The auction shown was a common one, with East opening the bidding and South making a weak jump overcall in spades. West passed, the usual tactic with

length and strength in the opponent's suit, and made a penalty pass when East reopened with a double.

Since East-West could make game in hearts, scoring at least 420, the defense needed to take eight tricks against two spades doubled, for a score of 500. It was not an easy task, and the number of trump tricks taken by the defenders was crucial. They could take two diamonds, one heart and one club, but could West win four trump tricks? The middle spot cards would decide.

The play often began with two rounds of hearts, South ruffing. The declarer could cross to the club king. Then he could exit in a heart, and cash the club king. Then he could exit in a minor suit. The defense could take three minor-suit tricks, but the position would be this with East to lead:

```
                NORTH
                ♠ 9 8
                ♥ 9
                ♦ J 10
                ♣ —
WEST                            EAST
♠ A Q J 5 4                     ♠ —
♥ 9             ▦▦▦▦           ♥ A
♦ —                             ♦ A 9 4
♣ —                             ♣ Q
                SOUTH
                ♠ K 10 7 6
                ♥ —
                ♦ —
                ♣ 9
```

West finds he has too many trumps. If East leads the diamond ace, South discards his club nine. West has to ruff, and South takes two trump tricks at the finish. The declarer has escaped for down two.

For the defense to collect 500, and score well, West needs to shift to diamonds at the second trick. Continuing that suit would permit a quick overruff, and eventually West would take three more trump tricks.

This demonstrates the importance of middle spot cards when two long suits are competing against each other. Think about this when you are considering a penalty pass of a double, holding length in the opponent's suit.

The New York Times

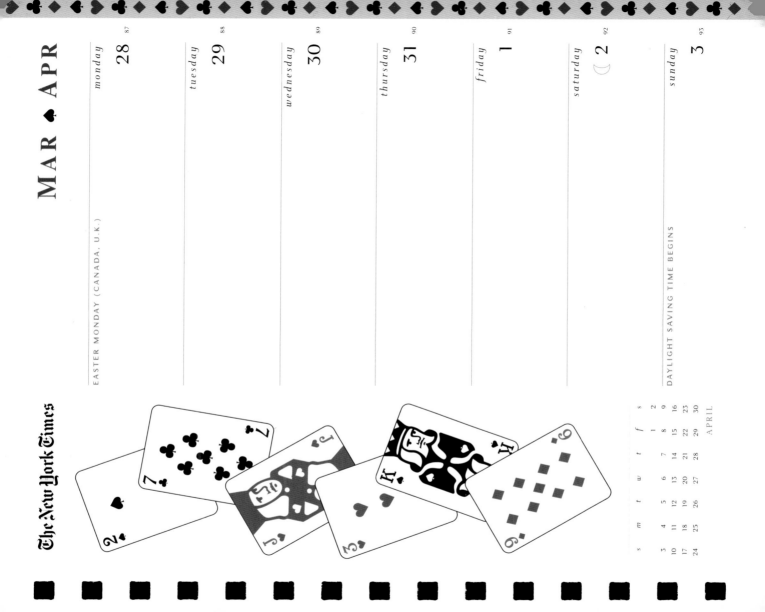

monday 28 87

EASTER MONDAY (CANADA, U.K.)

tuesday 29 88

wednesday 30 89

thursday 31 90

friday 1 91

saturday 2 92

sunday 3 93

DAYLIGHT SAVING TIME BEGINS

s	m	t	w	t	f	s
					1	2
3	4	5	6	7	8	9
10	11	12	13	14	15	16
17	18	19	20	21	22	23
24	25	26	27	28	29	30

APRIL

◆ AN ODD NAME FOR AN ODD DEAL. YOU HAVE NOT SEEN ONE.

Alan Truscott 4/6/02

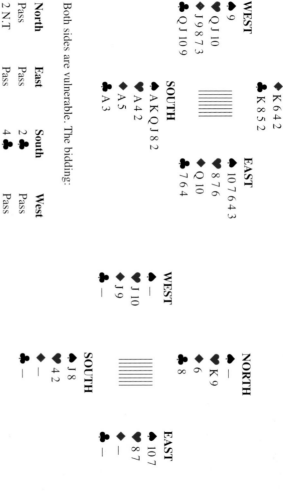

NORTH (D)
♠ 5
♥ K 9 5 3
♦ K 6 4 2
♣ K 8 5 2

WEST
♠ 9
♥ Q J 10
♦ J 9 8 7 3
♣ Q J 10 9

EAST
♠ 10 7 6 4 3
♥ 8 7 6
♦ Q 10
♣ 7 6 4

SOUTH
♠ A K Q J 8 2
♥ A 4 2
♦ A 5
♣ A 3

Both sides are vulnerable. The bidding:

North	East	South	West
Pass	Pass	2 ♣	Pass
2 N.T	Pass	4 ♣	Pass
4 ♦	Pass	5 ♣	Pass
5 N.T.	Pass	7 ♠	Pass
Pass	Pass	Pass	

West leads the heart queen.

Very few bridge deals have names, and those that do are usually very old. The diagramed example was created close to 70 years ago, and the reader should attempt to solve the problem of making seven spades after the lead of the heart queen. The hypothetical bidding features a Gerber auction: After a natural two no-trump response South discovers that his partner has no ace, not a surprise, and three kings.

South appears to have a trump loser, and even if he solves that problem there are only 12 tricks in view. He wins the first trick with the heart ace and cashes the spade ace and king. West had no trouble in giving up a diamond, but is in serious trouble when the spade queen is led. Suppose he gives up a club.

South now cashes the minor suits aces, crosses to the club king and ruffs a club. When he then leads to the diamond king the ending is this:

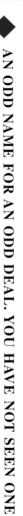

NORTH
♠ —
♥ K 9
♦ 6
♣ 8

WEST
♠ —
♥ J 10
♦ J 9
♣ —

EAST
♠ 10 7
♥ 8 7
♦ —
♣ —

SOUTH
♠ J 8
♥ 4 2
♦ —
♣ —

South leads the club eight from the dummy, now a winner, and East is at the crossroads. If he discards, his trumps are trapped in a coup position after the heart king is cashed. If he ruffs, South overruffs and draws the missing trump, in the process squeezing West in the red suits to make the grand slam. If West had discarded differently on the the third round of trumps, South would play the suit that was discarded with similar effect.

The creator of this remarkable deal described it as "the purple cow of bridgedom—a genuine squeeze coup." And it has been known ever since as Lennon's Purple Cow.

APRIL

monday 4

tuesday 5

wednesday 6

thursday 7

friday 8 ●

saturday 9

sunday 10

The New York Times

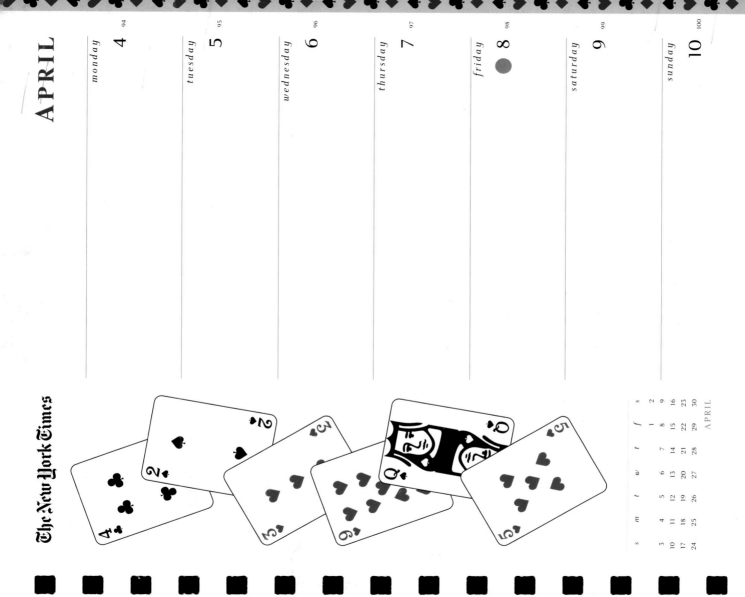

s	m	t	w	t	f	s
					1	2
3	4	5	6	7	8	9
10	11	12	13	14	15	16
17	18	19	20	21	22	23
24	25	26	27	28	29	30

APRIL

♣ ANTI-BATH COUP. IT DOESN'T CONSERVE WATER.

Alan Truscott 4/8/02

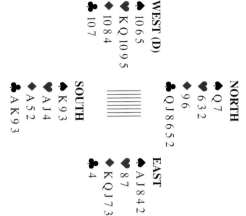

NORTH
♠ Q 7
♥ 6 3 2
♦ 9 6
♣ Q J 8 6 5 2

WEST (D)
♠ 10 6 5
♥ K Q 10 9 5
♦ 10 8 4
♣ 10 7

EAST
♠ A J 8 4 2
♥ 8 7
♦ K Q J 7 3
♣ 4

SOUTH
♠ K 9 3
♥ A J 4
♦ A 5 2
♣ A K 9 3

Neither side was vulnerable. The bidding:

West	North	East	South
			1 ♠
Pass	Pass	Pass	1 N.T.
2 ♥	3 ♣	3 ♦	3 N.T.
Pass	Pass	Pass	

West led the heart king.

Some 1900 years ago the Romans discovered hot springs in the west of England and built around them so that they could sample the waters. Two hundred years ago the British upper classes went to the town of Bath, the same place for the same purpose. They also played plenty of whist, the ancestor of bridge, which is why we have a Bath Coup, a fancy name for a simple play. If the opening lead is a king, the declarer holds up his ace with A-J-x so that a continuation will give him two tricks.

Far more interesting, and very rare, is the Anti-Bath Coup played on the diagramed deal. It occurred at the Fall Nationals in Las Vegas, and the hero was Lou Levy, perhaps the only living man to reach the highest levels in both bridge and chess. (That wording

excludes Irina Levitina, who has won women's world titles in both of the major intellectual games.)

Levy was South, and chose to overcall one spade with one no-trump holding slightly more than the normal requirements for that bid. He arrived in three no-trump after all the suits had been bid: clubs by his partner, hearts by West, and the pointed suits by East.

The final three no-trump contract would have been made easily with a black-suit lead. It would have been defeated automatically with a diamond lead, and was in the balance when West produced the heart king.

Levy could count eight tricks, and needed one from the spade suit to make his contract. He saw that either of the obvious first-trick plays was likely to be fatal. West was likely to have exactly five hearts, since with six he would have begun with a weak two-bid. So, winning with the ace would permit East to play a second heart when he gained the lead in spades, giving the defense five tricks.

Alternatively, it was likely that the play of the heart four, a normal Bath Coup, would cause West to shift to diamonds with decisive effect. East's diamond bid at the level of three suggested a very strong suit that he wished to have led.

So Levy used the Anti-Bath Coup. He dropped the heart jack under the king. West did not hesitate for a moment. He continued with the heart queen, in the belief that South had begun with A-J doubleton. South won with the ace and led a spade to the queen. East won with the ace but had no more hearts so Levy made his contract.

West would have solved the problem, perhaps, if he had looked carefully at the spots in hearts. East would not have played the seven from 8-7-4, so it followed that South was being tricky. But in the heat of battle players do not always pay attention to such details.

APRIL

monday 11 · 101

tuesday 12 · 102

wednesday 13 · 103

thursday 14 · 104

friday 15 · 105

saturday ☽ 16 · 106

sunday 17 · 107

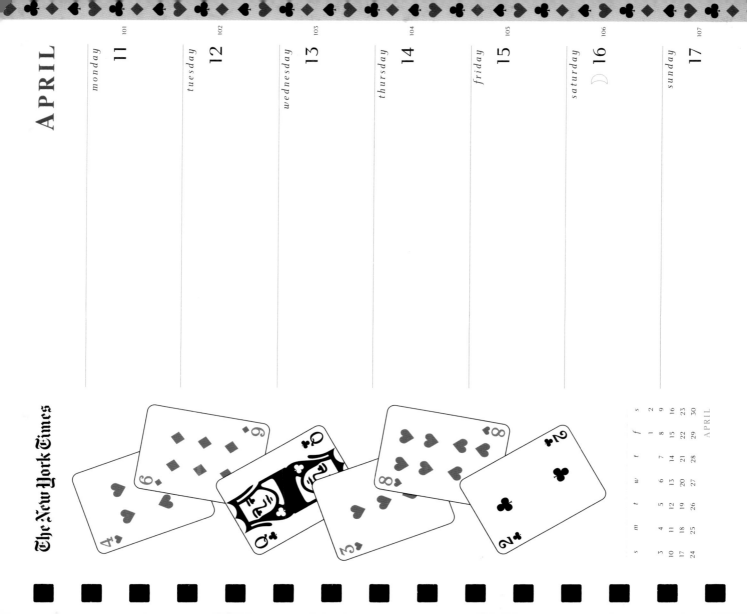

The New York Times

	s	m	t	w	t	f	s
						1	2
	3	4	5	6	7	8	9
	10	11	12	13	14	15	16
	17	18	19	20	21	22	23
	24	25	26	27	28	29	30

APRIL

THE RAREST CONTRACT TURNS OUT TO BE JUST RIGHT

Alan Truscott 4/20/02

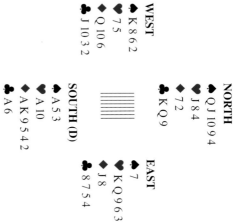

NORTH
- ♠ Q J 10 9 4
- ♥ J 8 4
- ♦ 7 2
- ♣ K Q 9

WEST
- ♠ K 8 6 2
- ♥ 7 5
- ♦ Q 10 6
- ♣ J 10 3 2

EAST
- ♠ 7
- ♥ K Q 9 6 3 2
- ♦ J 8
- ♣ 8 7 5 4

SOUTH (D)
- ♠ A 5 3
- ♥ A 10
- ♦ A K 9 5 4 2
- ♣ A 6

East and West were vulnerable. The bidding:

South	West	North	East
1 ♦	Pass	1 ♠	Pass
2 N.T.	Pass	3 ♠	Pass
5 N.T.	Pass	Pass	Pass

West led the club jack.

The commonest contract at the bridge-table is certainly three no-trump. But what is the rarest undoubled contract? The answer, oddly, depends on geographical location.

If you live in Italy, the answer is one club since that bid is almost invariably forcing. But in the United States and other countries in which standard methods prevail the answer is five no-trump. That contract was reached in a remarkable way on the diagramed deal, played in the 1999 Betty Kaplan Teams in Manhattan. This event requires rotation of partnerships, which generates some bidding confusion and did so in this case.

It is not clear how South should have bid, but his hand was clearly too good for the sequence chosen: one diamond followed by a jump to two no-trump. When his partner then rebid spades, he came to life with a jump to five no-trump. This was intended as a grand slam force and was entirely appropriate, for any North hand

including five or more spades headed by the king-queen was virtually sure to offer a good play for seven spades.

North could not believe that a partner who had limited his hand with two no-trump could then be justified in trying for a grand slam. He passed, irritating his partner, but the accidental contract of five no-trump proved to be a success.

The lead of the club jack was the best the defense could do. South won in his hand and set up the spades by playing the ace and another. West held up his king for one round and then led a second club. South won in dummy and cashed the spade winners, throwing a heart and a diamond. Abandoning the remaining club winner in the dummy, he gave up a diamond trick, making exactly 11 tricks when the suit split normally.

It might seem that North should have played six spades, as he would have done if he had responded to the grand slam force. Would that have succeeded after the lead of the heart king? The answer to this was demonstrated in the replay, when South landed in six spades. He had opened with two no-trump, and East had doubled the transfer response of three hearts. South bid three spades, and leaped majestically to six spades when his partner hinted at slam with a bid of four clubs.

A heart was duly led, and South captured the queen with the ace. He played three club winners, discarding a heart from his hand, and ruffed a heart. He then cashed his top diamonds and ruffed a diamond with the spade nine, preventing the predictable overruff. But when he then led the heart jack from dummy, covered by East, he was at the crossroads. He could have ruffed low and been overruffed, but he chose to ruff with the ace. That proved to be no better, for when a spade was led West could not be prevented from making two trump tricks.

South felt decidedly frustrated. He would have made the slam if the trumps had split evenly, or if the hearts had been divided in more normal fashion. The eight of spades in either hand, or the heart nine in dummy instead of the eight, would have been sufficient. The last straw was to discover that he had lost 11 imps because his opponents had ingeniously come to rest in five no-trump.

APRIL

monday 18 ¹⁰⁸

tuesday 19 ¹⁰⁹

wednesday 20 ¹¹⁰

thursday 21 ¹¹¹

friday 22 ¹¹²

EARTH DAY

saturday 23 ¹¹³

PASSOVER (BEGINS AT SUNSET)

sunday ◯ 24 ¹¹⁴

The New York Times

s	m	t	w	t	f	s
					1	2
3	4	5	6	7	8	9
10	11	12	13	14	15	16
17	18	19	20	21	22	23
24	25	26	27	28	29	30

APRIL

BEHAVE, LADIES ARE PRESENT

Alan Truscott 5/2/02

The diagramed deal occurred there in a mixed-pair event.

North and South were the eventual winners, Fred VanFleteren and Rose-Marie Loughnane, and they reached three no-trump by an obvious route. After a heart was led to the queen and king, South surveyed her prospects. There were seven tricks in clear view, and two more were needed from the diamond suit.

The danger was that East would win a quick diamond trick and return a heart, establishing his partner's suit while West had a diamond entry. The normal diamond play with a first-round finesse against the queen was due to fail with the actual distribution.

To guard against this, South made a Macchiavellian move. At the second trick, she led to dummy's club king and continued with a low diamond. An inspired East would have put up the queen with decisive effect, but he could not assume that South was abandoning a normal finesse. Playing the queen would have been an error if South held the ace, with or without the jack.

So East played low, and South's jack won the trick when West held up her ace. It was now clear that East held the queen, so when another diamond was led and West ducked again, the declarer put up the king. Loughnane made ten tricks, collecting all the match-points.

"I'm glad I had Rose-Marie for a partner," said VanFleteren after hearing the result announced. "You know, a woman is one of my favorite genders as a bridge partner."

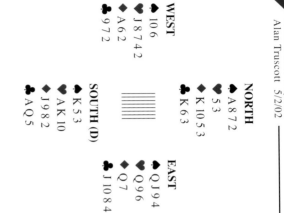

NORTH
♠ A 8 7 2
♥ 5 3
♦ K 10 5 3
♣ K 6 3

WEST
♠ 10 6
♥ J 8 7 4 2
♦ A 6 2
♣ 9 7 2

EAST
♠ Q J 9 4
♥ Q 9 6
♦ Q 7
♣ J 10 8 4

SOUTH (D)
♠ K 5 3
♥ A K 10
♦ J 9 8 2
♣ A Q 5

Both sides were vulnerable. The bidding:

South	West	North	East
1 N.T.	Pass	2 ♣	Pass
2 ♦	Pass	3 N.T.	Pass
Pass	Pass		

West led the heart four.

The battle to admit women to the gentlemen-only clubs of major cities was largely fought and won in the 20th century, but the first dent came, apparently, in Philadelphia at the end of the 19th. On January 30, 1893, the Hamilton Club there, after much debate, passed the following resolution: "The privileges and courtesies of the clubhouse are hereby given to wives, sisters and daughters of members and to the lady friends of members for any day of the week (except Sundays and legal holidays) from 9 A.M. to 3 P.M."

The women wanted to come to the Hamilton, then five years old, to play whist. Soon after, they were playing a newer game, with full membership privileges, and have been doing so ever since at the oldest bridge club on this side of the Atlantic, now in Bala Cynwyd, Pa.

monday 25 115

tuesday 26 116

wednesday 27 117

thursday 28 118

friday 29 119

saturday 30 120

sunday 1 121

The New York Times

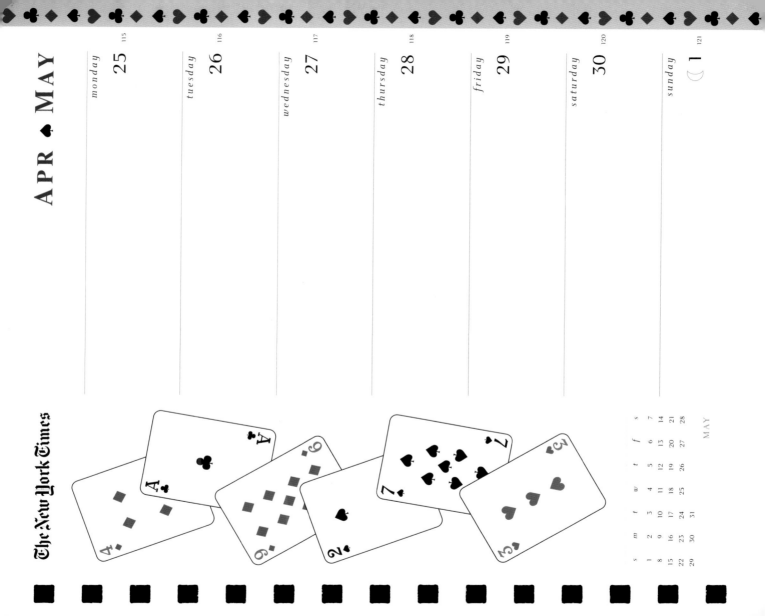

MAY

s	m	t	w	t	f	s
1	2	3	4	5	6	7
8	9	10	11	12	13	14
15	16	17	18	19	20	21
22	23	24	25	26	27	28
29	30	31				

◆ CALL OUT THE VICE SQUAD: SOMEONE'S CAUGHT IN A VISE

Alan Truscott 5/6/02

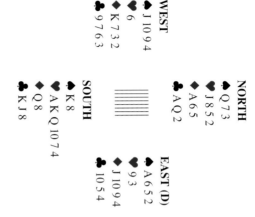

NORTH
♠ Q 7 3
♥ J 8 5 2
♦ A 6 5
♣ A Q 2

WEST
♠ J 10 9 4
♥ 6
♦ K 7 3 2
♣ 9 7 6 3

EAST (D)
♠ A 6 5 2
♥ 9 3
♦ J 10 9 4
♣ 10 5 4

SOUTH
♠ K 8
♥ A K Q 10 7 4
♦ Q 8
♣ K J 8

Neither side was vulnerable. The bidding:

East	South	West	North
	1 ♥	Pass	Pass
Pass	3 ♣	Pass	3 N.T.
Pass	4 ♣	Pass	4 ♦
Pass	4 N.T.	Pass	5 ♥
Pass	6 ♥	Pass	Pass
Pass			

West led the spade jack.

That vice is commoner in Britain than in America might seem a dubious proposition, but it is true, in a technical way, in the bridge communities. The explanation is that the gripping tool called a "vise" on this side of the Atlantic is a "vice" on the other.

The diagramed deal features a vice squeeze or a vice squeeze, depending on your citizenship. North and South, playing in a Norwegian Premier League match, were Geir Helgemo and Geir-Olav Tislevoll. The two no-trump response to one heart was a strong raise, and three clubs asked North to show a singleton if he had one. Three no-trump was a denial, and two cue-bids followed by Blackwood resulted in a decidedly poor slam contract.

West led the spade jack.

The spade jack was led and ducked around to the king. It might appear that the declarer's task was hopeless, but that is an illusion. Since the spade ace was clearly with East, South might well have decided to hope that the diamond king was also on his right. This would have made it possible to run all the winners in hearts and clubs, aiming for an endplay. East would have had to save the spade ace and the guarded diamond king, and a spade lead would have brought home the slam.

South set off on this track, but found he had another option. After drawing trumps, cashing his club winners, and playing three more hearts, Tislevoll reached this position:

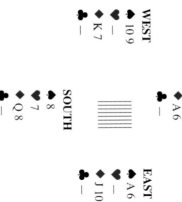

NORTH
♠ Q 7
♥ —
♦ A 6
♣ —

WEST
♠ 10 9
♥ —
♦ K 7
♣ —

EAST
♠ A 6
♥ —
♦ J 10
♣ —

SOUTH
♠ 8
♥ 7
♦ Q 8
♣ —

The Q 7 of spades were gripping West's 10 9 in vise, or vice. A spade discard would allow the declarer to lead the suit and establish a trick.

When the last trump was led West did throw a spade, in the hope that his partner held the eight. South discarded the diamond six from the dummy and followed with a spade lead to make his slam.

But if West had parted with the diamond seven, without any excessive display of agony, South would have had to guess the diamond situation. He might well have thrown a spade from the dummy, hoping to endplay East with a spade lead, and so failed in the slam.

monday 2 122

BANK HOLIDAY (U.K.)

tuesday 3 123

wednesday 4 124

thursday 5 125

CINCO DE MAYO

friday 6 126

saturday 7 127

sunday 8 128

MOTHER'S DAY

The New York Times

s	m	t	w	t	f	s
	1	2	3	4	5	6	7
8	9	10	11	12	13	14
15	16	17	18	19	20	21
22	23	24	25	26	27	28
29	30	31				

MAY

♣ ORGANIZERS NEVER WIN. NOT QUITE TRUE.

Alan Truscott 5/11/02

It is a truth universally acknowledged, as Jane Austen might have said, that the organizer of a major competition, with much on his mind, cannot expect to be a winner. Nevertheless, Bob Blanchard of Manhattan, one of the planners of the celebrated Cavendish tournament played annually in Las Vegas in May, roared to victory three years ago in the teams event.

Blanchard's partner was Sam Lev of Manhattan, with two Polish experts as teammates. They had a substantial lead going into their final match, and the diagramed deal settled the issue.

Both South players overcalled one heart with one no-trump, and at one table the bidding ended. When Blanchard sat North, however, he contributed an aggres-sive raise to two no-trump in the hope that his diamond suit would be worth five tricks. His partner, Lev, carried on to a game that hinged on the opening lead.

A low spade lead would have permitted the defense to score three tricks in the suit, together with two aces, and a heart to the ace combined with a spade shift would have had the same effect. But West led a club, which lost time for the defense and put the declarer in control.

South won with the jack and returned the king, taken by the ace. Now a spade shift would not have helped, since West no longer had a club entry. He returned a club, establishing two winners that were due to wither on the vine.

The declarer won, cashed the diamond king and overtook the queen with the ace. He continued with the jack and the gods of the game gave him the even split that he needed. After cashing the remaining diamonds the position was this:

NORTH
♠ J 3
♥ J 4
♦ A J 8 4 2
♣ 9 7 4 3

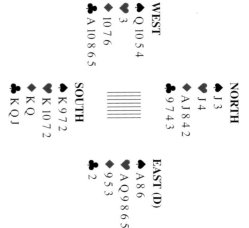

WEST
♠ Q 10 5 4
♥ 3
♦ 10 7 6
♣ A 10 8 6 5

EAST (D)
♠ A 8 6
♥ A Q 9 8 6 5
♦ 9 5 3
♣ 2

SOUTH
♠ K 9 7 2
♥ K 10 7 2
♦ K Q
♣ K Q J

Both sides were vulnerable. The bidding:

East	South	West	North
1 ♥	1 N.T.	Pass	Pass
Pass	2 ♣	Pass	2 N.T.
Pass	3 N.T.	Dbl.	Pass
Pass	Pass		

West led the club six.

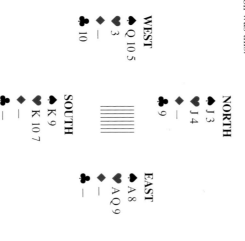

NORTH
♠ J 3
♥ J 4
♦ —
♣ 9

WEST
♠ Q 10 5
♥ 3
♦ —
♣ 10

EAST
♠ A 8
♥ A Q 9
♦ —
♣ —

SOUTH
♠ K 9
♥ K 10 7
♦ —
♣ —

The heart jack was led from dummy, and Lev could not be prevented from making the two additional tricks that he needed. A spade lead toward the king would have served equally well. His team gained 9 imps en route to the title.

monday
9 129

tuesday
10 130

wednesday
11 131

thursday
12 132

friday
13 133

saturday
14 134

sunday
15 135

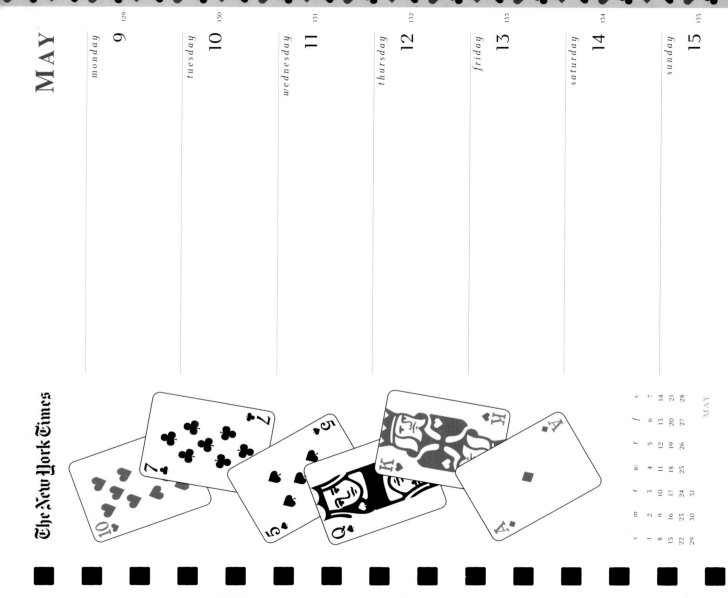

The New York Times

s	m	t	w	t	f	s
	1	2	3	4	5	6	7
8	9	10	11	12	13	14
15	16	17	18	19	20	21
22	23	24	25	26	27	28
29	30	31				

MAY

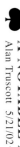

A NOTABLE FOURSOME THAT SCORED MANY VICTORIES

Alan Truscott 5/21/02

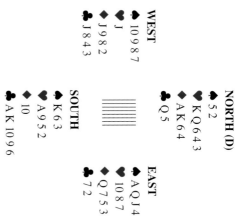

NORTH (D)
♠ 5 2
♥ K Q 6 4 3
♦ A K 6 4
♣ Q 5

WEST
♠ 10 9 8 7
♥ J
♦ J 9 8 2
♣ J 8 4 3

EAST
♠ A Q J 4
♥ 10 8 7
♦ Q 7 5 3
♣ 7 2

SOUTH
♠ K 6 3
♥ A 9 5 2
♦ 10
♣ A K 10 9 6

East and West were vulnerable. The bidding:

North	East	South	West
1 ♥	Pass	3 ♣	Pass
3 ♦	Pass	3 ♥	Pass
4 ♣	Pass	4 ♥	Pass
5 ♥	Pass	5 N.T.	Pass
6 N.T.	Pass	Pass	Pass

West led the spade ten.

Pavlicek, much the youngest, is still going strong, but his teammates are all dead. Kaplan died in 1997, Kay and Root in 2002.

The diagramed deal was played in the 1967 Vanderbilt, with Kaplan sitting North and Kay South. Since the ideal contract of six hearts by South was not available after the opening bid, the partnership maneuvered cleverly into six no-trump, protecting the spade king. Five hearts showed concern about spades, and five no-trump showed the spade king and suggested no-trump as an alternative to hearts. North selected six no-trump, which would have been simple if either player held the club jack. As it was, there was work to be done.

The opening spade ten was led to the ace, giving the declarer a trick in that suit and helping him gauge the distribution. East returned the queen, and South won with the king, noting the seven on his left. He then tested hearts, playing the ace and king. West discarded the spade eight, and Kay thought matters over.

It seemed almost certain that West had begun with exactly four spades. With a five-card diamond suit he would no doubt have discarded from that suit. There was therefore very good reason to believe that West had begun with 4-1-4-4 distribution.

The normal play in clubs had to be discarded: Playing the queen, king and ace would only succeed if East held a doubleton jack. West was twice as likely as East to hold the jack, so Kay backed his cardreading and his knowledge of percentages. He led the club ten and finessed. When this won he led to the club queen, and returned to his hand with the fourth round of hearts to cash his clubs, making the slam. Note that he had to take the club finesse before cashing the rest of the hearts, since he needed a reentry to his hand.

For the past three decades, nearly all the winning teams in the top American championships have consisted of six players, the maximum. One of the six has almost always been a sponsor who has subsidized the team and played the minimum number of deals, 50 percent.

The most important exception was a notable foursome: Edgar Kaplan, Norman Kay, Richard Pavlick and Bill Root. In the period 1982–1990, sometimes with a fifth player, they won the Reisinger Teams four times and the Vanderbilt twice, demonstrating remarkable stamina.

MAY

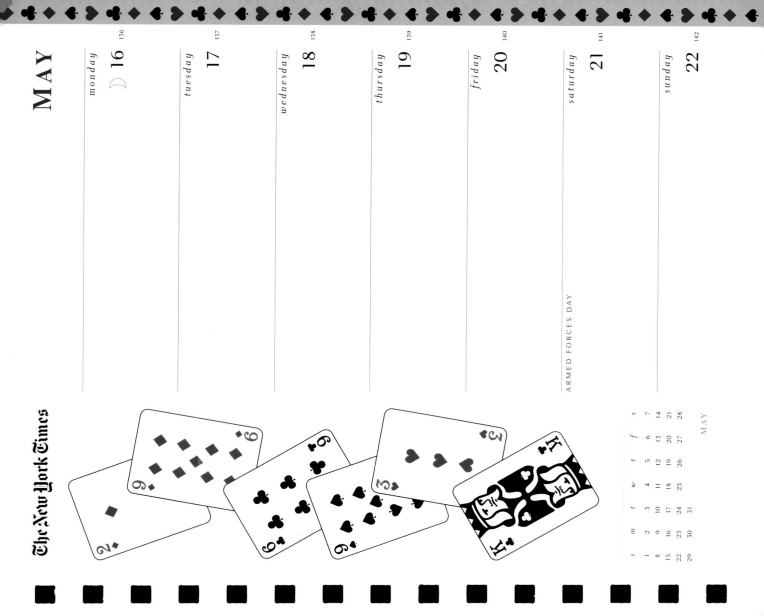

monday 16 · 136

tuesday 17 · 137

wednesday 18 · 138

thursday 19 · 139

friday 20 · 140

saturday 21 · 141

ARMED FORCES DAY

sunday 22 · 142

The New York Times

s	m	t	w	t	f	s
	1	2	3	4	5	6	7
8	9	10	11	12	13	14
15	16	17	18	19	20	21
22	23	24	25	26	27	28
29	30	31

MAY

A MOST UNLIKELY WINNER OF THE GOLDMAN PAIRS

Alan Truscott 5/30/02

```
                NORTH
                ♠ A K Q 5 3
                ♥ A K 8
                ♦ 10 7 4
                ♣ Q 3
WEST                              EAST (D)
♠ 10 8 4 2                        ♠ 9 6
♥ Q 6 5 2                         ♥ J 10
♦ A Q J                           ♦ 8 6 5 3 2
♣ J 8                             ♣ 10 5 4 2
                SOUTH
                ♠ J 7
                ♥ 9 7 4 3
                ♦ K 9
                ♣ A K 9 7 6
```

North and South were vulnerable. The bidding:

East	South	West	North
			Dbl.
Pass	Pass	1 ♦	
3 ♦	3 ♥	Pass	3 ♠
Pass	4 ♣	Pass	4 ♥
Pass	Pass	Pass	

West led the diamond ace.

The most predictable winner of the prestigious Goldman Pairs, always played late in May, was the first: In 1929, the title went to Oswald Jacoby, perhaps the greatest figure in the history of the game. The least predictable emerged in 2002. He was Boris Merson, who learned the game inductively 12 years before by reading this column and inferring the rules. He hardly ever touched a playing card, and his only previous experience of a major tournament came in the 1995 Goldman. He played occasionally on the Internet with Charles Moy, who was also unknown to bridge fame. But they became the Goldman champions, after defeating a star-studded field over four sessions of play. And Merson decided it was the right time to join the American Contract Bridge League. He was the first nonmember ever to win the title.

The diagramed deal offered problems in bidding and play. It was normal to bid game in no-trump, spades or

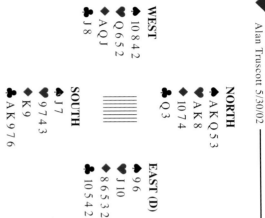

hearts. Those who made 11 tricks had a good score, but those who made only 10 did not. Because of the danger of a diamond lead, it was desirable for South to be the declarer.

When Merson and Moy were North and South, West opened one diamond, a third-seat action aimed at directing an eventual opening lead in that suit. Over Merson's take-out double, East jumped to three diamonds, trading on the favorable vulnerability. This is a weak action, and on this occasion was spectacularly so. If North-South had known how far out on a fragile limb their opponents were, they would have doubled and collected 1100. Not knowing, they continued bidding and landed in four hearts, a 4-3 fit. The question now was whether they could make a an overtrick, crucial at matchpoint scoring.

Moy, as declarer, would have had no trouble after a passive lead, for he would have led trumps effectively. But West led the diamond ace followed by the queen. South won and cashed the ace-king of hearts, noting the appearance of the jack-ten on his right. Since West had opened the bidding, the declarer could judge the position. He needed to find a way to neutralize West's six of trumps.

The queen, king and ace of clubs were played, and all would have been easy if West had ruffed, low or high. But West discarded a spade. Three rounds of spades followed, and the ending was this:

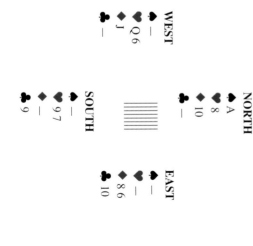

```
                NORTH
                ♠ —
                ♥ 8
                ♦ 10
                ♣ —
WEST                              EAST
♠ —                              ♠ —
♥ Q 6                            ♥ —
♦ J                              ♦ 8 6
♣ —                             ♣ 10
                SOUTH
                ♠ —
                ♥ 9 7
                ♦ —
                ♣ 9
```

MAY

The New York Times

Moy ruffed a diamond and played a club to collect the desired overtrick. He could also have achieved his goal by saving another spade in dummy instead of the diamond ten. Then he would have ruffed a spade with the heart nine, leaving the eight as the master trump if West overruffed.

monday
23 ○
143

VICTORIA DAY (CANADA)

tuesday
24
144

wednesday
25
145

thursday
26
146

friday
27
147

saturday
28
148

sunday
29
149

s	m	t	w	t	f	s
1	2	3	4	5	6	7
8	9	10	11	12	13	14
15	16	17	18	19	20	21
22	23	24	25	26	27	28
29	30	31				

MAY

♦ SECOND HAND LOW, RIGHT? MAYBE NOT THAT LOW

Alan Truscott 6/1/02

NORTH (D)
♠ J 10 8
♥ K J
♦ A 10 9 5
♣ J 6 4 2

WEST
♠ K 7 6 5 3 2
♥ 9 6
♦ —
♣ Q 9 7 5 3

EAST
♠ Q 9 4
♥ 5 4
♦ Q J 8 7 4 2
♣ K 10

SOUTH
♠ A
♥ A Q 10 8 7 3 2
♦ K 6 3
♣ A 8

North and South were vulnerable. The bidding:

North	East	South	West
Pass	2♦	3♥	Pass
4♥	Pass	4 N.T.	Pass
5♥	Pass	5 N.T.	Pass
6♥	Pass	Pass	Pass

West led the heart six.

The Reisinger Knockout Teams, a great tradition in New York bridge for 75 years, is now in progress. The diagramed deal was played in the 2002 contest, with Andy Stark and Franco Baseggio as North and South.

They reached six hearts as shown. After a weak two-bid in diamonds on his right, South underbid slightly with a strong jump to three hearts. He caught up, however, when his partner suggested higher things with a cue-bid of four diamonds, and was even able to hint at a grand slam with an eventual bid of five no-trump.

After a trump lead, Baseggio planned an endplay, knowing from the bidding and opening lead that all the diamonds were on his right. He intended to run his trumps and cash the diamond king, to reach a position something like this:

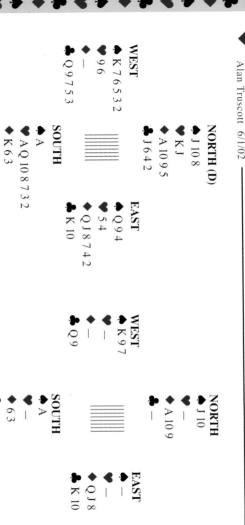

NORTH
♠ J 10
♥ —
♦ A 10 9
♣ —

WEST
♠ K 9 7
♥ —
♦ —
♣ Q 9

EAST
♠ —
♥ —
♦ Q J 8
♣ K 10

SOUTH
♠ A
♥ —
♦ 6 3
♣ A 8

Cashing the spade ace would force a club discard, to prevent a diamond duck. Then the club ace would strip East's remaining black card and allow a diamond duck-and-endplay. Alternatively, East could throw his clubs, in which case South would play the club ace with similar effect.

None of this happened, however, for Baseggio set a small trap. When East followed to the second round of trumps, South won that trick in the dummy. He called for the diamond five, and when East sleepily produced the four, confidently contributed the three and claimed his slam. Winning the first round of a suit with a five after an opponent has bid it may be unique.

monday 30 150

MEMORIAL DAY
BANK HOLIDAY (U.K.)

tuesday 31 151

wednesday 1 152

thursday 2 153

friday 3 154

saturday 4 155

sunday 5 156

The New York Times

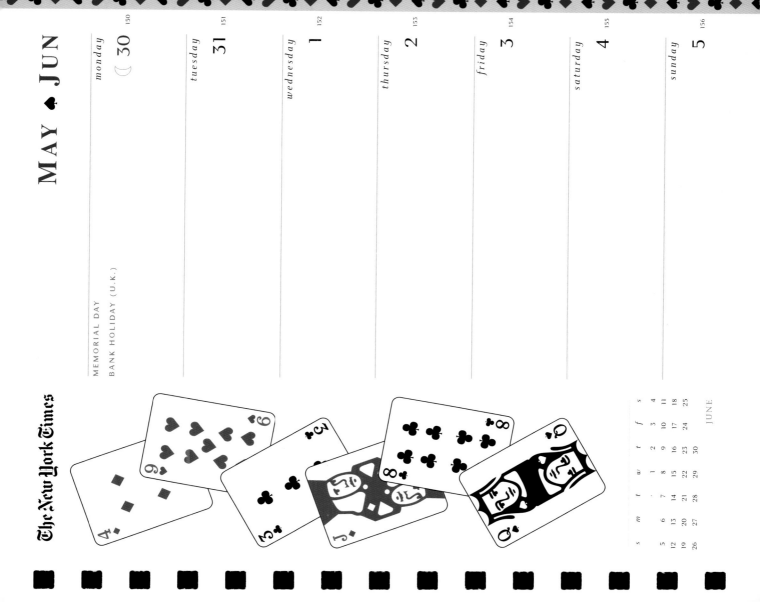

JUNE

s	m	t	w	t	f	s
						4
5	6	7	8	9	10	11
12	13	14	15	16	17	18
19	20	21	22	23	24	25
26	27	28	29	30		

Alan Truscott 6/15/02

NORTH
♠ 9 4 2
♥ A K 8 5
♦ A J 10 7 2
♣ 10

WEST (D)
♠ A 7 6
♥ 7 4 3 2
♦ —
♣ J 9 7 6 5 3

EAST
♠ 8 5 3
♥ J 9 6
♦ Q 9 4 3
♣ K Q 4

SOUTH
♠ K Q J 10
♥ Q 10
♦ K 8 6 5
♣ A 8 2

East and West were vulnerable. The bidding:

West	North	East	South
	1 ♦	Pass	1 ♠
Pass	2 ♦	Pass	4 ♠
Pass	Pass	Pass	

West led the club six.

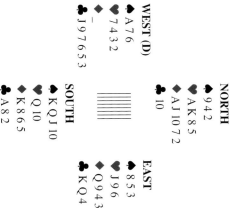

Brilliant software developed in England by Anna Gudge and Mark Newton makes it possible for players around the world to compete against each other in the Worldwide Bridge Contest, played annually in early June. In 2002, in the first of two similar events, an American pair finished top among players in 312 clubs in 41 countries. Ken Barbour and Markland Jones scored 76 percent playing at the Arizona Bridge Center in Phoenix, Ariz.

Six diamonds would be an acceptable contract on the diagramed deal, but, as it happens, is doomed by the bad trump split. If North-South are going to play a game, the best choice is four spades. The winners hit this target on the diagramed deal by reaching four spades with a simple sequence. A 4-3 trump fit is often

desirable when the four-card suit is strong and ruffs can be taken in the short hand.

Jones, as South, could have made two overtricks by winning the club lead with the ace, ruffing a club, and maneuvering a second club ruff. But that would require a 3-3 trump split, which was unlikely. Instead, he made a good play by permitting East to win the first club trick, preserving his ace to keep control.

It did not occur to East to return a diamond and give his partner a ruff. He returned a club, which was ruffed in the dummy. When South embarked on trumps, West held up his ace for one round and then led a third club. South won with the ace, drew trumps, and had no trouble making the remaining tricks. The lucky heart position, with the nine and jack falling in three rounds, made it unnecessary for declarer to guess the diamond position. This result gave Barbour and Jones 4098.6 match points, which is not a number players are used to. It represented 81.55 percent of the maximum.

Three pairs actually bid and made slams with the North-South cards. One did so in spades, which is understandable. One did so in diamonds and another in no-trump, both of which appear impossible.

JUNE

The New York Times

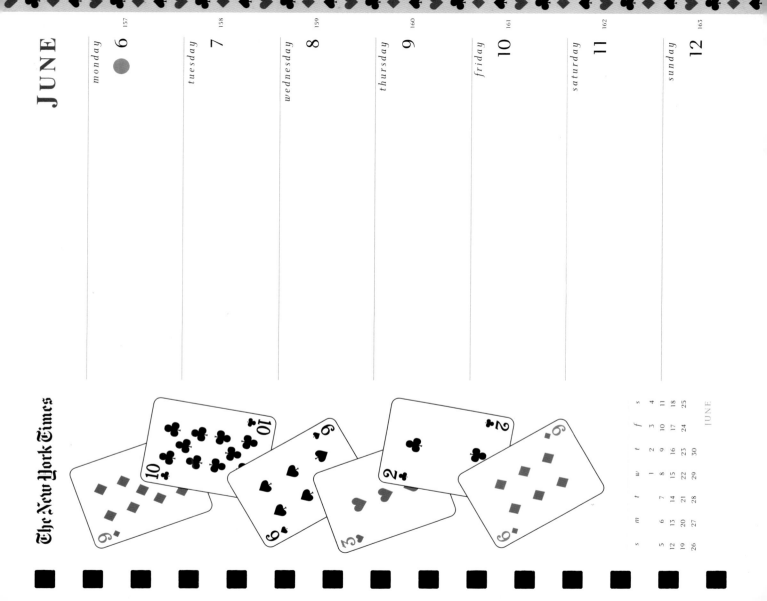

	s	m	t	w	t	f	s
				1	2	3	4
	5	6	7	8	9	10	11
	12	13	14	15	16	17	18
	19	20	21	22	23	24	25
	26	27	28	29	30		

JUNE

LIFE'S LEARNING EXPERIENCES, ETCHED FOREVER IN MEMORY

Alan Truscott 6/6/02

NORTH
- ♠ K 9 4
- ♥ K 10 7 6
- ♦ 4 3
- ♣ K Q 6 2

WEST
- ♠ A J 5
- ♥ J 8 2
- ♦ Q 10 6
- ♣ J 8 7 3

EAST
- ♠ 10 7 6 3 2
- ♥ A 5 4 3
- ♦ 5 2
- ♣ 10 9

SOUTH (D)
- ♠ Q 8
- ♥ Q 9
- ♦ A K J 9 8 7
- ♣ A 5 4

Both sides were vulnerable. The bidding:

South	West	North	East
1 N.T.	Pass	Pass	Pass
Pass	Pass	3 N.T.	Pass

West led the spade jack.

Many players have a sad memory of one that got away imprinted on their bridge psyche. For this columnist, it happened more than half a century ago, in my first international championship. The contract was three no-trump, and the defense had four obvious tricks. The only possible fifth was in a suit in which I held Q x x and my partner J x x. I hit on the rare lead of the queen, deceiving the declarer, and my partner eventually scored his jack. But he then failed to find the play to cash our five tricks.

For Andrew Arkin, the diagramed deal, also played many years ago, is even sadder. In a money game, he sat West, and also had to lead against three no-trump. As the expert declarer acknowledged afterwards, any orthodox lead would have given him no trouble at all. But Arkin was inspired to lead the spade jack.

The lead was made in the hope of finding his partner with length and some strength in the suit. East had the length but not much strength. What he did have, however, was crucial.

South played low from dummy without hesitation and won with the queen. He crossed to dummy with a club lead and finessed the diamond jack, losing to the queen. Arkin now followed up his unorthodox lead by playing the five. South confidently finessed dummy's nine, and was headed for a two-trick defeat, since East had the ace of hearts as an entry after the spades were cleared.

Alas for Arkin's hopes, the opening lead had fooled not only South but also East. That player "knew" that South had the spade ace and did not bother to play his ten on dummy's nine. Arkin did not say much, but he has neither forgotten nor forgiven.

JUNE

monday **13** 164

tuesday **14** 165

wednesday ☽ **15** 166

thursday **16** 167

friday **17** 168

saturday **18** 169

sunday **19** 170

FLAG DAY

FATHER'S DAY

The New York Times

s	m	t	w	t	f	s
			1	2	3	4
5	6	7	8	9	10	11
12	13	14	15	16	17	18
19	20	21	22	23	24	25
26	27	28	29	30		

JUNE

A CANDIDATE FOR THE MOST REMARKABLE LEAD EVER MADE

Alan Truscott 6/10/02

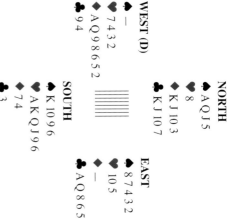

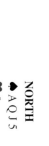

```
                    NORTH
                    ♠ A Q J 5
                    ♥ 8
                    ♦ K J 10 3
                    ♣ K J 10 7

WEST (D)                              EAST
♠ —                                   ♠ 8 7 4 3 2
♥ 7 4 3 2                             ♥ 10 5
♦ A Q 9 8 6 5 2                       ♦ —
♣ 9 4                                 ♣ A Q 8 6 5 2

                    SOUTH
                    ♠ K 10 9 6
                    ♥ A K Q J 9 6
                    ♦ 7 4
                    ♣ 3
```

Both sides were vulnerable. The bidding:

West	North	East	South
Pass	1 ♦	Pass	3 ♥
Pass	3 ♣	Pass	3 ♥
Pass	3 N.T.	4 ♣	4 ♦
Pass	4 ♥	Pass	4 N.T.
Pass	5 ♦	Pass	5 ♥
Pass	6 ♥	Dbl.	Pass
Pass	Pass		

West led the diamond queen.

The most remarkable lead reported so far in this decade occurred on the diagramed deal. Indeed, the queen from a seven-card suit headed by the A Q against a suit slam may be unique and is a candidate for the strangest ever made. It occurred in the 2002 New York Von Zedtwitz Double Knockout Teams, and the East-West cards were held by Sue Picus of Manhattan and Jillian Levin of Riverdale in the Bronx, both world champions.

The North-South bidding went seriously off the rails. Knowing that North had some strength in clubs, South should have been content to bid four hearts over three no-trump. When his Blackwood bid revealed that there

were two aces missing, he attempted to sign off in five hearts and North should certainly have subsided. That contract would not have been doubled and would have had a faint chance of succeeding: West would probably have led her partner's club suit and East might have attempted to take two tricks there with disastrous consequences.

East doubled six hearts as a Lightner move, suggesting a lead in diamonds rather than clubs. If West had heeded this warning, he would have retreated to six no-trump. That contract makes 11 tricks if the declarer judges to develop a club trick rather than a diamond trick. Even six spades would have been an improvement, failing by at most two tricks.

West, however, was listening to the bidding and selected a dramatic lead: the diamond queen. She knew that her partner's double indicated a diamond void, and the queen was a suit-preference indication showing a strong desire for a spade return.

East won the first trick by ruffing dummy's diamond king, and took a slight risk by cashing the club ace. She then played a spade, as requested by the lead, and the defense had a merry time crossruffing to collect 1100. The penalty would have been 1400 if East had led a spade at the second trick, maneuvering an extra ruff for her partner.

In the replay, North-South were again over-exuberant. North bid three no-trump over a three-diamond opening by West, and South raised directly to six no-trump. The result was another slam missing two aces, but this one was not doubled. After a spade lead, the declarer made an early diamond play from his dummy and the result was down two. He should instead have made a club play from the South side, failing by just one trick with a slight chance to succeed: West might have held a singleton or doubleton club queen.

monday **20** 171

tuesday **21** 172

wednesday ○ **22** 173

SUMMER SOLSTICE 6:46 A.M. (GMT)

thursday **23** 174

friday **24** 175

saturday **25** 176

sunday **26** 177

The New York Times

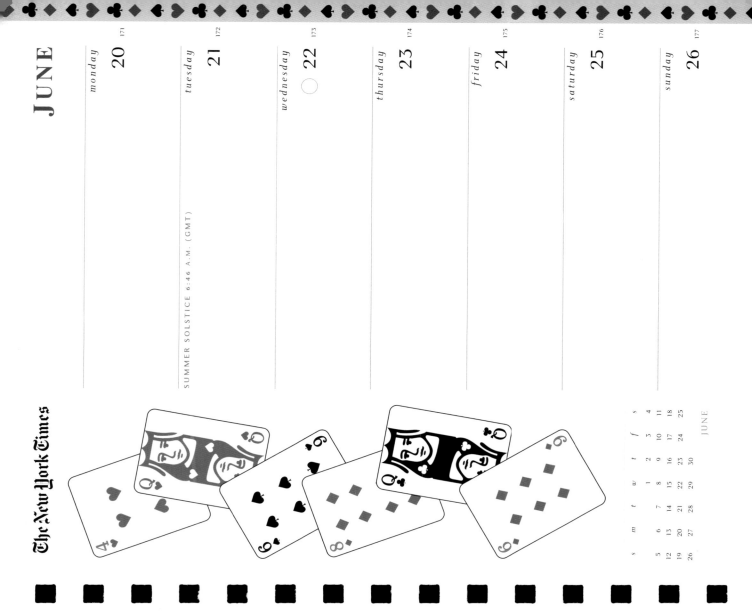

s	m	t	w	t	f	s
			1	2	3	4
5	6	7	8	9	10	11
12	13	14	15	16	17	18
19	20	21	22	23	24	25
26	27	28	29	30		

JUNE

GENERALIZATIONS ARE NOT ABSOLUTE—THERE ARE ALWAYS EXCEPTIONS

Alan Truscott 7/8/02

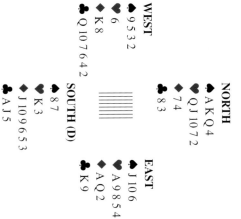

NORTH
- ♠ A K Q 4
- ♥ Q J 10 7 2
- ♦ 7 4
- ♣ 8 3

WEST
- ♠ 9 5 3 2
- ♥ 6
- ♦ K 8
- ♣ Q 10 7 6 4 2

EAST
- ♠ J 10 6
- ♥ A 9 8 5 4
- ♦ A Q 2
- ♣ K 9

SOUTH (D)
- ♠ 8 7
- ♥ K 3
- ♦ J 10 9 6 5 3
- ♣ A J 5

Neither side was vulnerable. The bidding:

South	West	North	East
Pass	Pass	1 ♥	Pass
1 N.T.	Pass	2 ♣	Pass
2 ♦	Pass	Pass	Pass

West led the heart six.

Consider these two generalizations: An eight-card trump fit can be expected to take at least as many tricks as a seven-card trump fit; and declarer does better if his trumps split evenly than if they split very unevenly. Both these are cast into some doubt by the diagramed deal played in a Pro-Am event in Manhattan.

North had a hand that every expert hates to pick up: 4-5-2-2 with 12–16 high-card points. A few, therefore, use Flannery to show four-five in the major suits, and South bids two hearts, becoming declarer. Using a modern standard method, however, the danger is that one heart will receive a forcing one no-trump response. North must grit his teeth and bid two clubs with a doubleton, which may result in a foolish contract. It does

not here, because South will rebid two hearts or two diamonds.

The situation is different when, as here, South is a passed hand: He can respond two diamonds, non-forcing. This suggests a six-card suit with slightly less than opening values, and a sensible contract is reached when North passes. Alternatively, South can bid one no-trump, non-forcing. North can pass this with disastrous consequences: After a club lead the contract fails by three tricks.

North-South avoided this fate because they were playing one no-trump as forcing, even by a passed hand. The result was two diamonds, which would have failed if West had led a club. However, a heart was led to the ace and the suit was returned for a ruff. Now West shifted to a club, the king forcing the ace.

Now South should have succeeded by playing three rounds of spades and throwing a club. A heart winner would follow, for another club discard, and West would have to ruff with a winning trump. Instead, South played a heart winner from dummy prematurely, and the defense took a club trick as well as the heart ace and four trumps for down one.

East and West were Kelley Hwang and Hilary Skolnick, who won the event. The curious feature of the deal is that two diamonds is defeated by the best lead of a club, while two hearts is unbeatable: The declarer will take four black-suit tricks and, in one way or another, four trump tricks. So a 5-2 fit, with the missing trumps breaking very badly, proves to be more successful than a 6-2 fit with a normal split.

JUN ♠ JUL

monday
27
178

tuesday
28
179

wednesday
29
180

thursday
30
181

friday
1
182

CANADA DAY (CANADA)

saturday
2
183

sunday
3
184

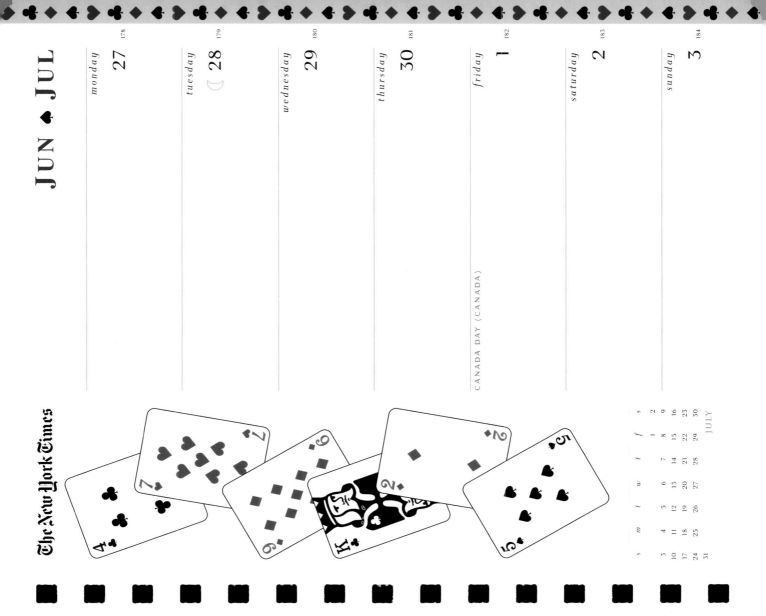

s	m	t	w	t	f	s
					1	2
3	4	5	6	7	8	9
10	11	12	13	14	15	16
17	18	19	20	21	22	23
24	25	26	27	28	29	30
31						

JULY

♣ BIG BUSINESS AND SMALL CARDS GO WELL TOGETHER

Alan Truscott 7/11/02

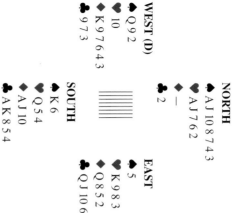

```
             NORTH
             ♠ A J 10 8 7 4 3
             ♥ A J 7 6 2
             ♦ —
             ♣ 2

WEST (D)                       EAST
♠ Q 9 2                        ♠ 5
♥ 10                           ♥ K 9 8 3
♦ K 9 7 6 4 3                  ♦ Q 8 5 2
♣ 9 7 3                        ♣ Q J 10 6

             SOUTH
             ♠ K 6
             ♥ Q 5 4
             ♦ A J 10
             ♣ A K 8 5 4
```

Neither side was vulnerable. The bidding:

West	North	East	South
Pass	1♠	Pass	2♣
Pass	2♦	Pass	3 N.T.
Pass	4♠	Pass	6 N.T.
Pass	Pass	Pass	

West led the heart ten.

Throughout bridge history, there have been enthusiasts with big reputations in the corporate and financial worlds. First there was Charles Schwab, head of Bethlehem Steel, who in 1933 presented the Schwab Cup for international competition, now awarded to the winners of the World Pairs. Second came Ira Corn Jr., chief executive of Michigan General, a major conglomerate, and founder of the Aces team that won several world team titles.

Among current players, the veteran is George Rosenkranz of Mexico, retired president of Syntex Corporation, who has won the Spingold Knockout twice and is still contending at the age of 88. James Cayne, CEO of Bear Stearns Inc. brokerage, has won 10 national titles and been in the running at world level. Warren Buffet, legendary head of Berkshire Hathaway, has played all his adult life and makes occasional tournament appearances.

One new recruit to the game is Bill Gates of Microsoft, who has played twice in the Summer Nationals, which are always held in July. Another is Peter Lynch, noted author of "One Up on Wall Street," whose wife, Carolyn, moved One Up on her spouse by winning four team events at her first tournament. It was the 2002 Regional Championships in Cherry Hill, N.J., where she played with her teacher, Dennis Dawson. They were strongly supported by four world-class players, David Berkowitz, Larry Cohen, Mike Lawrence and John Sutherlin. As South on the diagramed deal from the Swiss Teams, Dawson insisted on six no-trump, which was not the contract his partner had anticipated.

West looked for a safe lead, and decided that dummy's second suit was less dangerous than South's first suit or the unbid diamonds. South studied the heart ten, and was sure that the king was on his right. He put up dummy's ace, in the faint hope, unfulfilled, of collecting a singleton king. There was no hurry to play spades, so he called for a low heart. East played low, and the queen won in the closed hand.

South cashed the spade king and led the six. When the nine appeared on his left he brooded. Where was the queen? There was a slight clue. West was known to have begun with a singleton heart, and therefore three spades was slightly more likely than two.

A tripleton spade with West thus seemed slightly more likely than a doubleton, so Dawson called for the ten, taking a heart-in-mouth finesse. When it succeeded he had 12 tricks and his slam. If it had failed he would have struggled home with seven tricks for a loss of 250. In the replay six spades failed by a trick when the declarer did not guess the trump position, and the Lynch team gained 14 imps en route to victory in the event with eight wins and no losses.

JULY

monday 4 — 185
INDEPENDENCE DAY

tuesday 5 — 186

wednesday ● 6 — 187

thursday 7 — 188

friday 8 — 189

saturday 9 — 190

sunday 10 — 191

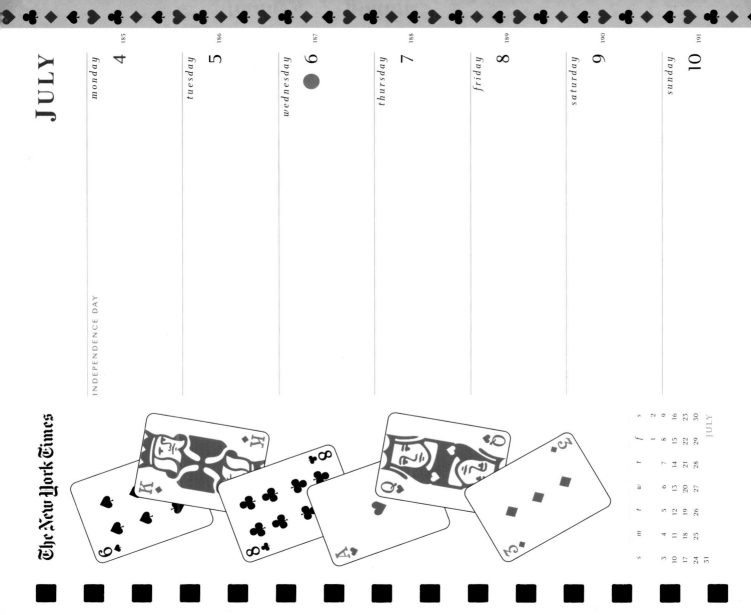

s	m	t	w	t	f	s
					1	2
3	4	5	6	7	8	9
10	11	12	13	14	15	16
17	18	19	20	21	22	23
24	25	26	27	28	29	30
31						

JULY

♠ HOW TO PRACTICE FOR THE SUMMER NATIONALS

Alan Truscott 7/13/02

NORTH
♠ Q 7 3
♥ K 7
♦ K Q 9 2
♣ A K 7 6

WEST
♠ K 6 5 4 2
♥ Q 10 8
♦ J 7 6 5
♣ J

EAST
♠ J 10 9 8
♥ 9 5 3
♦ 10
♣ Q 10 8 5 3

SOUTH (D)
♠ A
♥ A J 6 4 2
♦ A 8 4 3
♣ 9 4 2

Both sides were vulnerable. The bidding:

South	West	North	East
1 ♥	Pass	2 ♣	Pass
2 ♦	Pass	3 ♦	Pass
4 ♣	Pass	4 ♥	Pass
4 ♠	Dbl.	4 ♠	Pass
5 ♣	Pass	6 ♦	Pass
Pass	Pass	Pass	

West led the spade two.

The Summer Nationals will begin this week in Atlanta, Ga. Many of the experts practice online with their intended partners before they make the trip.

Marty Fleisher and Ron Gerard had good reason to be pleased with the diagramed deal, played in an imp game on the Swan network in such a practice game. They reached an excellent contract of six diamonds, which would have been relatively easy with a normal 3-2 trump split. As it was, it would appear that the defense was likely to take a trump trick and a club trick.

Gerard, South, won the opening third-and-fifth spade lead with the ace and played three rounds of hearts, ruffing the third with the diamond nine. He then cashed the king-queen of diamonds, uncovering the bad split. Reading the distribution correctly, he took the club ace, removing West's singleton jack, and led to the diamond ace. The position was this:

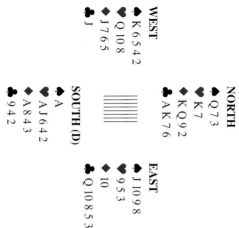

NORTH
♠ Q 7
♥ —
♦ —
♣ K 7 6

WEST
♠ K 6 5 4
♥ —
♦ J
♣ —

EAST
♠ J 10
♦ —
♣ Q 10 8

SOUTH
♠ —
♥ J 6
♦ 8
♣ 9 4

The heart jack was led, and West would have end-played himself if he had ruffed: Dummy's spade queen would have scored a trick. West therefore discarded a spade, but was in the same bind when the declarer threw a club from the dummy and continued with the last heart.

West discarded again, but it did not save him. South gave up the spade seven from dummy and led a club. This time a ruff would have eliminated the declarer's club loser, so West discarded for the third time. Gerard won with the club king and ruffed the spade queen. He had his 12th trick, and East's club winner and West's trump winner collided on the last trick.

JULY

monday 11

tuesday 12

wednesday 13

thursday ☽ 14

friday 15

saturday 16

sunday 17

BANK HOLIDAY (N. IRELAND)

The New York Times

s	m	t	w	t	f	s
					1	2
3	4	5	6	7	8	9
10	11	12	13	14	15	16
17	18	19	20	21	22	23
24	25	26	27	28	29	30
31						

JULY

A CLEVER TRAP IS LAID—AND AVOIDED

Alan Truscott 7/20/02

NORTH
- ♠ J 8 3
- ♥ A 8 6
- ♦ K Q 10 9 5
- ♣ 10 3

WEST
- ♠ Q 7 5
- ♥ J 10 9 5 2
- ♦ 7 6 2
- ♣ J 4

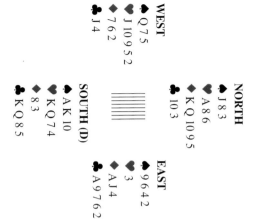

EAST
- ♠ 9 6 4 2
- ♥ 3
- ♦ A J 4
- ♣ A 9 7 6 2

SOUTH (D)
- ♠ A K 10
- ♥ K Q 7 4
- ♦ 8 3
- ♣ K Q 8 5

Both sides were vulnerable. The bidding:

South	West	North	East
1 N.T.	Pass	3 N.T.	Pass
Pass	Pass		

West led the heart jack.

The Summer Nationals of the American Contract Bridge League are almost always played in July. They are now in progress in Atlanta, Ga.

The major team games always produce some close struggles. One of them, five years ago in Washington, D.C., furnished a battle of wits between Chris Willenken, East, and Roger Bates, South, on the diagramed deal.

An obvious auction led to three no-trump. The declarer won the heart-jack lead with the king and ran the diamond eight for a finesse. He was in the paradoxical position of hoping that this would lose to the jack, for if that happened he could be sure of making three diamond tricks, with nine winners a virtual certainty. But he did not lose to the jack, for Willenken promptly

allowed the eight to win, a brilliant move. This tempted South to repeat the finesse, in which case the contract would have failed.

After much thought, Bates decided to allow for the possibility that East had made a tricky play. So, instead of finessing the ten and guaranteeing the contract if West did indeed hold the ten, South led to the diamond king. This gave him two chances.

One was that the diamond suit would be established, and it was: When the jack appeared on the third round he made 11 tricks. If that had failed he would have attempted the spade finesse, hoping to collect three tricks in spades, together with three in hearts, two in diamonds and one in clubs.

In the replay, the play began similarly but East won the second trick with the jack. The declarer made 10 tricks, losing one imp.

JULY

monday 18   199

tuesday 19   200

wednesday 20   201

thursday ○ 21   202

friday 22   203

saturday 23   204

sunday 24   205

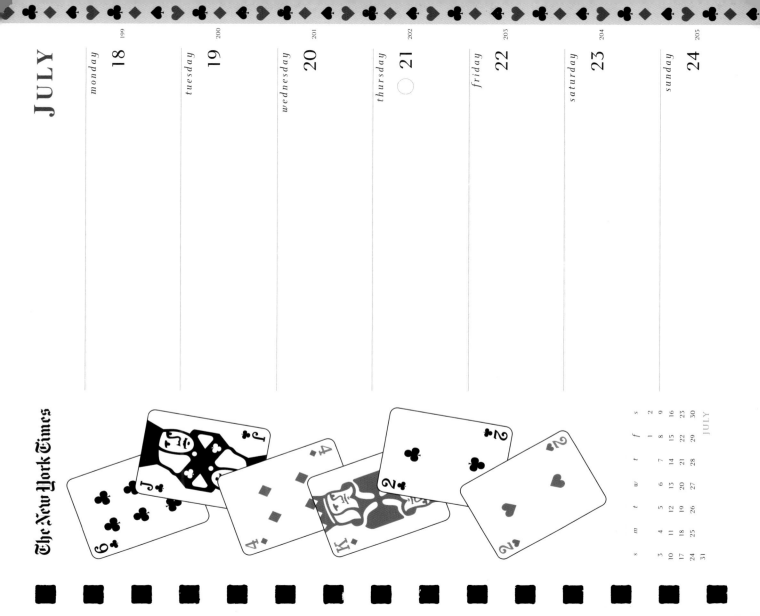

The New York Times

s	m	t	w	t	f	s
					1	2
3	4	5	6	7	8	9
10	11	12	13	14	15	16
17	18	19	20	21	22	23
24	25	26	27	28	29	30
31						

JULY

WHEN YOU ARE ABOUT TO DIE, RUN AWAY AND SAVE THE DAY

Alan Truscott 7/27/02

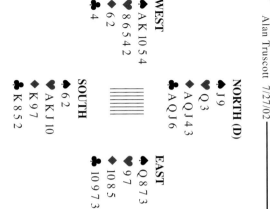

NORTH (D)
♠ J 9
♥ Q 3
♦ A Q J 4 3
♣ A Q J 6

WEST
♠ A K 10 5 4
♥ 8 6 5 4 2
♦ 6 2
♣ 4

EAST
♠ Q 8 7 3
♥ 9 7
♦ 10 8 5
♣ 10 9 7 3

SOUTH
♠ 6 2
♥ A K J 10
♦ K 9 7
♣ K 8 5 2

Neither side was vulnerable. The bidding:

North	East	South	West
1 N.T.	Pass	2 ♣	2 ♦
Pass	Pass	3 ♣	Pass
4 ♦	Pass	4 ♥	Pass
Pass			

West led the spade ace.

The Summer Nationals are just ending in Atlanta, Ga. The final championship is traditionally the Mixed Teams, which uses board-a-match scoring. One of the most sensational deals ever played in this event occurred on the diagramed deal played three years ago.

The North-South hands should obviously avoid three no-trump, lacking a stopper in spades. But what is the right contract? The obvious answer is either five clubs or five diamonds, which would be the correct choice at imp scoring or rubber bridge. But at board-a-match or match points, when small advantages have a big impact, a brilliant pair might reach the unexpected contract of four hearts.

Although outnumbered in trumps, South will succeed with a normal four-three trump split. (He actually makes an overtrick). That has a 62 percent chance, and

North-South can therefore expect to outscore a rival pair playing in a minor-suit game.

Two Canadians, Rhoda Habert and Marshall Lewis, sitting North-South, hit this difficult target with the diagramed auction. West's overcall of two spades warned about a possible weakness in no-trump, and the partnership maneuvered into hearts, a brilliant effort.

Virtue had to be its own reward, for the player who was known to have long spades turned out, unexpectedly, to have long hearts also. West led a top spade and shifted to a trump. When South attempted to draw trumps he lost control and was finished three.

East-West thought they had won the board by collecting 150 when their opponents could have made a minor-suit game. They would have been quite happy if their teammates had reached three no-trump, failing by one trick, but the result in the replay was sensational.

Larry Cohen, sitting North, opened one club, strong and artificial in the Precision System he was using. Lisa Berkowitz responded two no-trump. This shut West out of the bidding, and North had a problem. He took a shot at six no-trump, which was about to fail by four tricks, losing the board. But West came to the rescue by doubling, as many would.

North knew that West, for his double, must have either two aces or an ace-king combination. If the latter, it was quite possible that East would not know which suit to lead. Cohen therefore retreated to seven clubs, hoping that a possible four-four fit would be effective.

West doubled with rather less confidence, and, sure enough, East did not know what to lead. When he failed to find a spade, Cohen was able to draw trumps and claim the grand slam.

North-South scored 1630, and were even more confident than their teammates that they had won the board. But they were not entirely happy: It would have been even better, they realized, if it had been imp scoring. But their team did win the title.

JULY

monday 25   206

tuesday 26   207

wednesday 27   208

thursday 28   209

friday 29   210

saturday 30   211

sunday 31   212

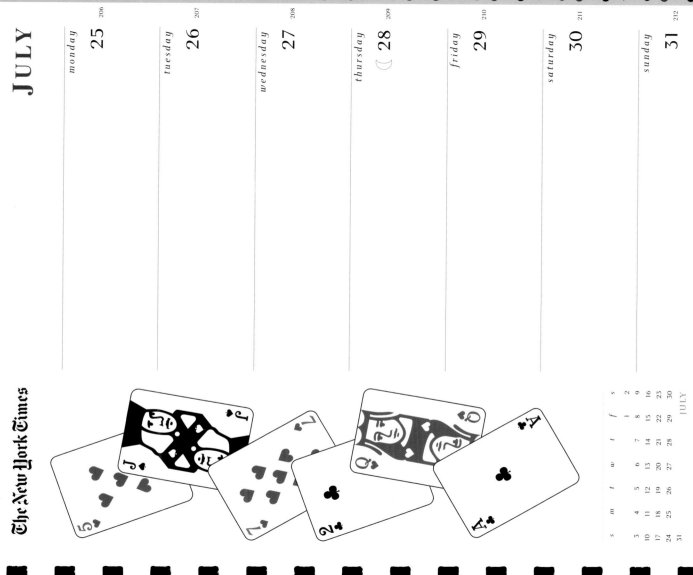

The New York Times

JULY

s	m	t	w	t	f	s
					1	2
3	4	5	6	7	8	9
10	11	12	13	14	15	16
17	18	19	20	21	22	23
24	25	26	27	28	29	30
31						

A DAMAGING LEAD FORCES DECLARER TO MAKE HIS SLAM

Alan Truscott 8/8/02

NORTH
♠ A 10 5 3 2
♥ A K Q 10 9
♦ A
♣ 8 5

WEST (D)
♠ K 4
♥ J 5 2
♦ Q 10 4 3 2
♣ 7 3 2

EAST
♠ J 9 7 6
♥ 7 6 3
♦ K 9
♣ J 10 6 4

SOUTH
♠ Q 8
♥ 8 4
♦ J 8 7 6 5
♣ A K Q 9

Both sides were vulnerable. The bidding:

West	North	East	South
Pass	1 ♠	Pass	2 ♣
Pass	2 ♥	Pass	2 N.T.
Pass	3 ♣	Pass	3 ♠
Pass	6 N.T.	Pass	Pass
Pass			

West led the diamond three.

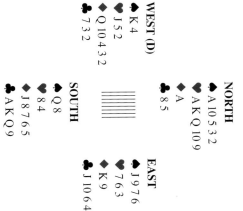

Anyone who can combine great luck and great skill will do well at bridge, or almost any other activity. The diagramed deal from the final of the Spingold Knockout Teams in Washington, D.C., five years ago illustrates the point.

North and South were two Canadian champions, Bryan Maksymetz and Allan Graves, who had impressed the pundits with their play throughout the week. They were members of the Michael Moss team that had eliminated several top-ranked squads en route to the final, in which they faced George Jacobs, Ralph Katz, and four Italian stars.

Graves chose to respond two clubs to one spade, bidding strength rather than length. This slight eccentricity proved to have a major impact on the outcome. When the bidding reached three spades, North had considerable undisclosed strength. He stretched with a bid of six no-trump, and Graves was now in a totally terrible contract.

The chance of success seemed to diminish when West led a diamond, removing dummy's ace. If South had bid diamonds, West would probably have led a club or a heart. The declarer would then have tried to make use of the spade suit, starting with a low card from dummy toward the queen. This would have failed.

After a diamond lead, playing spades was virtually hopeless. South therefore tried for a long shot: He led a club from dummy and finessed the nine. When this won the trick, a glimmer of hope appeared. The declarer played hearts, and felt even better when the jack appeared on the third round. He took two more heart tricks and two of his club winners to reach this ending:

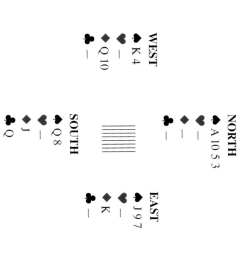

NORTH
♠ A 10 5 3
♥ —
♦ —
♣ —

WEST
♠ K 4
♥ —
♦ —
♣ —

EAST
♠ J 9 7
♥ —
♦ K
♣ —

SOUTH
♠ Q 8
♥ —
♦ J
♣ Q

When the club queen was led, West threw a diamond, North a spade, and East also a spade. East was thrown into the lead with a diamond and was forced to break the spade suit. Graves now had a good reason to make the winning guess. He played the eight, forcing the king and making his slam. Graves judged that East would have discarded his diamond king if he had held the spade king.

Wild applause erupted in the Vugraph theater, particularly from the Canadian supporters. Since the rival

AUGUST

CIVIC HOLIDAY (CANADA, MOST PROVINCES)

BANK HOLIDAY (SCOTLAND)

The New York Times

North-South played in three no-trump, Graves and his teammates gained 13 imps. They would have lost 12 if the gods of the game had not been smiling so favorably. Paradoxically, the menacing diamond lead had forced South to make his improbable slam.

s	m	t	w	t	f	s
	1	2	3	4	5	6
7	8	9	10	11	12	13
14	15	16	17	18	19	20
21	22	23	24	25	26	27
28	29	30	31			

AUGUST

OVERCOMING A MEDICAL PROBLEM AND AN ITALIAN OPPONENT

Alan Truscott 8/10/02

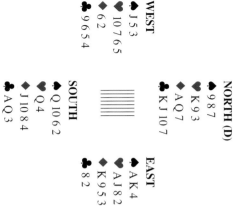

NORTH (D)
- ♠ 9 8 7
- ♥ K 9 3
- ♦ A Q 7
- ♣ K J 10 7

WEST
- ♠ J 5 3
- ♥ 10 7 6 5
- ♦ 6 2
- ♣ 9 6 5 4

EAST
- ♠ A K 4
- ♥ A J 8 2
- ♦ K 9 5 3
- ♣ 8 2

SOUTH
- ♠ Q 10 6 2
- ♥ Q 4
- ♦ J 10 8 4
- ♣ A Q 3

Neither side was vulnerable. The bidding:

North	East	South	West
1 ♣	Dbl.	Redbl.	1 ♥
Pass	Pass	2 N.T.	Pass
3 N.T.	Pass	Pass	Pass

West led the heart five.

A familiar figure on the national bridge scene was center stage once again at the American Contract Bridge League's Summer Nationals in Washington, D.C. five years ago. Michael Moss of Manhattan, known for his will to win on any occasion, came close to winning a world team title 15 years ago. In 2001, he was an unexpected runner-up in the Spingold Knockout, playing on a four-man team in an event that is always a test of stamina. In 2002 he again battled his way to the Spingold final in a totally different four-man team, originally seeded 22nd in the field of 103 teams.

His march to the final included a win over the third seed by the crushing margin of 102 imps. It also included a medical problem. After the first session of one match, he was taken to hospital following a dia-

betic reaction, but returned for the evening play after a talented substitute had taken his place for 16 deals.

On the diagrammed deal from the final, Moss got the better of a battle of wits with an Italian world champion. When his partner's opening bid of one club was doubled, Moss redoubled and followed with a jump to two no-trump, undeterred by his weakness in the heart suit that West had bid. When his partner, Martin Schifko, continued to three no-trump, Moss had the advantage of knowing that almost all the high-card strength was on his right.

A heart was led and dummy played low, Alfredo Versace, sitting East, did well by playing the eight and forcing the queen, since he would know that his contract was doomed if West could win the trick to play a second heart.

But Versace made a strange and subtle play: He cashed the heart before leading the spade four. This seemed foolish, but when the commentators thought this over they realized that it gave Moss a losing option: He could finesse the ten and make his contract if the spade jack was on his right and the ace or king on his left.

Moss put his head in his hands and thought for three minutes, a long time at the bridge table. Finally he produced the spade queen, making his contract and collecting a round of applause, which he could not hear, from the audience of 200 in the Vugraph theater. Moss had realized that if West held a top spade, East would not have cashed the the heart ace and given him a chance to succeed. The heart ace could be recognized as a red herring, and the smell of fish was perceptible.

In the replay, North-South did not reach game and Moss had earned a profit for his team.

They were sure that he would make the winning guess by playing the queen, since he would know that his contract was doomed if West could win the trick to play a second heart.

But Versace made a strange and subtle play: He cashed the heart before leading the spade four. This seemed foolish, but when the commentators thought this over they realized that it gave Moss a losing option: He could finesse the ten and make his contract if the spade jack was on his right and the ace or king on his left.

finesse lost to the king. The commentators were now sure that the contract would succeed. They expected the lead of the spade four, setting Moss a problem.

AUGUST

monday 8 220

tuesday 9 221

wednesday 10 222

thursday 11 223

friday 12 224

saturday 13 225

sunday 14 226

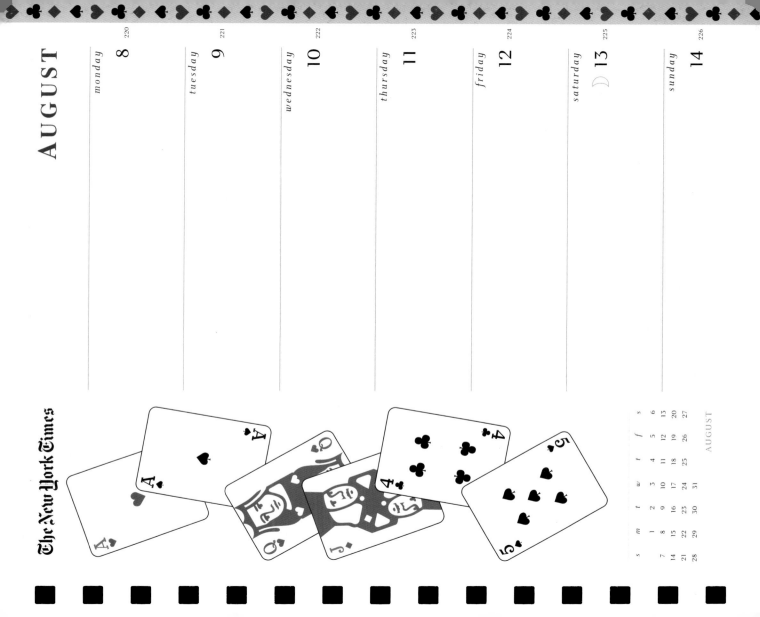

The New York Times

s	m	t	w	t	f	s
	1	2	3	4	5	6
7	8	9	10	11	12	13
14	15	16	17	18	19	20
21	22	23	24	25	26	27
28	29	30	31			

AUGUST

THE BEST-PLAYED DEAL IN THE 2002 WORLD CHAMPIONSHIP

Alan Truscott 8/22/02

NORTH (D)
♠ K 3 2
♥ 7 3
♦ A 4
♣ A K Q 10 8 4

WEST
♠ 10 9 8 5 4
♥ A J 10
♦ J 10 8 2
♣ 7

EAST
♠ J
♥ Q 9 8 6 5
♦ Q 9 5
♣ 9 6 3 2

SOUTH
♠ A Q 7 6
♥ K 4 2
♦ K 7 6 3
♣ J 5

North and South were vulnerable. The bidding:

North	East	South	West
1 ♣	Pass	1 ♦	Pass
3 ♣	Pass	4 ♣	Pass
4 ♦	Pass	4 N.T.	Pass
5 ♦	Pass	6 N.T.	Pass
Pass	Pass	Pass	

West led the spade ten.

When the world championships were staged in Montreal three years ago, the diagramed deal from the Mixed Pairs was widely considered to be the best-played.

Sitting North and South were Judi Radin and Zia Mahmood, and their bidding followed a natural course. The raise to four clubs provisionally agreed a trump suit, and four diamonds was a cue-bid. The five-diamond response to Blackwood showed zero or three key cards in the style favored by the partnership, and South settled in six no-trump. He knew that there was one key card missing, either an ace or the club king.

West was not inclined to lead a heart, which would have given Zia his 12th trick. The actual lead was the spade ten, which appeared safe but was fatal. Dummy

played low, and East put up the jack. This was not a likely falsecard, and South took it at face value. West's failure to lead a heart made it quite likely that he held the ace. After winning with the spade ace, South proceeded on that assumption, rather than try for a heart trick by direct means. At the second trick he led the spade six, and this won the trick, giving South his slam, when West played low and dummy did likewise.

It might appear that West had erred by failing to cover the six with the eight, but Zia had a plan to deal with this. He would have won with dummy's king and cashed six club winners followed by the diamond ace. The position would have been this:

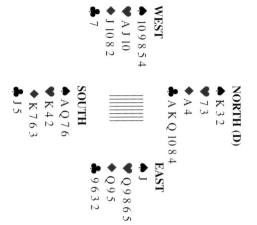

NORTH
♠ 3
♥ 7 3
♦ 4
♣ —

WEST
♠ 9 5
♥ A J
♦ —
♣ —

EAST
♠ —
♥ Q 9
♦ Q 9
♣ —

SOUTH
♠ Q 7
♥ K
♦ K
♣ —

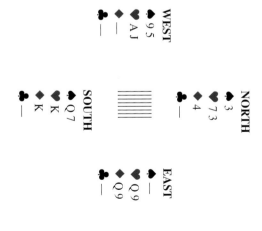

A diamond lead to the king would then have settled the issue. West would have had to choose between a spade discard, allowing South to score two tricks in that suit, and the heart jack, allowing a heart lead to force a spade return at the 12th trick.

The lead of the nine or eight of spades would have had led a diamond, a club or a low spade originally. The lead of the nine or eight of spades would have left the issue in doubt, with the declarer unsure about the spade distribution.

monday 15 227

tuesday 16 228

wednesday 17 229

thursday 18 230

friday ○ 19 231

saturday 20 232

sunday 21 233

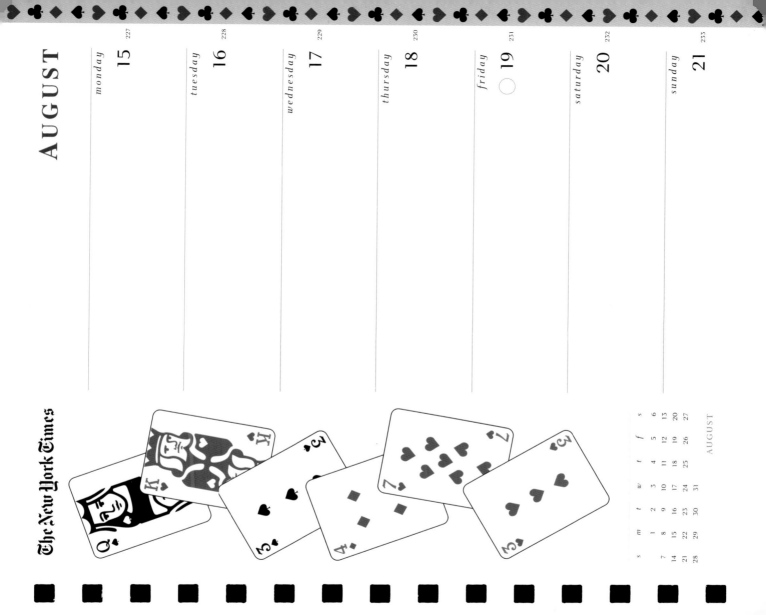

The New York Times

AUGUST

s	m	t	w	t	f	s
	1	2	3	4	5	6
7	8	9	10	11	12	13
14	15	16	17	18	19	20
21	22	23	24	25	26	27
28	29	30	31			

A BRILLIANT OPENING LEAD ALMOST SAVES THE DAY

Alan Truscott 8/29/02

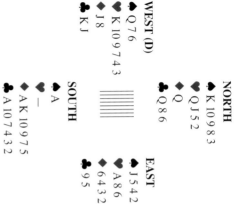

NORTH
- ♠ K 10 9 8 3
- ♥ Q J 5 2
- ♦ Q
- ♣ Q 8 6

WEST (D)
- ♠ Q 7 6
- ♥ K 10 9 7 4 3
- ♦ J 8
- ♣ K J

EAST
- ♠ J 5 4 2
- ♥ A 8 6
- ♦ 6 4 3 2
- ♣ 9 5

SOUTH
- ♠ A
- ♥ —
- ♦ A K 10 9 7 5
- ♣ A 10 7 4 3 2

Neither side was vulnerable. The bidding:

West	North	East	South
2 ♥	2 ♠	3 ♥	4 ♦
Pass	4 ♠	Pass	6 ♦
Pass	Pass	Pass	

West led the heart king.

Perhaps the biggest surprise of the 2002 World Team Championship in Montreal occurred in the round of 16 when Nick Nickell's star team, winner of three world titles, lost by six to an unheralded Italian group led by Dano Attanasio. On the diagramed deal, a brilliant opening lead by Paul Soloway, sitting West for the Nickell team, almost, but not quite, averted disaster for the Americans.

He opened two hearts, weak, and was raised by his partner, Bob Hamman, when North overcalled in spades. South bid diamonds and then jumped to six clubs, reaching an excellent slam that hinged on the declarer's handling of the trump suit.

The standard play is to cash the ace and continue. Barring an unlikely 4-0 split, this succeeds unless East

has exactly K J x. But Soloway provided some clever disinformation. His opening lead was the heart king rather than a small card, strongly suggesting that he had an ace-king combination. From South's point of view, it was now unlikely that West held the club king, for with an ace-king combination plus a king he would presumably have opened one heart, not two.

South therefore ruffed the opening lead, crossed to the diamond queen, and then led the club queen, finessing. He was disconcerted when this lost to the king and the diamond jack was returned. Still deluded by the opening lead, he ruffed in dummy and took another club finesse. He believed it impossible that West held the club jack, together with a king and a presumed ace-king. When West produced the jack, the slam failed by a trick.

In the replay West played three hearts doubled, losing 500. The Nickell team therefore gained 11 imps, and would probably have lost nine but for Soloway's inspired opening lead.

AUGUST

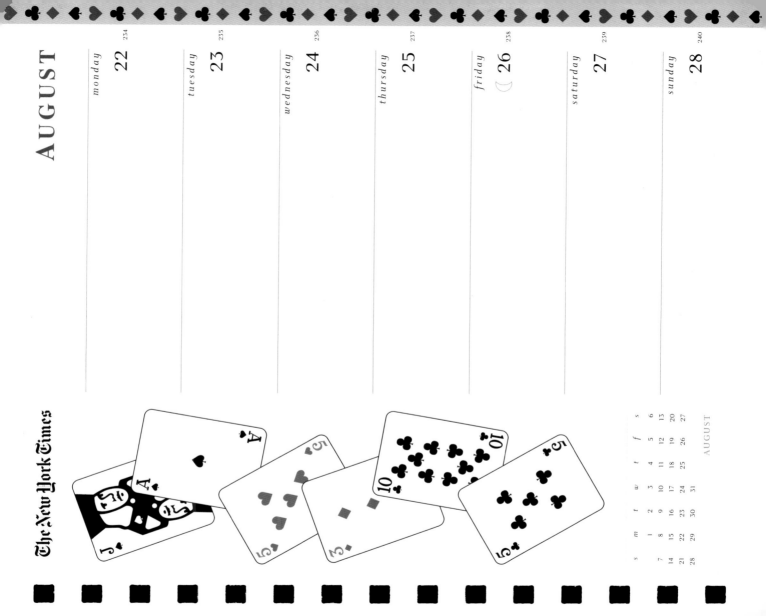

monday 22 [234]

tuesday 23 [235]

wednesday 24 [236]

thursday 25 [237]

friday 26 [238]

saturday 27 [239]

sunday 28 [240]

The New York Times

s	m	t	w	t	f	s
	1	2	3	4	5	6
7	8	9	10	11	12	13
14	15	16	17	18	19	20
21	22	23	24	25	26	27
28	29	30	31			

AUGUST

A VICTORY FOR A PRACTICAL PATRIARCH

Alan Truscott 9/11/02

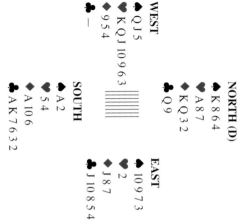

NORTH (D)
♠ K 8 6 4
♥ A 8 7
♦ K Q 3 2
♣ —

WEST
♠ Q J 5
♥ K Q J 10 9 6 3
♦ 9 5 4
♣ Q 9

EAST
♠ 10 9 7 3
♥ 2
♦ J 8 7
♣ J 10 8 5 4

SOUTH
♠ A 2
♥ 5 4
♦ A 10 6
♣ A K 7 6 3 2

Both sides were vulnerable. The bidding:

North	East	South	West
1♦	Pass	2♣	2♥
2 N.T.	Pass	4♦	Pass
4♥	Pass	4♠	Pass
5♣	Pass	6♣	Pass
Pass	Pass		

West led the heart king.

There is some scientific evidence to support the contention that playing bridge is conducive to a long life. Whether it is valid or not, octogenarians and nonagenarians fight regularly for small victories in clubs all across North America. One of them is octogenarian Kenneth Cox, who has been associated with the game for more than half a century. For 12 years, he was the Executive Secretary of the small American Bridge Association, and he continues to play each week at his club in Harlem, N.Y.

An authority once described Cox as "one of the finest analytical players in the game" and offered the diagramed deal as an example. It was played in 1957 at an A.B.A. tournament in New York, and Cox sat South. His second-round jump to four clubs was a good practical move, made necessary by the fact that three clubs

would have been non-forcing. He was not handicapped by the modern idea that a jump from two no-trump to four clubs should be Gerber, asking for aces.

The final contract of six clubs was excellent, and on a good day 13 tricks would roll in. But this was not a good day. Out of respect for Cox's ability, East, looking at two probable tricks, resisted the temptation to double.

South won the opening heart lead with dummy's ace and played the club queen, discovering the bad split when West threw a heart. The club nine was led, and covered with the ten and king. The ace and king of spades were cashed and a spade was ruffed. A diamond lead to dummy allowed a second spade ruff, and the ace and king of diamonds were taken. Luckily for the declarer, East had to follow suit and was reduced to his three trumps. The ending was this:

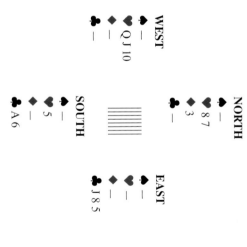

NORTH
♠ —
♥ 8 7
♦ 3
♣ —

WEST
♠ —
♥ Q J 10
♦ —
♣ —

EAST
♠ —
♥ —
♦ —
♣ J 8 5

SOUTH
♠ —
♥ 5
♦ —
♣ A 6

When the last diamond was led from dummy East was helpless. He chose to ruff with the club eight, and Cox promptly threw his heart five. The ace-six of clubs scored the last two tricks over the jack-five to bring home the slam.

monday **29** 241

BANK HOLIDAY (U.K. EXCEPT SCOTLAND)

tuesday **30** 242

wednesday **31** 243

thursday **1** 244

friday **2** 245

saturday ● **3** 246

sunday **4** 247

The New York Times

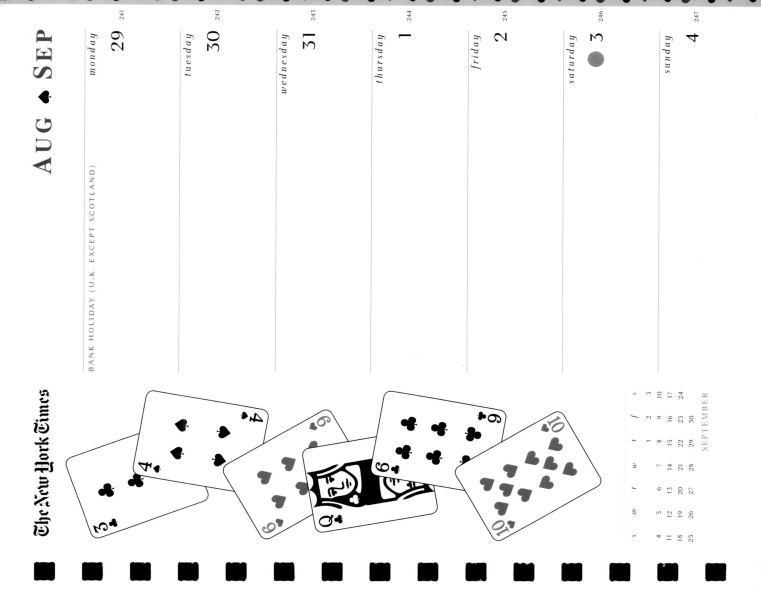

s	m	t	w	t	f	s
				1	2	3
4	5	6	7	8	9	10
11	12	13	14	15	16	17
18	19	20	21	22	23	24
25	26	27	28	29	30	

SEPTEMBER

EXPERT DEFENDER GIVES CREDIT WHERE IT IS DUE: TO DECLARER

Alan Truscott 9/21/02

The world's great players always attract a following of kibitzers, watching their every move. When the kibitzer sees something memorable, he eagerly reports it to the press, hoping for reflected glory. But this can happen in reverse, in a man-bites-dog scenario.

Zia Mahmood, a cosmopolitan with a home in London and a residence in Manhattan, is around the top of any list of world-best players, either in tournaments or at rubber bridge. On the diagramed deal he was the reporter rather than the reportee of a fine play. He was West in a money-bridge game at the Regency Whist Club in Manhattan. Sitting South was Amos Kaminsky, who once won the celebrated Cavendish Pairs but seldom takes part in tournaments.

The contract was a borderline three no-trump.

NORTH
- ♠ 9 7 2
- ♥ K 10 7 5 4
- ♦ A K 2
- ♣ A J

WEST
- ♠ 10 6
- ♥ Q 9
- ♦ 8 7 4 3
- ♣ K 10 8 7 3

EAST (D)
- ♠ A K J 8 5
- ♥ J 6 3
- ♦ 9 6
- ♣ Q 5 4

SOUTH
- ♠ Q 4 3
- ♥ A 8 2
- ♦ Q J 10 5
- ♣ 9 6 2

North and South were vulnerable. The bidding:

East	South	West	North
1 ♠	Pass	1 N.T.	2 ♥
Pass	2 N.T.	Pass	3 N.T.
Pass	Pass	Pass	

West led the spade ten.

reached, unexpectedly, after the opponents had opened the bidding and responded. The opening lead was the spade ten, and East carefully played the jack. This forced South to win with the queen, leaving the defenders ready to take the setting tricks when they gained the lead.

South cashed all of his diamonds and gave up a heart from dummy. East, under pressure, reluctantly surrendered two clubs. The position was this:

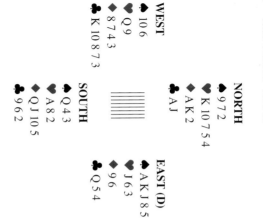

NORTH
- ♠ 9 7
- ♥ K 10 7 5
- ♦ —
- ♣ A J

WEST
- ♠ 6
- ♥ Q 9
- ♦ —
- ♣ K 10 8 7 3

EAST
- ♠ A K 8 5
- ♥ J 6 3
- ♦ —
- ♣ Q

SOUTH
- ♠ 4 3
- ♥ A 8 2
- ♦ —
- ♣ 9 6 2

Reading the position perfectly, Kaminsky led to the club ace, removing the queen from the East hand, and called for a spade. East was welcome to take his spades, but then had to break the heart suit. The three went to the queen and king, and the ten was led. This pinned West's nine, and South had his ninth trick whether or not East covered with the jack.

Realizing what had happened, Zia raised his eyebrows, congratulated Kaminsky on his brilliant effort, and hastened to tell the waiting world.

SEPTEMBER

LABOR DAY (U.S., CANADA)

The New York Times

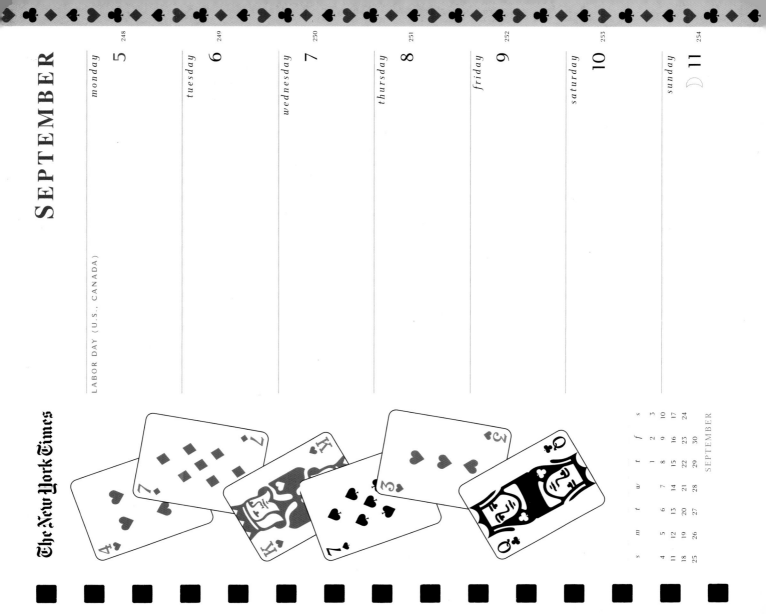

s	m	t	w	t	f	s
				1	2	3
4	5	6	7	8	9	10
11	12	13	14	15	16	17
18	19	20	21	22	23	24
25	26	27	28	29	30	

SEPTEMBER

♠ UNSUNG HERO OF THE SLIDING TRAY SHOWS HIS SKILL

Alan Truscott 9/28/01

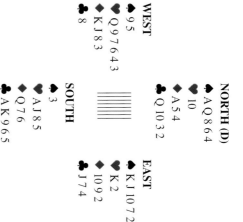

NORTH (D)
♠ A Q 8 6 4
♥ 10
♦ A 5 4
♣ Q 10 3 2

WEST
♠ 9 5
♥ Q 9 7 6 4 3
♦ K J 8 3
♣ 8

EAST
♠ K J 10 7 2
♥ K 2
♦ 10 9 2
♣ J 7 4

SOUTH
♠ 3
♥ A J 8 5
♦ Q 7 6
♣ A K 9 6 5

North and South were vulnerable. The bidding:

North	East	South	West
1 ♠	Pass	2 ♣	2 ♥
3 ♣	Pass	3 N.T.	Pass
4 ♣	Pass	5 ♣	Pass
Pass	Pass		

West led the diamond three.

For players at the top of the tournament pyramid, some equipment items are now taken for granted, but the efforts of those who introduced them are generally forgotten. Some recall that bidding boxes, now used routinely, were developed by the Jannersten organization in Sweden, whose name is still on most of them. Few remember that the bidding screens that cross the table diagonally in major national and international competitions were introduced in 1975 by Jaime Ortiz-Patino, then president of the World Bridge Federation. And not one in ten thousand could say who thought of the sliding tray, which goes underneath the bidding screen and avoids the need for monitors announcing bids as they are made.

The unsung hero of the sliding tray was Henny Dorsman of Aruba, whose idea was immediately adopted around the world. He now lives in Virginia,

and competed in the 2002 Summer Nationals in Washington, D.C. On the diagramed deal from the IMP Pairs, he landed in five clubs from the South position. He might have played in three no-trump, which could have been made, though with considerable difficulty, but his partner, fearing the heart suit, persevered in clubs.

At first sight, it appears that five clubs is due to fail, since the spades break badly and two important kings, in spades and diamonds, are badly placed. But analysis shows the contract can always succeed. Suppose, for example, that a spade is led. South can win with dummy's ace, ruff a spade, cash the ace of hearts, and ruff a heart. A club to the ace and a heart ruff with the club queen permits South to take a finesse against East's club jack. A spade ruff leaves South with the lead in this position:

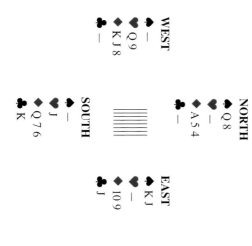

NORTH
♠ Q 8
♥ —
♦ A 5 4
♣ —

WEST
♠ —
♥ Q 9
♦ K J 8
♣ —

EAST
♠ K J
♥ —
♦ 10 9
♣ J

SOUTH
♠ —
♥ J
♦ Q 7 6
♣ K

The play of the club king draws East's jack but sets up West for an endplay. Whatever he does, South can lead the heart jack and eventually score the diamond queen.

In practice, Dorsman was put to a different test. West led the diamond three, permitting the queen to score, but there were only ten tricks in view. South cashed the club ace, unblocking dummy's ten, and suspected that West's eight was a singleton in view of the known heart

SEPTEMBER

The New York Times

and diamond length. He fin-essed the spade queen unsuc-cessfully, and won East's heart shift with the ace.

South's next moves were to ruff a heart and to discard a heart on the spade ace. Trusting his view of the club lay-out, Dorsman finessed the club nine, and when this won he ruffed a heart with dummy's club queen. He made his contract, losing a diamond at the finish.

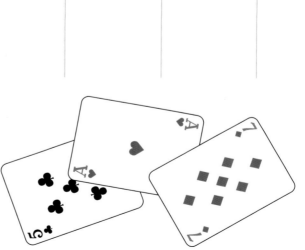

s	m	t	w	t	f	s
				1	2	3
4	5	6	7	8	9	10
11	12	13	14	15	16	17
18	19	20	21	22	23	24
25	26	27	28	29	30	

SEPTEMBER

WHAT IS TRUMP SUPPORT? IT VARIES

Alan Truscott 9/30/02

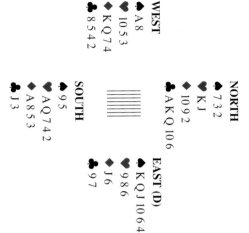

NORTH
- ♠ 7 3 2
- ♥ K J
- ♦ 10 9 2
- ♣ A K Q 10 6

WEST
- ♠ A 8
- ♥ 10 5 3
- ♦ K Q 7 4
- ♣ 8 5 4 2

EAST (D)
- ♠ K Q J 10 6 4
- ♥ 9 8 6
- ♦ J 6
- ♣ 9 7

SOUTH
- ♠ 9 5
- ♥ A Q 7 4 2
- ♦ A 8 5 3
- ♣ J 3

East and West were vulnerable. The bidding:

East	South	West	North
2 ♠	3 ♥	Pass	4 ♥
Pass	Pass	Pass	

West led the spade ace.

Street. North and South were Terry Heled and Margie Gwozdzinsky, who faced a weak two spades from East. The overcall of three hearts was aggressive, which is a way of saying that South did not quite have the qualifications for her bid. North was entitled to expect a six-card suit, and the raise to four hearts was entirely appropriate.

The defense began with three rounds of spades, and South knew that West was in a position to overruff. She also knew that her contract was safe barring a disastrous trump split. A likely division was four with West and two with East, and she prepared for that.

The spade lead was ruffed with the heart ace, and dummy's king-jack of trumps were cashed. The closed hand was entered with a club to the jack, and the heart queen was played. As it happened, both defenders followed and an overtrick rolled in. If West had begun with four hearts, South would have played a fourth round. This would have converted the play to no-trump, and South would have made the remaining tricks in the minor suits.

Notice that ruffing low would have been equally effective in dealing with a 4–2 trump split, but the useful overtrick would not have materialized. This deal helped North-South to win a charity game.

The number of trumps needed to support partner depends, obviously, on the length indicated by his bid. Eight cards in the combined hands are sufficient, with seven acceptable at a pinch. At one extreme is the raise of a one-club opening bid, which needs four cards and might lead to a seven-card fit if partner has three—but that is only one chance in six. At the other extreme is the raise of a preemptive opening, three clubs or higher. Since partner is known to have at least seven cards, a raise with a singleton is common and a raise with a void may be right in rare cases.

An important case arises when an overcall is made at the level of two or higher. Such bids are usually based on a six-card or longer suit, and a raise is therefore acceptable with a doubleton. An example is the diagramed deal, played at the Town Club, 9 East 86th

SEPTEMBER

monday 19 262

tuesday 20 263

wednesday 21 264

thursday 22 265

friday 23 266

saturday 24 267

sunday 25 268

AUTUMNAL EQUINOX 10:23 P.M. (GMT)

The New York Times

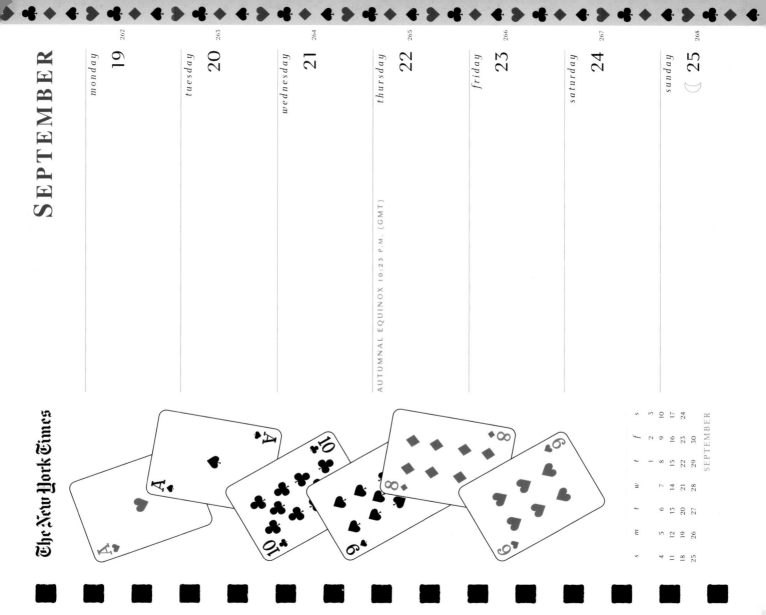

s	m	t	w	t	f	s
				1	2	3
4	5	6	7	8	9	10
11	12	13	14	15	16	17
18	19	20	21	22	23	24
25	26	27	28	29	30	

SEPTEMBER

A COSMOPOLITAN TEAM JUST MISSED MEDALS

Alan Truscott 10/5/02

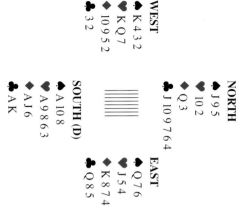

NORTH
♠ J 9 5
♥ 10 2
♦ Q 3
♣ J 10 9 7 6 4

WEST
♠ K 4 3 2
♥ K Q 7
♦ 10 9 5 2
♣ 3 2

EAST
♠ Q 7 6
♥ J 5 4
♦ K 8 7 4
♣ Q 8 5

SOUTH (D)
♠ A 10 8
♥ A 9 8 6 3
♦ A J 6
♣ A K

Neither side was vulnerable. The bidding:

South	West	North	East
2 N.T.	Pass	3 N.T.	Pass
Pass	Pass		

West led the spade two.

Almost all American players were eliminated early in the 2002 World Team Championship in Montreal. The exceptions were Christal Henner and Jimmy Rosenbloom, who played with four Swedish experts, Peter Fredin, Magnus Lindkvist, Frederik Nystrom and Peter Bertheau. They reached the semifinal stage, and just missed winning the bronze medals. En route they defeated several favored teams.

On the diagramed deal, in a close match, Henner was South in three no-trump, which in theory was due to be defeated by any lead. However, West tabled the two of spades, presumably indicating a four-card suit, and East had a problem when the five was played from dummy. The queen would have been right with this lay-out for a subtle reason: It would have forced the ace, and allowed the defenders to duck a spade later to preserve communications.

In practice East played the six, which would have been a good move if South had held K x x. The declarer won with the eight, and could have prevailed by leading a low heart. She could then duck a risky low-spade return from West, win the third round of spades, and reach this tricky position:

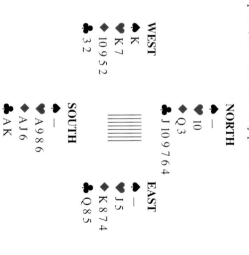

NORTH
♠ —
♥ 10
♦ Q 3
♣ J 10 9 7 6 4

WEST
♠ K
♥ K 7
♦ 10 9 5 2
♣ 3 2

EAST
♠ —
♥ J 5
♦ K 8 7 4
♣ Q 8 5

SOUTH
♠ —
♥ A 9 8 6
♦ A J 6
♣ A K

Now South can lead the heart ace, and West is on the horns of a dilemma. If he plays low South will cash her club winners and play a third heart. West will be able to win the spade king, but he will then be endplayed, forced to lead a diamond and give South her ninth trick. Alternatively, West can unblock the heart king under the ace. South will then be able to play a third heart immediately, and develop her ninth trick in diamonds.

In practice, South made the tempting play of cashing her top clubs at the second and third tricks. This was a delicate error, since it established East's queen, but she survived. When she next led a low heart, West won and did not know that another spade lead was safe. He tried the diamond ten, and South was able to establish her hearts and claim nine tricks, winning seven imps. In the replay, North-South very reasonably rested in one no-trump and made eight tricks. If three no-trump had failed, the Swedish-American team would have lost the match by two imps instead of winning by ten.

monday 26 269

tuesday 27 270

wednesday 28 271

thursday 29 272

friday 30 273

saturday 1 274

sunday 2 275

The New York Times

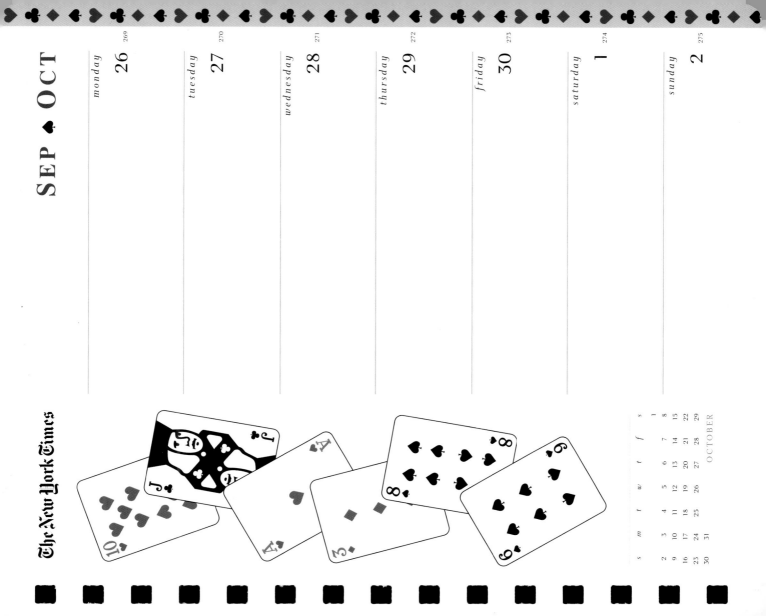

s	m	t	w	t	f	s
						1
2	3	4	5	6	7	8
9	10	11	12	13	14	15
16	17	18	19	20	21	22
23	24	25	26	27	28	29
30	31					

OCTOBER

NORTH
♠ A Q 10 7 6
♥ 8 7 6 5 2
♦ 7 3
♣ 2

WEST
♠ 9 5 2
♥ A 4
♦ K 5 2
♣ A J 10 9 4

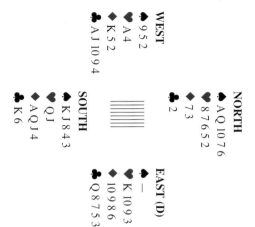

EAST (D)
♠ —
♥ K 10 9 3
♦ 10 9 8 6
♣ Q 8 7 5 3

SOUTH
♠ K J 8 4 3
♥ Q J
♦ A Q J 4
♣ K 6

North and South were vulnerable. The bidding:

South	West	North	East
1 N.T.	Pass	2 ♥	Pass
3 ♦	Pass	3 ♥	Pass
3 ♠	Pass	4 ♠	Pass
Pass	Pass		

West led the spade two.

The 2002 World Women's Pairs title was won by Karen McCallum and Debbie Rosenberg, representing the United States. McCallum had won the same title 12 years earlier, with Kerri Shuman.

The diagramed deal from the event illustrates how far styles have changed in selecting one-no-trump opening bids. Seventy years ago, Ely Culbertson and his group had stringent standards, and hardly ever made the bid, even if the requirements were met, because their responding methods were unreliable. McCallum and Rosenberg believe in opening one no-trump at the drop of a hat, reasoning that they can usually find the right contract and that this policy will make life difficult for the opponents.

In this case, McCallum as South opened one no-trump with a 5-2-4-2 hand, a choice that few would make. It had the useful effect of silencing the opposition, who could have made at least 11 tricks in a club contract.

After North's transfer response, showing spades, three diamonds promised at least a four-card spade fit. Three hearts was a re-transfer, and four spades became the contract. The North-South hands offered two chances: The club king might provide a diamond discard in the dummy, and the diamonds could provide a discard for dummy's singleton club. Both these plans were due to fail against accurate defense.

A trump was led, and South won in her hand and crossed to dummy with a second trump. East discarded a discouraging club and a discouraging diamond, causing South to suspect that the minor-suit honors were badly placed for her. She therefore took an immediate diamond finesse, leaving a harmless trump at large. It was harmful to West, however, because it gave her a losing option. When she won the third trick with the diamond king she thought it was safe to exit with her remaining trump. McCallum showed that this was a misconception by winning and playing the ace-jack of diamonds to discard dummy's singleton club. Then she could claim her game, conceding two heart tricks.

OCTOBER

ROSH HASHANAH (BEGINS AT SUNSET)

monday
3
276

tuesday
4
277

wednesday
5
278

thursday
6
279

friday
7
280

saturday
8
281

sunday
9
282

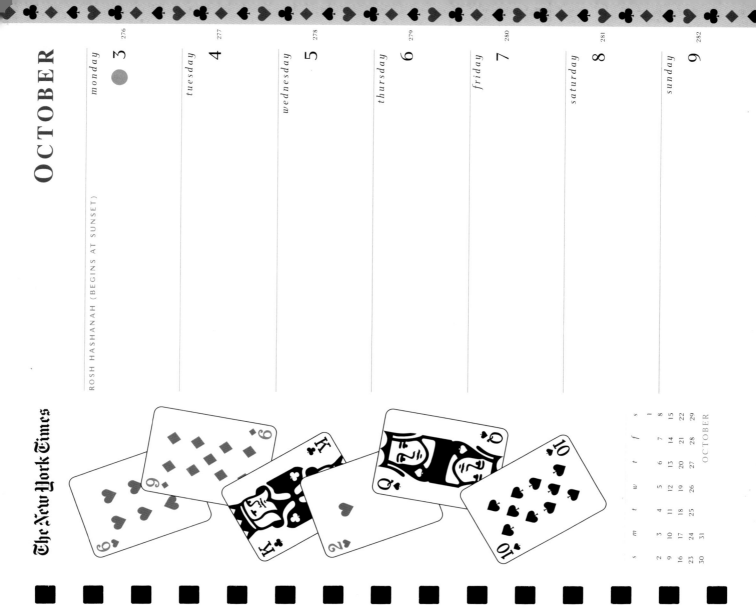

s	m	t	w	t	f	s
						1
2	3	4	5	6	7	8
9	10	11	12	13	14	15
16	17	18	19	20	21	22
23	24	25	26	27	28	29
30	31					

OCTOBER

DECLARERS MAY HAVE TO THINK POETICALLY

Alan Truscott 10/14/02

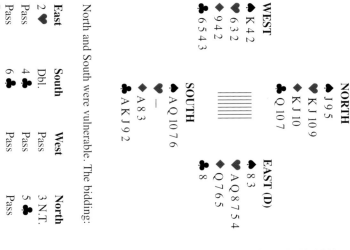

NORTH
♠ J 9 5
♥ K J 10 9
♦ K J 10
♣ Q 10 7

WEST
♠ K 4 2
♥ 6 3 2
♦ 9 4 2
♣ 6 5 4 3

EAST (D)
♠ 8 3
♥ A Q 8 7 5 4
♦ Q 7 6 5
♣ 8

SOUTH
♠ A Q 10 7 6
♥ —
♦ A 8 3
♣ A K J 9 2

North and South were vulnerable. The bidding:

East	South	West	North
2 ♥	Dbl.	Pass	3 N.T.
Pass	4 ♣	Pass	5 ♣
Pass	6 ♣	Pass	Pass
Pass			

West led the heart two.

When the poet Tennyson demanded, "Break, break, break," he might well have been a bridge player studying his trump suit. That gives rise to an interesting question: Is it better to have a bad break in the trump suit or in a significant side suit? There is no clear answer, but the diagramed deal sheds a little light.

It was played in a private game, and the South cards were held by Jack Sonnenblick of Rye, N.Y. Six spades and six clubs were both excellent contracts, and he reached the latter. Four clubs was natural and forcing, and the spades were left undisclosed. From South's angle, North was more likely to have clubs than spades in view of the jump to three no-trump.

A heart was led, and dummy's nine was covered by the queen. South ruffed, and was now worried about the possibility of losing a spade finesse and finding a 4-1 trump split. Both those transpired, but he survived.

The club ace was cashed, and a club to the ten revealed the bad break. A spade to the queen lost to the king; and West was happy to play a second heart to force a ruff. The declarer had one trump in each hand and West had two—but they did him no good.

South led a spade to dummy's jack, threw a diamond on a heart winner, and played a spade to the ace. He was relieved when West followed, and the position was then this:

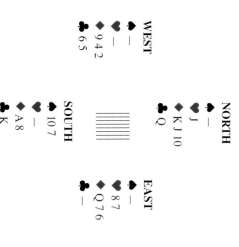

NORTH
♠ —
♥ J
♦ K J 10
♣ Q

WEST
♠ —
♥ —
♦ 9 4 2
♣ 6 5

EAST
♠ —
♥ 8 7
♦ Q 7 6
♣ —

SOUTH
♠ 10 7
♥ —
♦ A 8
♣ K

South led spade winners, and West was helpless. If he had ruffed, the declarer would have overruffed, crossed to the diamond ace, and drawn trumps. West chose to discard diamonds, and dummy did likewise. A diamond winner was taken and the last two tricks were crossruffed with West underruffing helplessly. So Sonnenblick made his slam.

Now consider what would have happened in six spades, with the trumps breaking. That contract would be in serious jeopardy if West was inspired to lead a club. South could then survive by cashing the spade ace and leading a second round, but that would not be obvious. Taking a spade finesse would be essential if East held a doubleton king and all the remaining clubs. On balance, it is better to have the trumps split evenly, since there may be no way to overcome a bad break. But it is far from being an absolute rule.

OCTOBER

monday ☽ 10   283

COLUMBUS DAY OBSERVED

THANKSGIVING DAY (CANADA)

tuesday 11   284

wednesday 12   285

COLUMBUS DAY

YOM KIPPUR (BEGINS AT SUNSET)

thursday 13   286

friday 14   287

saturday 15   288

sunday 16   289

s	m	t	w	t	f	s
						1
2	3	4	5	6	7	8
9	10	11	12	13	14	15
16	17	18	19	20	21	22
23	24	25	26	27	28	29
30	31					

OCTOBER

GOOD BIDDING, BAD RESULT, AND A SEMIFINAL DEFEAT

Alan Truscott 10/24/02

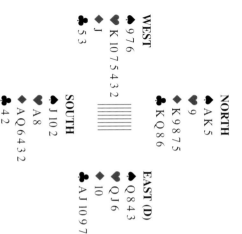

NORTH
- ♠ A K 5
- ♥ 9
- ♦ K 9 8 7 5
- ♣ K Q 8 6

WEST
- ♠ 9 7 6
- ♥ K 10 7 5 4 3 2
- ♦ J
- ♣ 5 3

EAST (D)
- ♠ Q 8 4 3
- ♥ Q J 6
- ♦ 10
- ♣ A J 10 9 7

SOUTH
- ♠ J 10 2
- ♥ A 8
- ♦ A Q 6 4 3 2
- ♣ 4 2

Neither side was vulnerable. The bidding:

East	South	West	North
Pass	2 ♦	Pass	Pass
Pass	5 ♥	Pass	4 N.T.
Pass	6 ♦	Pass	Pass
Pass			

West led the spade six.

The result of the 2002 World Team Championship in Montreal hung on some very slender threads. Poland lost to Indonesia by 15 after suffering a sad blow on the diagramed deal from the last session of the semifinal.

North and South were Leandro Burgay and Carlo Mariani, two Italians who were recruited by the Polish team. They were the only one of four pairs to reach the excellent six-diamond contract. In Burgay's bidding methods, the opening bid of two diamonds showed, in principle, a six-card diamond suit with 12–15 high-card points. That was all the information North needed to ask for aces and settle in six diamonds.

The slam would have been simple to make if South had held one more heart and one card fewer in the black suits. As it was, it was due to succeed if West

held either the spade queen or the club ace, a 75 percent chance.

These chances were due to fail, but even so South would have had a chance in the absence of the spade lead chosen by West. That is not entirely obvious, but consider how the play might develop after, for example, a club lead. Dummy would have played the queen, and East would have taken the ace and returned the jack, hoping for a ruff. South can win with dummy's club king, draw the missing trumps, and take a heart ruff. Then the play of three more trumps can result in this ending:

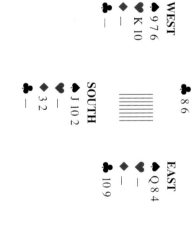

NORTH
- ♠ A K 5
- ♥ —
- ♦ —
- ♣ 8 6

WEST
- ♠ 9 7 6
- ♥ K 10
- ♦ —
- ♣ —

EAST
- ♠ Q 8 4
- ♥ —
- ♦ —
- ♣ 10 9

SOUTH
- ♠ J 10 2
- ♥ —
- ♦ 3 2
- ♣ —

If he reads the position correctly, South can lead another last trump and throw the spade five from the dummy. East is caught in a trump squeeze: Whatever he discards will allow South to develop his 12th trick.

In theory, the slam should have been played from the North position, preventing a spade lead. As it was, the Italian players and their Polish team-mates lost 11 when a gain of 13 was to be expected. The gods of the game had deprived them of a chance to play in the final of a world championship.

monday	17	290
tuesday	18	291
wednesday	19	292
thursday	20	293
friday	21	294
saturday	22	295
sunday	23	296

The New York Times

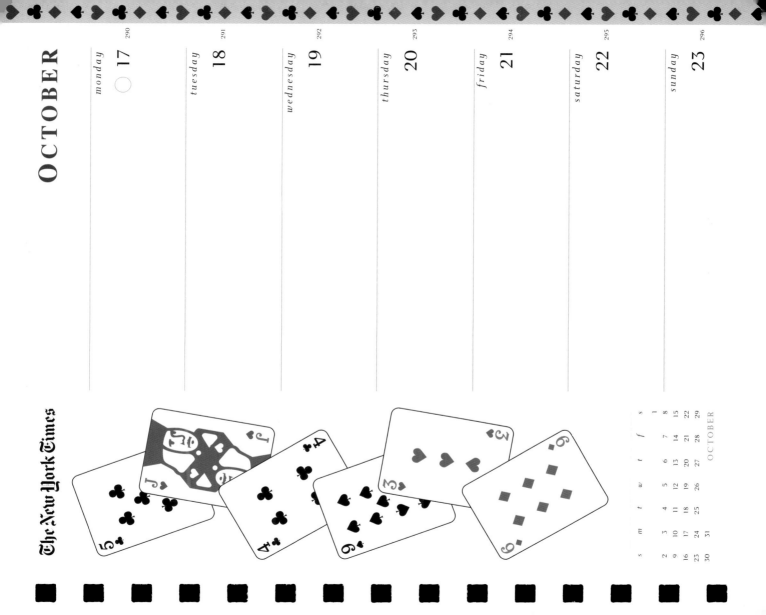

OCTOBER

s	m	t	w	t	f	s
						1
2	3	4	5	6	7	8
9	10	11	12	13	14	15
16	17	18	19	20	21	22
23	24	25	26	27	28	29
30	31					

♣ IF ALL THE PLAYERS ARE EXPERT, THEY MAY CUT THE PLAY SHORT

Alan Truscott 10/21/02

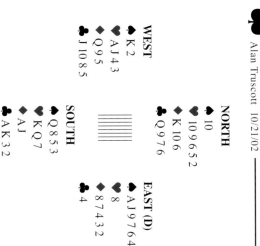

NORTH
♠ 10
♥ 10 9 6 5 2
♦ K 10 6
♣ Q 9 7 6

WEST
♠ K 2
♥ A J 4 3
♦ Q 9 5
♣ J 10 8 5

EAST (D)
♠ A J 9 7 6 4
♥ 8
♦ 8 7 4 3 2
♣ 4

SOUTH
♠ Q 8 5 3
♥ K Q 7
♦ A J
♣ A K 3 2

East and West were vulnerable. The bidding:

East	South	West	North
2 ♠	Dbl.	Pass	Pass
Pass	3 N.T.	Pass	3 ♥
Pass	Pass	Pass	

West led the spade king.

Some bridge deals are cut short because an expert declarer can see through complexities that lesser players would struggle with. An example is the diagrammed deal from the quarterfinal stage of the 2002 World Open Team Championships in Montreal. Sitting North and South were Adam Zmudzinski and Cezary Balicki of Poland, who were on the way to capturing bronze medals.

They were aided by a popular convention. After doubling a weak two-bid they were using Lebensohl, so North would have bid two no-trump with a very weak hand. His three-heart bid promised modest strength, so South was happy to continue. Since his partner could have held a four-card suit, he chose three no-trump rather than four hearts.

The defense began with the king and ace of spades, with South discarding a heart from the dummy. Since East had no chance of an entry in the other suits he shifted to his singleton heart. South played the king, and after winning with the ace West continued with a low heart, as good as anything.

South won with the ten in dummy, and tried the ace and king of clubs. The bad break was a disappointment, and on the face of it declarer did not have nine tricks. The position was this:

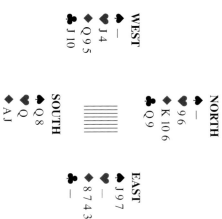

NORTH
♠ —
♥ 9 6
♦ K 10 6
♣ Q 9

WEST
♠ —
♥ J 4
♦ Q 9 5
♣ J 10

EAST
♠ J 9 7
♥ —
♦ 8 7 4 3
♣ —

SOUTH
♠ Q 8
♥ Q
♦ A J
♣ 3 2

Balicki knew a lot about the hand, but he did not know which opponent held the queen of diamonds. Nevertheless, he claimed nine tricks, with this explanation to West. "I play the spade queen, and you must throw a diamond. I throw a heart from dummy, and then play queen and nine of clubs. Whatever you return, I can play queen of hearts and ace of diamonds. Your partner must guard spades, so nobody can guard the diamonds. I make a ninth trick whoever has the queen of diamonds."

His British opponents, also highly expert, took a look and agreed. The Polish players gained seven imps en route to victory in the match. In the replay East made seven tricks in two spades doubled.

OCTOBER

monday **24** 297

tuesday **25** 298

wednesday **26** 299

thursday **27** 300

friday **28** 301

saturday **29** 302

sunday **30** 303

UNITED NATIONS DAY

DAYLIGHT SAVING TIME ENDS

SUMMER TIME ENDS (U.K.)

The New York Times

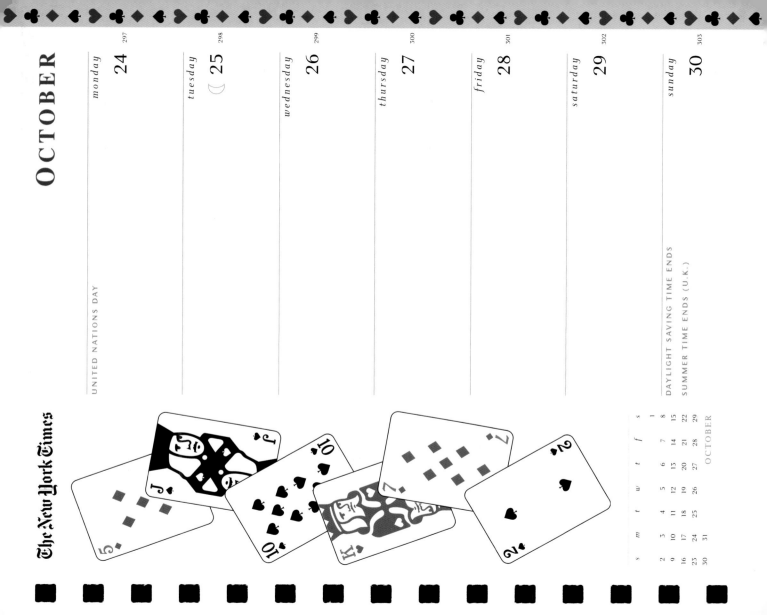

	s	m	t	w	t	f	s
							1
	2	3	4	5	6	7	8
	9	10	11	12	13	14	15
	16	17	18	19	20	21	22
	23	24	25	26	27	28	29
	30	31					

OCTOBER

BRITISH TWINS ARE AN EBULLIENT PARTNERSHIP

Alan Truscott 11/7/02

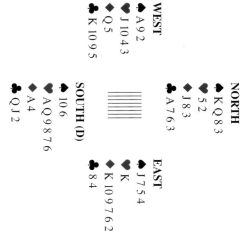

NORTH
- ♠ K Q 8 3
- ♥ 5 2
- ♦ J 8 3
- ♣ A 7 6 3

WEST
- ♠ A 9 2
- ♥ J 10 4 3
- ♦ Q 5
- ♣ K 10 9 5

EAST
- ♠ J 7 5 4
- ♥ K
- ♦ K 10 9 7 6 2
- ♣ 8 4

SOUTH (D)
- ♠ 10 6
- ♥ A Q 9 8 7 6
- ♦ A 4
- ♣ Q J 2

Neither side was vulnerable. The bidding:

South	West	North	East
1 ♥	Pass	1 ♠	Pass
2 ♥	Pass	3 ♥	Pass
4 ♥	Pass	Pass	Pass

West led the club ten.

Bridge-playing brothers are not uncommon, but Britain has a curious monopoly. James and Robert Sharples, Gerald and Stuart Tredinnick. Jason and Justin Hackett have all represented that country internationally and all are twins, believed to be the only examples around the world.

The Hacketts, now 38, are vastly experienced, with a resume that includes the 1995 World Junior Teams title. They retain some youthful ebullience, as a result of which they sometimes bid more than others would do. An example is the diagramed deal from the 2002 world championships in Montreal.

Most North players would pass the two-heart rebid but Jason pushed on with three hearts and Justin had to play a shaky four-heart contract. Luckily for him, the lead was the club ten. He would have been defeated by a diamond lead or a low heart lead, and even by the bizarre choice of the club king, which would have

removed dummy's sure entry prematurely before spades have been played.

The club lead ran around to the queen, and a spade was led. West ducked, the queen won in dummy, and a heart was played. The appearance of the king was good news and bad news. South won with the ace and tried another spade. West took the ace and exited with his remaining spade, allowing declarer to win in dummy and discard a diamond.

South led to his diamond ace and played a low heart. West won with the ten, and his only safe play was his remaining diamond. South ruffed, cashed the queen of hearts, and gave West his second trump trick. That player was reduced to his K-9-5 of clubs, and had to lead away from them to give Justin Hackett his contract.

The analysts at first thought that West could have prevailed by shifting to a diamond after taking the spade ace, but that was not the case. South would have taken his ace, crossed to the club ace, and discarded his diamond loser on the spade king. The position would then have been this:

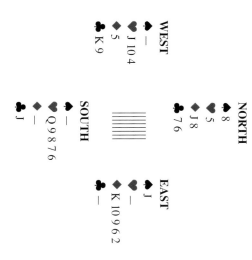

NORTH
- ♠ 8
- ♥ 5
- ♦ J 8
- ♣ 7 6

WEST
- ♠ —
- ♥ J 10 4
- ♦ 5
- ♣ K 9

EAST
- ♠ J
- ♥ —
- ♦ K 10 9 6 2
- ♣ —

SOUTH
- ♠ —
- ♥ Q 9 8 7 6
- ♦ —
- ♣ J

South can then ruff a diamond and lead the club jack. West can win and lead his last club, but is endplayed when South ruffs and leads a low heart.

monday 31
304

HALLOWEEN

tuesday 1
305

wednesday ● 2
306

thursday 3
307

friday 4
308

saturday 5
309

sunday 6
310

The New York Times

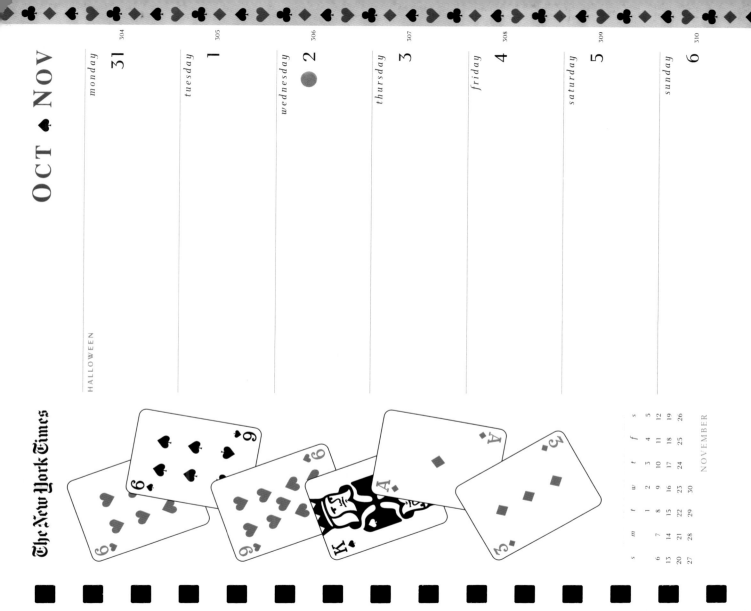

s	m	t	w	t	f	s
		1	2	3	4	5
6	7	8	9	10	11	12
13	14	15	16	17	18	19
20	21	22	23	24	25	26
27	28	29	30			

NOVEMBER

IS A HURRICANE WORSE THAN A BIG PENALTY?

Alan Truscott 11/14/02

NORTH
- ♠ J 5 3
- ♥ 7 6 5 4
- ♦ 7 4 2
- ♣ 8 5 3

WEST (D)
- ♠ Q 2
- ♥ Q 10 2
- ♦ K J 6 3
- ♣ Q 7 6 4

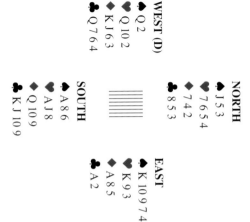

EAST
- ♠ K 10 9 7 4
- ♥ K 9 3
- ♦ A 8 5
- ♣ A 2

SOUTH
- ♠ A 8 6
- ♥ A J 8
- ♦ Q 10 9
- ♣ K J 10 9

North and South were vulnerable. The bidding:

West	North	East	South
		1 ♠	Pass
Pass	Pass	Pass	1 N.T.
Dbl.	Pass	Pass	

West led the spade queen.

Whether one should run from a hurricane is a question not easily answered: It depends on circumstances. The same is true of the diagramed deal, played when the tournament resumed. Should South run from impending disaster when his one no-trump overcall is doubled? In general, the answer is no. An attempt to escape tends to make matters worse, given that South will have to play at a higher level. But this deal suggests that there are exceptions when there is a suit with internal strength. In two clubs doubled South can be sure of making four tricks, but he may have only two in no-trump. The one no-trump overcall of the one-spade opening, with a minimum, was questionable: A x x in the opposing suit is an unsatisfactory holding for this purpose. Note that East and West would probably not have reached the unbeatable three no-trump contract if left to themselves.

Rosenkranz, sitting East, was in the process of earning his 15,000th master points, joining a select group of 88 top players in that category. He and Reygadas, West, imposed the maximum penalty.

The spade queen was led and allowed to win. South held up his ace until the third round, but was helpless. The defense had to take four spades, two hearts, four diamonds and one club. The penalty was 1400, slightly worse than South would have done in two clubs doubled.

"It's just one disaster after another," grumbled South. "Losing 1400 is even worse than a hurricane."

For a tournament to have to cancel two days of play is a very rare occurrence. It happened at the 2002 regional championships in Puerto Vallarta, Mexico, because the town was struck by Hurricane Kenna. Some condominiums were destroyed, but the hotel that was the headquarters of the tournament was almost unscathed. However, lack of electricity prevented play from continuing, and the active players had to descend, and then climb, seven flights of stairs to bring food to the less active. This was the first hurricane in half a century for the small resort town.

Play resumed in another hotel, and the big winners of the tournament were Dr. George Rosenkranz, Miguel Reygadas, Eddie Wold and Bob Morris. They won four team events, and Edith Rosenkranz shared in three of these wins.

monday 7 _311_

tuesday 8 _312_

wednesday ☽ 9 _313_

thursday 10 _314_

friday 11 _315_

VETERANS DAY
REMEMBRANCE DAY (CANADA)

saturday 12 _316_

sunday 13 _317_

The New York Times

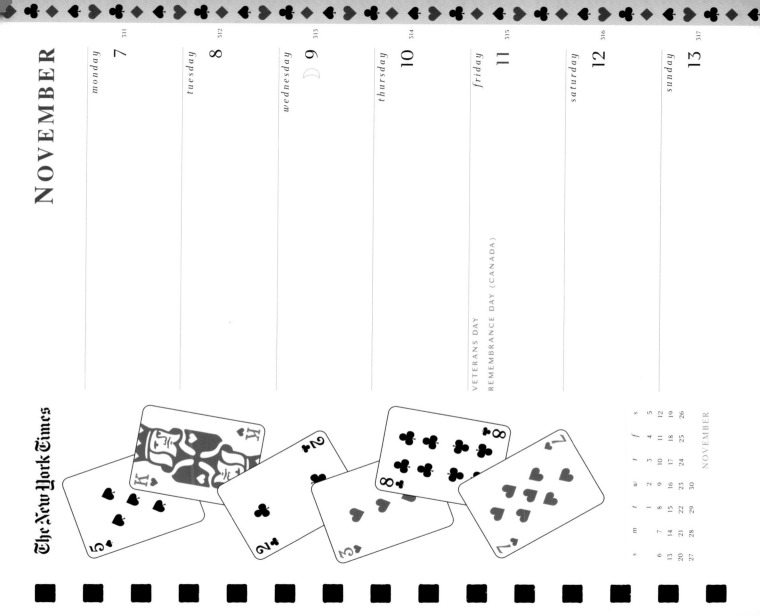

s	m	t	w	t	f	s
		1	2	3	4	5
6	7	8	9	10	11	12
13	14	15	16	17	18	19
20	21	22	23	24	25	26
27	28	29	30			

NOVEMBER

BEWARE OF BEARDED STRANGERS WHO KIBITZ IN CYBERSPACE

Alan Truscott 11/18/02

Tradition holds that a man who is lost in a blizzard in Alaska and desperate for human company should play a game of solitaire. Within a few minutes a bearded stranger is sure to lean over the man's shoulder and point out something he has overlooked: "Play the red six on the black seven."

The modern bridge equivalent occurs in cyberspace. If you post a deal on rec.games.bridge (reachable via search engines like Google and Yahoo, or bridge newsgroups) and make a sweeping generalization, a stranger is sure to point out an error.

In the diagramed deal from a club duplicate game, North-South reached an optimistic six-spade contract. Perhaps North should have slowed things down by bidding three no-trump at his third turn.

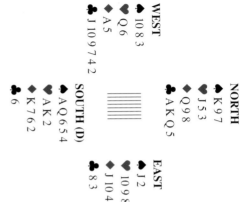

```
                NORTH
                ♠ K 9 7
                ♥ J 5 3
                ♦ Q 9 8
                ♣ A K Q 5

WEST                          EAST
♠ 10 8 3                      ♠ J 2
♥ Q 6                         ♥ 10 9 8 7 4
♦ A 5                         ♦ J 10 4 3
♣ J 10 9 7 4 2                ♣ 8 3

                SOUTH (D)
                ♠ A Q 6 5 4
                ♥ A K 2
                ♦ K 7 6 2
                ♣ 6
```

Both sides were vulnerable. The bidding:

South	West	North	East
1 ♠	Pass	2 ♣	Pass
2 ♦	Pass	2 ♠	Pass
3 ♣	Pass	4 ♦	Pass
4 N.T.	Pass	5 ♥	Pass
6 ♠	Pass	Pass	Pass

West led the club jack.

West led the club jack, attacking South's communications. The declarer, Barry Rigal, won with the queen in dummy and led to the diamond king, hoping that it would win. Then he intended to cash a string of winners: three spades, two clubs, one heart, and the last two spades. If East held the heart queen along with the diamond ace, he would be set up for an endplay in the red suits.

But West won the diamond king with the ace and played a second club. South won in dummy, discarding a diamond from his hand. He took the ace, queen and king of spades, followed by the remaining club winner for a heart discard. A heart to the king and a trump led to this ending:

```
                NORTH
                ♠ —
                ♥ J 3
                ♦ Q
                ♣ 6

WEST                          EAST
♠ —                           ♠ —
♥ Q                           ♥ 10 9
♦ 5                           ♦ J 10
♣ 10 9                        ♣ —

                SOUTH
                ♠ 5
                ♥ A
                ♦ 7 6
                ♣ —
```

On the last trump, clubs were discarded by West and dummy. The declarer thought he was squeezing East, who was known to have begun with nine cards on the red suits. East threw a diamond, and South played that suit, scoring the last trick with the seven to make his slam.

When South discovered the original distribution, with the heart queen due to fall doubleton, he decided that he was going to make the contract whatever he did. But when he reported this in cyberspace, the bearded stranger duly arrived with a comment.

"Not necessarily. If West ducked the diamond king

NOVEMBER

The New York Times

smoothly, you'd be in for quite a shock with your original plan."

The comment came from Richard Pavlicek, who has long been one of the country's finest players, analysts and teachers. But he does not have a beard.

s	m	t	w	t	f	s
		1	2	3	4	5
6	7	8	9	10	11	12
13	14	15	16	17	18	19
20	21	22	23	24	25	26
27	28	29	30			

NOVEMBER

♣ FOUR BACK-TO-BACK WINS ARE A BACK RECORD

Alan Truscott 11/28/02

NORTH (D)
- ♠ Q 10 9 8 6 5 2
- ♥ A 10 2
- ♦ 6
- ♣ —

WEST
- ♠ K J 7 3
- ♥ Q 7 6 5
- ♦ 6 5
- ♣ 9 5 2

EAST
- ♠ 4
- ♥ K 9 8 4 3
- ♦ —
- ♣ A K Q J 6 4 3

SOUTH
- ♠ A
- ♥ J
- ♦ K Q J 9 7 4 3 2
- ♣ 10 8 7

Both sides were vulnerable. The bidding:

North	East	South	West
1 ♠	2 ♣	2 ♦	3 ♣
3 ♠	5 ♣	5 ♦	Pass
6 ♣	Pass	7 ♦	Pass
Pass	Pass		

West led the diamond six.

Regional championships invariably schedule stratified open pairs events, in which all players compete together but awards are made on the basis of experience measured by master points. To win in the top bracket is an achievement. Back-to-back victories are very rare. To do so on three consecutive days is extraordinary.

In 2002, in Virginia Beach, Va., a New York partnership won four days in a row (Nov. 5, 6, 7, 8) which is believed to be an all-time record. Beverly Perry of Manhattan and Kent Mignocchi of Riverdale, N.Y., were the heroes, and one of their favorite deals is shown in the diagram.

The opponents succeeded in crowding the auction with club bids, but they did not prevent North-South from reaching their grand slam. Mignocchi, who is a reigning world junior team champion, made an intelli-

gent cue-bid of six clubs with the North hand, inviting seven diamonds. Perry recognized that this grand-slam invitation indicated that her partner held both red aces, as well as club control, and accepted the suggestion. She knew that her singleton spade ace was exactly what was required.

With a routine club lead, South would have cross-ruffed happily, scoring 11 trump tricks and the two major-suit aces. But West cleverly led a trump, making matters harder. This prevented one of the club ruffs, and South worked on spades after winning the first trick. She immediately cashed the spade ace, and won the next four tricks with club ruffs and spade ruffs. This would have insured 13 tricks if the spade king had appeared, but it did not.

However, Perry had a third string to her bow. She led six more trump winners and reached this ending:

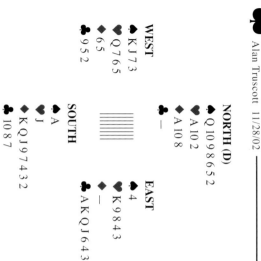

NORTH
- ♠ Q
- ♥ A 10
- ♦ —
- ♣ —

WEST
- ♠ K
- ♥ Q 7
- ♦ —
- ♣ —

EAST
- ♠ —
- ♥ K 9
- ♦ —
- ♣ A

SOUTH
- ♠ —
- ♥ J
- ♦ 7
- ♣ 10

The lead of the last trump executed a classic double squeeze. West had to throw a heart, and dummy parted with the spade queen, now useless. East had to save the ace of clubs, and dummy's heart ten took the final trick.

Notice that this would not have worked if West had held a club honor. He would have been able to protect both black suits, leaving his partner to guard hearts.

NOVEMBER

monday 21 · 325

tuesday 22 · 326

wednesday ☾ 23 · 327

thursday 24 · 328

friday 25 · 329

saturday 26 · 330

sunday 27 · 331

THANKSGIVING DAY

The New York Times

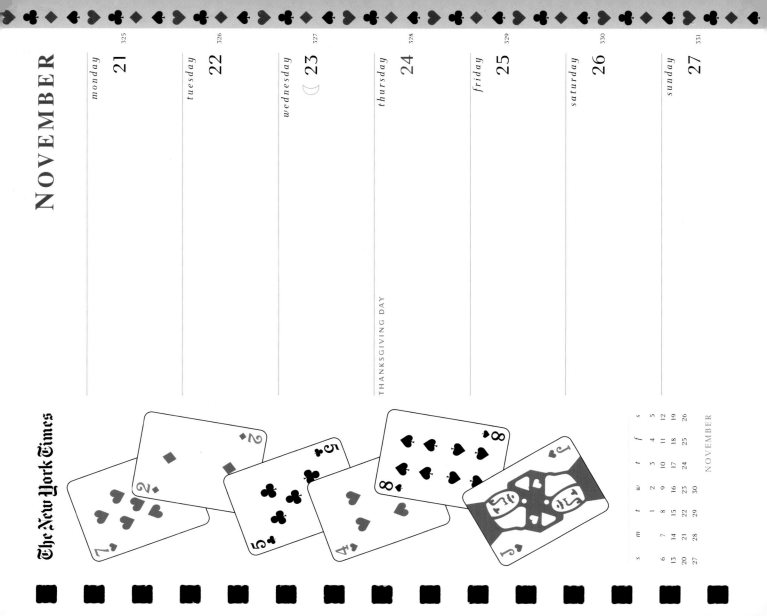

s	m	t	w	t	f	s
		1	2	3	4	5
6	7	8	9	10	11	12
13	14	15	16	17	18	19
20	21	22	23	24	25	26
27	28	29	30			

NOVEMBER

♠ AYN RAND'S PHILOSOPHY CAN HELP AT THE BRIDGE TABLE

Alan Truscott 12/1/02

```
NORTH (D)
♠ A Q 10 8 3
♥ 3
♦ A 10 9
♣ Q 10 7 6
```

```
WEST                          EAST
♠ 5 2                         ♠ J 9 7 4
♥ A 10 9 2                    ♥ 8 6
♦ K J 7 6 4                   ♦ Q 8 5 2
♣ 9 3                         ♣ K J 8
```

```
SOUTH
♠ K 6
♥ K Q J 7 5 4
♦ 3
♣ A 5 4 2
```

North and South were vulnerable. The bidding:

North	East	South	West
1 ♠	Pass	2 ♥	Pass
2 N.T.	Pass	4 ♥	Pass
Pass	Pass		

West led the diamond six.

Two of the winners of the 2002 Reisinger Teams in Phoenix, Ariz., Doug Doub and Adam Wildavsky, claim that they were aided by the objectivist philosophy of Ayn Rand. It stresses the importance of reason and keeping emotion in its proper place.

One of the decisive boards from the final round is shown in the diagram. Doub landed in four hearts, a contract that appears doomed by the bad trump split. The two no-trump rebid by Wildavsky, North, was non-forcing.

A diamond was led, and won with dummy's ace. A heart to the king lost to the ace, and another diamond lead was ruffed in the closed hand. South persevered

with trumps, surrendering the fourth round to West. East was already in trouble for discards, and the position was this:

```
NORTH
♠ A Q 10 8
♥ —
♦ —
♣ Q 10 7
```

```
WEST                          EAST
♠ 5 2                         ♠ J 9 7 4
♥ —                           ♥ —
♦ K J 7                       ♦ —
♣ 9 3                         ♣ K J 8
```

```
SOUTH
♠ K 6
♥ 7
♦ —
♣ A 5 4 2
```

There was no escape for the defense. West led another diamond, which forced East to throw a club. South ruffed and surrendered a club to make his game. If West had shifted to a club in the diagramed position, South would have won in his hand and led the last trump, discarding a club from dummy. Then South could have cashed the king and ace of spades, with a club lead to follow, endplaying East.

In the replay North-South team attempted four spades unsuccessfully. Doub and his teammates won the board and surged to their Reisinger victory.

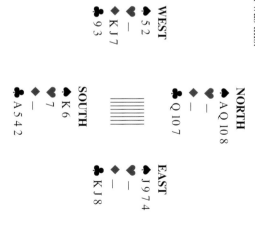

monday 28 332

tuesday 29 333

wednesday 30 334

thursday ● 1 335

friday 2 336

saturday 3 337

sunday 4 338

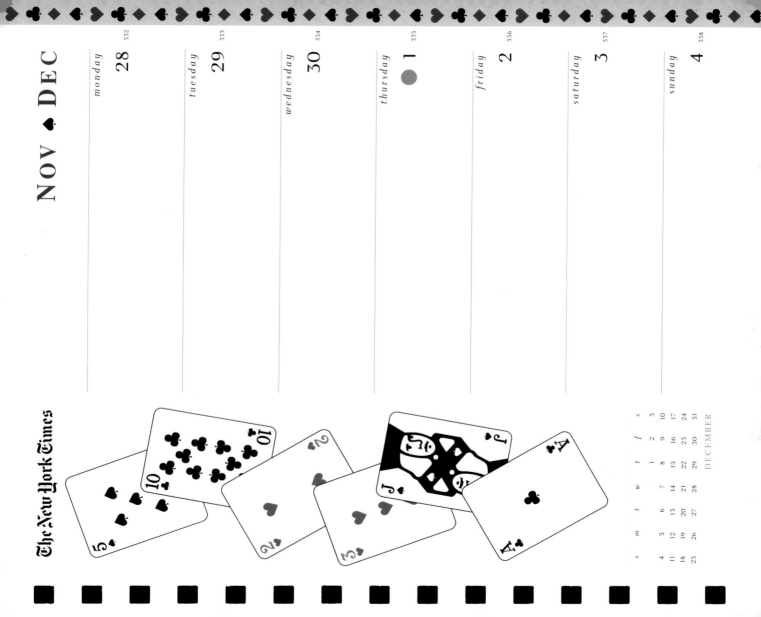

The New York Times

s	m	t	w	t	f	s
				1	2	3
4	5	6	7	8	9	10
11	12	13	14	15	16	17
18	19	20	21	22	23	24
25	26	27	28	29	30	31

DECEMBER

LEAGUE PRESIDENT REMEMBERS A FAVORITE DEAL

Alan Truscott 12/16/02

NORTH (D)
♠ Q
♥ A 10 7 5 2
♦ A 7 6 5 4
♣ 8 7

WEST
♠ K 7 5 3
♥ 9 8
♦ J 10 9 8
♣ 10 3 2

EAST
♠ A 10 8 6 4
♥ Q J 6 3
♦ Q 3 2
♣ 9

SOUTH
♠ J 9 2
♥ K 4
♦ K
♣ A K Q J 6 5 4

Both sides were vulnerable. The bidding:

North	East	South	West
Pass	Pass	3 N.T.	Pass
6 N.T.	Pass	Pass	Pass

West led the diamond jack.

Each year, the American Contract Bridge League chooses a new president, who takes office in January. In 2003, that title was held by Alvin Levy of Stony Brook, Long Island, a retired aerospace research engineer. In recent years he has organized the annual World Computer Championship, in which programs from around the globe can prevail in a team competition.

Levy's favorite deal, shown in the diagram, took place in a club some 38 years ago, when he was a graduate student at Columbia University. He had just read a book about squeeze play, and found himself in a hopeless contract of six no-trump.

There was a misunderstanding in the bidding. Levy was using the newfangled—at that time—gambling three no-trump based on a long, solid minor suit. His partner was a traditionalist, and thought three no-trump showed a balanced hand with a wealth of high cards. If North had been on the right wavelength he could have bid six clubs, playing the slam from the "wrong" side of the table. That could have been defeated if, and only if, East had led his singleton trump.

Six no-trump would obviously have gone down at once with a spade lead, but West understandably led the diamond jack. South won and could only see 11 tricks. He boldly led the spade deuce, and West put up his king. East shouted for a spade continuation by dropping the ten, but West paid no attention. Not only did he not lead a spade, nor shift to a heart effectively, he persevered with diamonds. Now South was able to win with dummy's ace and run six club winners to reach this position:

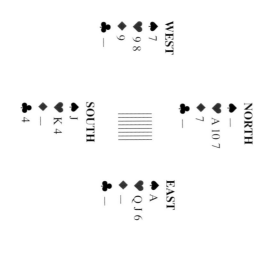

NORTH
♠ —
♥ A 10 7
♦ 7
♣ —

WEST
♠ 7
♥ 9 8
♦ 9
♣ —

EAST
♠ A
♥ Q J 6
♦ —
♣ —

SOUTH
♠ J
♥ K 4
♦ —
♣ 4

Levy, with his newfound mastery of squeezes, led his last club and threw the diamond seven from the dummy. East discarded a heart, and South made his 12th trick with dummy's heart ten.

DECEMBER

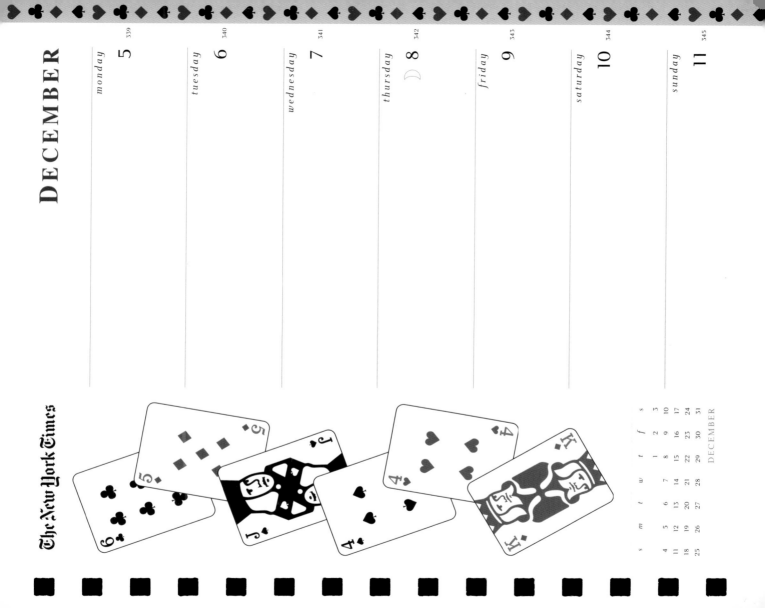

The New York Times

monday 5 ³³⁹

tuesday 6 ³⁴⁰

wednesday 7 ³⁴¹

thursday 8 ³⁴²

friday 9 ³⁴³

saturday 10 ³⁴⁴

sunday 11 ³⁴⁵

DECEMBER

s	m	t	w	t	f	s
				1	2	3
4	5	6	7	8	9	10
11	12	13	14	15	16	17
18	19	20	21	22	23	24
25	26	27	28	29	30	31

HE MAY BE NEW TO THE GAME, BUT HE CERTAINLY CAUGHT ON

Alan Truscott 12/23/02

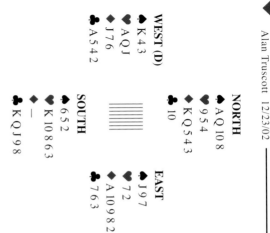

NORTH
♠ A Q 10 8
♥ 9 5 4
♦ K Q 5 4 3
♣ 10

WEST (D)
♠ K 4 3
♥ A Q J
♦ J 7 6
♣ A 5 4 2

EAST
♠ J 9 7
♥ 7 2
♦ A 10 9 8 2
♣ 7 6 3

SOUTH
♠ 6 5 2
♥ K 10 8 6 3
♦ —
♣ K Q J 9 8

North and South were vulnerable. The bidding:

West	North	East	South
1 N.T.	Pass	Pass	2 ♥
Pass	4 ♥	Pass	Pass
Pass			

West led the spade three.

Those who learn the game after the age of 18, like those who attempt to master a new language, rarely achieve the highest levels of expertise. The South player on the diagrammed deal may represent an exception. He is a 28-year-old Dane named Sebastian Kristensen, who played the deal superbly two and a half years after he learned the game.

The balancing bid of two hearts showed hearts and a minor, a popular agreement in modern tournament play. North was happy to raise to game. West led a spade, and the declarer finessed dummy's queen successfully. He then led the club ten, overtaking with the jack. West won with the ace, and South now had four established club tricks. How many of those do you suppose he made?

When another spade was led, South won with dummy's ace, led the diamond king, and ruffed out East's ace. It was now clear that virtually all of the remaining high-card points were with West, and that three probable trump tricks with that player would doom the contract. But South did not give up. He ruffed a club winner in the dummy and threw a spade on the diamond queen. Then he ruffed a spade, another club winner, and a diamond. The position was this:

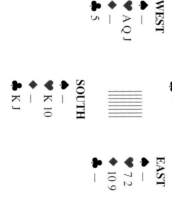

NORTH
♠ 10
♥ 9
♦ 5 4
♣ —

WEST
♠ —
♥ A Q J
♦ —
♣ 5

EAST
♠ —
♥ 7 2
♦ 10 9
♣ —

SOUTH
♠ —
♥ K 10
♦ —
♣ K J

Yet another club winner was ruffed in the dummy, and West was left clutching his three trumps. South led something from the dummy and discarded his last club. He took his tenth trick with the heart king, and had made his contract without scoring a single one of his club winners.

This effort earned him the the International Bridge Press Association's Digital Fountain Award for the best-played deal of 2002. Kristensen hopes to come to the United States and eventually become a professional bridge player. Judging by this effort, he may well succeed.

monday 12 *346*

tuesday 13 *347*

wednesday 14 *348*

thursday ○ 15 *349*

friday 16 *350*

saturday 17 *351*

sunday 18 *352*

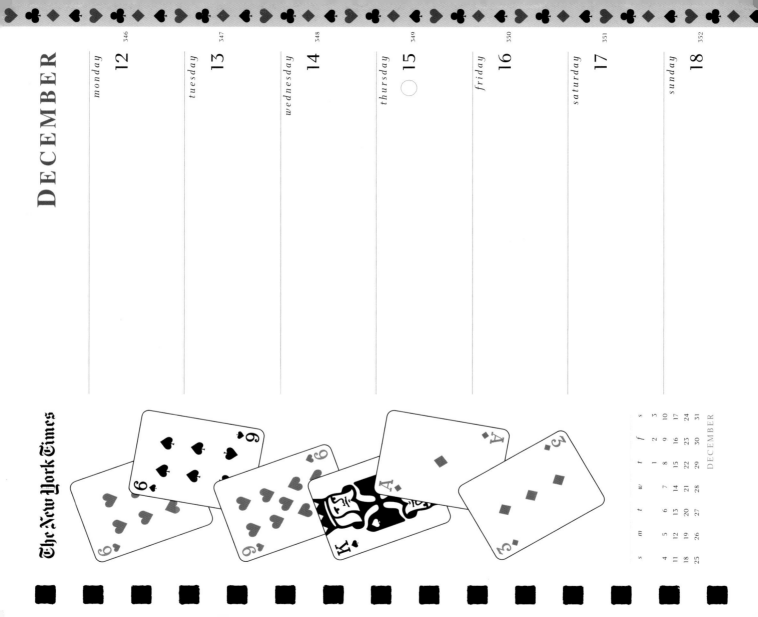

The New York Times

s	m	t	w	t	f	s
				1	2	3
4	5	6	7	8	9	10
11	12	13	14	15	16	17
18	19	20	21	22	23	24
25	26	27	28	29	30	31

DECEMBER

WINNING THE PLAYER OF THE YEAR TITLE, BY A WHISKER

Alan Truscott 12/26/02

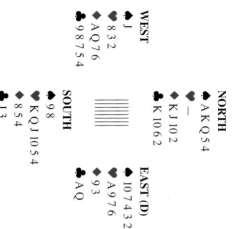

NORTH
♠ A K Q 5 4
♥ —
♦ K J 10 2
♣ K 10 6 2

WEST
♠ J
♥ 8 3 2
♦ A Q 7 6
♣ 9 8 7 5 4

EAST (D)
♠ 10 7 4 3 2
♥ A 9 7 6
♦ 9 3
♣ A Q

SOUTH
♠ 9 8
♥ K Q J 10 5 4
♦ 8 5 4
♣ J 3

Neither side was vulnerable. The bidding:

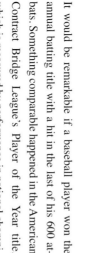

East	South	West	North
		Pass	Pass
Pass	3 ♥	Pass	Pass
Pass			

West led the spade jack.

It would be remarkable if a baseball player won the annual batting title with a hit in the last of his 600 at-bats. Something comparable happened in the American Contract Bridge League's Player of the Year title, which is measured by performance in national championships. It came down to the last trick of the national year, in the 2002 Reisinger Board-a-Match Teams in Phoenix, Ariz. However, in this case it was decided by a miss, not a hit.

Larry Cohen won the title, by a whisker, because a player on another team, at another table, misguessed a queen. Cohen's favorite deal of the tournament came in the Blue Ribbon Pairs, earlier in the week. He sat West, playing with David Berkowitz, and defended three hearts. South opened with that bid, a slight stretch

based on the solidity of his suit, and probably regretted his enterprise when he saw the dummy.

Superficially, South was due to lose one heart trick, one diamond and two clubs. But there were some rocks on the road to that result. West led his singleton spade jack and dummy won. Another top spade was led, and West ruffed, noting that his partner had played low cards to signal for clubs. Cohen shifted to that suit, and East took his two tricks there.

A spade was returned, and South ruffed high, following with another high trump. East won and led a fourth round of spades. South was not enjoying this. He ruffed high and followed with a high trump. But when he played another heart, hoping to clear the last two trumps, East won in this position:

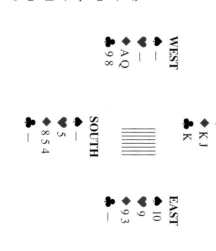

NORTH
♠ K
♥ —
♦ K J
♣ K

WEST
♠ —
♥ —
♦ A Q
♣ 9 8

EAST
♠ 10
♥ 9
♦ 9 3
♣ —

SOUTH
♠ —
♥ 5
♦ 8 5 4
♣ —

The lead of the heart nine by Berkowitz removed South's last trump, and Cohen threw a club. The result was a remarkable triple squeeze without the count, of the dummy. The declarer reluctantly parted with the diamond jack from the dummy, and Cohen scored two diamond tricks.

DECEMBER

The New York Times

The result was down four, in a contract South had hoped to make, and Cohen and Berkowitz collected 111 match points out of a possible 116.

monday **19**

tuesday **20**

wednesday **21**

WINTER SOLSTICE 6:35 P.M. (GMT)

thursday **22**

friday **23**

saturday **24**

sunday **25**

CHRISTMAS DAY

HANUKKAH (BEGINS AT SUNSET)

s	m	t	w	t	f	s
				1	2	3
4	5	6	7	8	9	10
11	12	13	14	15	16	17
18	19	20	21	22	23	24
25	26	27	28	29	30	31

DECEMBER

SOMETIMES THE BEST DEFENSE IS A GOOD IDEA FOR AN AWARD

Alan Truscott 12/30/02

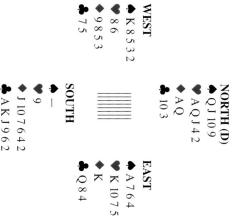

NORTH (D)
- ♠ Q J 10 9
- ♥ A Q J 4 2
- ♦ A Q
- ♣ 10 3

WEST
- ♠ K 8 5 3 2
- ♥ 8 6
- ♦ 9 8 5 3
- ♣ 7 5

EAST
- ♠ A 7 6 4
- ♥ K 10 7 5 3
- ♦ K
- ♣ Q 8 4

SOUTH
- ♠ —
- ♥ 9
- ♦ J 10 7 6 4 2
- ♣ A K J 9 6 2

Neither side was vulnerable. The bidding:

North	East	South	West
1 ♥	Pass	2 ♦	Pass
2 ♠	Pass	3 ♦	Pass
3 N.T.	Pass	4 ♣	Pass
6 ♦	Pass	Pass	Pass

West led the spade three.

A group of European stars regularly competes in American national championships. One of them is Tony Forrester of England, who has a large collection of titles acquired on both sides of the Atlantic. Playing in the Fall Nationals in Las Vegas four years ago, he defended brilliantly on the diagramed deal, and for his effort he eventually received the International Bridge Press Association's award for the Best Defense of the Year.

Forrester sat East, and his partner was a well-known British television journalist, James Mates, whose father, Michael Mates, is a Conservative member of Parliament and former Cabinet Minister. The partners

sat silently while their opponents climbed to the sensible contract of six diamonds.

South's bid of three clubs, the fourth suit, did not necessarily show clubs. It would often be a waiting move, with nothing much in the club suit. But the subsequent bid of four clubs showed that he had a freakish two-suited hand with some slam interest. North decided that his ace-queen of diamonds were golden cards, which indeed they were, and made a spectacular leap to six diamonds.

On a good day, South can take all 13 tricks, and this does not necessarily require a periscope to see the singleton diamond king on his right. After ruffing an opening spade lead in six diamonds, it is quite reasonable to play clubs, ruffing the third round with dummy's diamond queen. Then the diamond king drops fortuitously under the ace, and all the tricks roll in.

South started on this route, but unluckily for him he had Forrester on his right. On the second round of clubs, the English star dropped the club queen, a piece of spectacular "generosity." Now South did not need a club ruff, and he thought he could afford to take a diamond finesse. The sequel proved him wrong.

After taking the diamond king, East returned a spade. South ruffed, and led to the diamond ace. The bad trump division now doomed the slam. He could not return to his hand without forcing himself again, and finished down four. He had made eight tricks, and would have made 13 but for Forrester's "generosity."

The New York Times

monday 26 · 360
KWANZAA BEGINS
BOXING DAY (CANADA, U.K.)

tuesday 27 · 361
BANK HOLIDAY (U.K.)

wednesday 28 · 362

thursday 29 · 363

friday 30 · 364

saturday ● 31 · 365

sunday 1 · 1
NEW YEAR'S DAY

s	m	t	w	t	f	s
1	2	3	4	5	6	7
8	9	10	11	12	13	14
15	16	17	18	19	20	21
22	23	24	25	26	27	28
29	30	31				

JANUARY

2005 INTERNATIONAL HOLIDAYS

Following are major (bank-closing) holidays for selected countries in 2005. Islamic observances are subject to adjustment. Holidays for the U.S., U.K., and Canada and major Jewish holidays appear on this calendar's grid pages. Pomegranate is not responsible for errors or omissions in this list. Users of this information should confirm dates with local sources before making international travel or business plans.

ARGENTINA

1 Jan	New Year's Day
24 Mar	Holy Thursday
25 Mar	Good Friday
27 Mar	Easter
4 Apr	Malvinas Islands Memorial
1 May	Labor Day
25 May	National Holiday
20 Jun	Flag Day
9 Jul	Independence Day
15 Aug	Gen. San Martín Anniversary
10 Oct	Columbus Day
8 Dec	Immaculate Conception
25 Dec	Christmas

AUSTRALIA

1–3 Jan	New Year's Holiday
26 Jan	Australia Day
7 Mar	Labor Day (Western Australia)
14 Mar	Labor Day (Victoria)
25 Mar	Good Friday
26 Mar	Easter Saturday (New South Wales)
27–28 Mar	Easter Holiday
25 Apr	Anzac Day
2 May	Labor Day (Queensland)
13 Jun	Queen's Birthday
1 Aug	Bank Holiday (New South Wales, Northern Territory)
3 Oct	Labor Day (New South Wales, Australian Capital Territory, and South Australia)
1 Nov	Melbourne Cup Day (Victoria)
25–26 Dec	Christmas Holiday
27 Dec	Boxing Day

BRAZIL

1 Jan	New Year's Day
20 Jan	Foundation Day (Rio de Janeiro)
25 Jan	Foundation Day (São Paulo)
7–8 Feb	Carnival
25 Mar	Good Friday
27 Mar	Easter
21 Apr	Tiradentes Day
1 May	Labor Day
26 May	Corpus Christi
1 Jul	Civic Holiday (São Paulo)
9 Jul	Independence Day (São Paulo)
7 Sep	Independence Day
12 Oct	Our Lady of Aparecida
2 Nov	All Souls' Day
15 Nov	Proclamation of the Republic
25 Dec	Christmas
31 Dec	New Year's Eve

CHINA (SEE ALSO HONG KONG)

1 Jan	New Year's Day
9–11 Feb	Lunar New Year
1–3 May	Labor Day Holiday
1–3 Oct	National Holiday

FRANCE

1 Jan	New Year's Day
25 Mar	Good Friday
27–28 Mar	Easter Holiday
1 May	Labor Day
8 May	Armistice Day (1)
5 May	Ascension Day
16 May	Whitmonday
14 Jul	Bastille Day
15 Aug	Assumption Day
1 Nov	All Saints' Day
11 Nov	Armistice Day (2)
25 Dec	Christmas

GERMANY

1 Jan	New Year's Day
6 Jan	Epiphany (Munich)
25 Mar	Good Friday
27–28 Mar	Easter Holiday
1 May	Labor Day
5 May	Ascension Day
16 May	Whitmonday
26 May	Corpus Christi
15 Aug	Assumption Day (Munich)
3 Oct	National Day
1 Nov	All Saints' Day (Munich)
24 Dec	Christmas Eve
25 Dec	Christmas
26 Dec	Boxing Day
31 Dec	New Year's Eve

HONG KONG

1 Jan	New Year's Day
9–11 Feb	Lunar New Year
25–28 Mar	Easter Holiday
5 Apr	Ching Ming Festival
1 May	Labor Day
15 May	Buddha's Birthday
11 Jun	Tuen Ng Day
1 Jul	SAR Establishment Day
19 Sep	Mid-Autumn Festival
1 Oct	Chinese National Holiday
11 Oct	Chung Yeung Day
25–27 Dec	Christmas Holiday

INDIA

21 Jan	Bakr-Id (Eid-al-Adha)
26 Jan	Republic Day
19 Feb	Muharram
25 Mar	Good Friday
27 Mar	Easter
1 Apr	Half-yearly bank closing
21 Apr	Prophet Muhammad's Birthday
1 May	Maharashtra Day (Mumbai)
15 Aug	Independence Day
30 Sep	Half-yearly bank closing
2 Oct	Mahatma Gandhi's Birthday
1 Nov	Diwali (Deepavali)
3 Nov	Ramzan Id (Eid-al-Fitr)
25 Dec	Christmas
(Additional holidays to be declared)

IRELAND

1 Jan	New Year's Day
17 Mar	St. Patrick's Day
25 Mar	Good Friday
27–28 Mar	Easter Holiday
2 May	May Day
6 Jun	Summer Holiday
1 Aug	Autumn Holiday
31 Oct	Halloween
25 Dec	Christmas
26 Dec	St. Stephen's Day

ISRAEL

25 Mar	Purim
24 Apr	First day of Pesach
30 Apr	Last day of Pesach
14 May	National Independence Day
13 Jun	Shavuot
14 Aug	Fast of Av
4–5 Oct	Rosh Hashanah
13 Oct	Yom Kippur
18 Oct	First day of Sukkot
25 Oct	Shemini Atzeret

ITALY

1 Jan	New Year's Day
6 Jan	Epiphany
27–28 Mar	Easter Holiday
25 Apr	Liberation Day
1 May	Labor Day
2 Jun	Republic Day
29 Jun	Sts. Peter and Paul (Rome)
15 Aug	Assumption Day
1 Nov	All Saints' Day
8 Dec	Immaculate Conception
25 Dec	Christmas
26 Dec	St. Stephen's Day

2005 INTERNATIONAL HOLIDAYS

JAPAN
1 Jan	New Year's Day
10 Jan	Coming of Age Day
11 Feb	National Foundation Day
21 Mar	Vernal Equinox Holiday
29 Apr	Greenery Day
3 May	Constitution Day
4 May	National Holiday
5 May	Children's Day
20 Jul	Marine Day
19 Sep	Respect for the Aged Day
23 Sep	Autumnal Equinox Holiday
10 Oct	Health and Sports Day
3 Nov	Culture Day
23 Nov	Labor Thanksgiving Day
23 Dec	Emperor's Birthday
31 Dec	New Year's Eve

KENYA
1 Jan	New Year's Day
25 Mar	Good Friday
27–28 Mar	Easter Holiday
1 May	Labor Day
1 Jun	Madaraka Day
10 Oct	Moi Day
20 Oct	Kenyatta Day
4 Nov	Eid-al-Fitr
12 Dec	Jamhuri Day
25 Dec	Christmas
26 Dec	Boxing Day

MALAYSIA
1 Jan	New Year's Day
21 Jan	Hari Raya Haji (Eid-al-Adha)
1 Feb	Federal Territory Day
9–10 Feb	Lunar New Year
10 Feb	First day of Muharram
21 Apr	Prophet Muhammad's Birthday
1 May	Labor Day
23 May	Vesak Day (Buddha's Birthday)
4 Jun	Yang DiPertuan Agong's Birthday
31 Aug	National Day
1 Nov	Deepavali
3–4 Nov	Hari Raya Puasa (Eid-al-Fitr)
25 Dec	Christmas

MEXICO
1 Jan	New Year's Day
5 Feb	Constitution Day
21 Mar	Benito Juárez's Birthday
24 Mar	Holy Thursday
25 Mar	Good Friday
26 Mar	Holy Saturday
27 Mar	Easter
1 May	Labor Day
5 May	Battle of Puebla
1 Sep	Bank Holiday
16 Sep	Independence Day
20 Nov	Revolution Day
12 Dec	Our Lady of Guadalupe
25 Dec	Christmas

NETHERLANDS
1 Jan	New Year's Day
25 Mar	Good Friday
27–28 Mar	Easter Holiday
30 Apr	Queen's Birthday
5 May	Ascension Day/Liberation Day
16 May	Whitmonday
25 Dec	Christmas
26 Dec	Boxing Day

NEW ZEALAND
1–4 Jan	New Year's Holiday
24 Jan	Wellington Provincial Anniversary
31 Jan	Auckland Provincial Anniversary
6 Feb	Waitangi Day
25 Mar	Good Friday
27–28 Mar	Easter Holiday
25 Apr	Anzac Day
6 Jun	Queen's Birthday
24 Oct	Labor Day
25–26 Dec	Christmas Holiday
27 Dec	Boxing Day

PUERTO RICO
1 Jan	New Year's Day
6 Jan	Three Kings Day (Epiphany)
11 Jan	Eugenio María de Hostos's Birthday
17 Jan	Martin Luther King Jr. Day
21 Feb	Presidents' Day
22 Mar	Emancipation Day
25 Mar	Good Friday
27 Mar	Easter
16 Apr	José de Diego's Birthday
30 May	Memorial Day
24 Jun	St. John the Baptist
4 Jul	U.S. Independence Day
17 Jul	Luis Muñoz Rivera's Birthday
25 Jul	Constitution Day
27 Jul	José Celso Barbosa's Birthday
5 Sep	Labor Day
10 Oct	Columbus Day
11 Nov	Veterans Day
19 Nov	Discovery of Puerto Rico
24 Nov	Thanksgiving Day
25 Dec	Christmas

SAUDI ARABIA
16–24 Jan	Eid-al-Adha
29 Oct–8 Nov	Eid-al-Fitr

SINGAPORE
1 Jan	New Year's Day
21 Jan	Hari Raya Haji (Eid-al-Adha)
9–11 Feb	Lunar New Year
25 Mar	Good Friday
27 Mar	Easter
1 May	Labor Day
23 May	Vesak Day (Buddha's Birthday)
9 Aug	National Day
1 Nov	Deepavali
3 Nov	Hari Raya Puasa (Eid-al-Fitr)
25 Dec	Christmas

SOUTH AFRICA
1 Jan	New Year's Day
21 Mar	Human Rights Day
25 Mar	Good Friday
27 Mar	Easter
28 Mar	Family Day
27 Apr	Freedom Day
1 May	Labor Day
16 Jun	Youth Day
9 Aug	National Women's Day
24 Sep	Heritage Day
16 Dec	Day of Reconciliation
25 Dec	Christmas
26 Dec	Day of Goodwill

SPAIN
1 Jan	New Year's Day
6 Jan	Epiphany
24 Mar	Holy Thursday
25 Mar	Good Friday
27 Mar	Easter
1 May	Labor Day
2 May	Independence Day
15 May	San Isidro's Day
15 Aug	Assumption Day
12 Oct	Hispanity Day
1 Nov	All Saints' Day
9 Nov	Our Lady of Almudena
6 Dec	Constitution Day
8 Dec	Immaculate Conception
25 Dec	Christmas

SWITZERLAND
1 Jan	New Year's Day
2 Jan	Berchtoldstag
25 Mar	Good Friday
27–28 Mar	Easter Holiday
1 May	Labor Day
5 May	Ascension Day
16 May	Whitmonday
1 Aug	National Day
25 Dec	Christmas
26 Dec	St. Stephen's Day

2005

JANUARY
s	m	t	w	t	f	s
						1
2	3	4	5	6	7	8
9	10	11	12	13	14	15
16	17	18	19	20	21	22
23	24	25	26	27	28	29
30	31					

FEBRUARY
s	m	t	w	t	f	s
		1	2	3	4	5
6	7	8	9	10	11	12
13	14	15	16	17	18	19
20	21	22	23	24	25	26
27	28					

MARCH
s	m	t	w	t	f	s
		1	2	3	4	5
6	7	8	9	10	11	12
13	14	15	16	17	18	19
20	21	22	23	24	25	26
27	28	29	30	31		

APRIL
s	m	t	w	t	f	s
					1	2
3	4	5	6	7	8	9
10	11	12	13	14	15	16
17	18	19	20	21	22	23
24	25	26	27	28	29	30

MAY
s	m	t	w	t	f	s
1	2	3	4	5	6	7
8	9	10	11	12	13	14
15	16	17	18	19	20	21
22	23	24	25	26	27	28
29	30	31				

JUNE
s	m	t	w	t	f	s
			1	2	3	4
5	6	7	8	9	10	11
12	13	14	15	16	17	18
19	20	21	22	23	24	25
26	27	28	29	30		

JULY
s	m	t	w	t	f	s
					1	2
3	4	5	6	7	8	9
10	11	12	13	14	15	16
17	18	19	20	21	22	23
24	25	26	27	28	29	30
31						

AUGUST
s	m	t	w	t	f	s
	1	2	3	4	5	6
7	8	9	10	11	12	13
14	15	16	17	18	19	20
21	22	23	24	25	26	27
28	29	30	31			

SEPTEMBER
s	m	t	w	t	f	s
				1	2	3
4	5	6	7	8	9	10
11	12	13	14	15	16	17
18	19	20	21	22	23	24
25	26	27	28	29	30	

OCTOBER
s	m	t	w	t	f	s
						1
2	3	4	5	6	7	8
9	10	11	12	13	14	15
16	17	18	19	20	21	22
23	24	25	26	27	28	29
30	31					

NOVEMBER
s	m	t	w	t	f	s
		1	2	3	4	5
6	7	8	9	10	11	12
13	14	15	16	17	18	19
20	21	22	23	24	25	26
27	28	29	30			

DECEMBER
s	m	t	w	t	f	s
				1	2	3
4	5	6	7	8	9	10
11	12	13	14	15	16	17
18	19	20	21	22	23	24
25	26	27	28	29	30	31

2006

JANUARY

s	m	t	w	t	f	s
1	2	3	4	5	6	7
8	9	10	11	12	13	14
15	16	17	18	19	20	21
22	23	24	25	26	27	28
29	30	31				

FEBRUARY

s	m	t	w	t	f	s
			1	2	3	4
5	6	7	8	9	10	11
12	13	14	15	16	17	18
19	20	21	22	23	24	25
26	27	28				

MARCH

s	m	t	w	t	f	s
			1	2	3	4
5	6	7	8	9	10	11
12	13	14	15	16	17	18
19	20	21	22	23	24	25
26	27	28	29	30	31	

APRIL

s	m	t	w	t	f	s
						1
2	3	4	5	6	7	8
9	10	11	12	13	14	15
16	17	18	19	20	21	22
23	24	25	26	27	28	29
30						

MAY

s	m	t	w	t	f	s
	1	2	3	4	5	6
7	8	9	10	11	12	13
14	15	16	17	18	19	20
21	22	23	24	25	26	27
28	29	30	31			

JUNE

s	m	t	w	t	f	s
				1	2	3
4	5	6	7	8	9	10
11	12	13	14	15	16	17
18	19	20	21	22	23	24
25	26	27	28	29	30	

JULY

s	m	t	w	t	f	s
						1
2	3	4	5	6	7	8
9	10	11	12	13	14	15
16	17	18	19	20	21	22
23	24	25	26	27	28	29
30	31					

AUGUST

s	m	t	w	t	f	s
		1	2	3	4	5
6	7	8	9	10	11	12
13	14	15	16	17	18	19
20	21	22	23	24	25	26
27	28	29	30	31		

SEPTEMBER

s	m	t	w	t	f	s
					1	2
3	4	5	6	7	8	9
10	11	12	13	14	15	16
17	18	19	20	21	22	23
24	25	26	27	28	29	30

OCTOBER

s	m	t	w	t	f	s
1	2	3	4	5	6	7
8	9	10	11	12	13	14
15	16	17	18	19	20	21
22	23	24	25	26	27	28
29	30	31				

NOVEMBER

s	m	t	w	t	f	s
			1	2	3	4
5	6	7	8	9	10	11
12	13	14	15	16	17	18
19	20	21	22	23	24	25
26	27	28	29	30		

DECEMBER

s	m	t	w	t	f	s
					1	2
3	4	5	6	7	8	9
10	11	12	13	14	15	16
17	18	19	20	21	22	23
24	25	26	27	28	29	30
31						

It happened fast, the two grabbed Rembert and spun him around

The taller of the two men put a knife to her cameraman's throat, while the other produced a second knife and held it to his stomach. Rembert dropped his camera and flailed his arms up, but stopped moving when the one named Gaston jabbed the tip hard enough to draw blood.

"Stay still," Gaston said.

Annja had been reaching for the sword in her mind, had felt the sensation of the pommel against her palm, but she left the blade hanging in the otherwhere.

"I told the kid the money is at the hotel." Annja squinted through the driving rain, taking in Rembert's panic. "I only have a few Euros with me. You can have them, but—"

"We don't want your money, Annja Creed. We want your sword."

His accent. Annja recognized Gaston. He was one of the gang she'd fought in Paris outside the old train station. He was one of the gang who'd fled before the police arrived. What was he doing here? Had he overheard her talking to Roux, telling him she was coming to this city for another episode of *Chasing History's Monsters?*

"The sword! If you hand over the sword, we'll let your friend live."

Titles in this series:

ROGUE Angel

Alex Archer

CITY OF SWORDS

A GOLD EAGLE BOOK FROM
WORLDWIDE®

TORONTO • NEW YORK • LONDON
AMSTERDAM • PARIS • SYDNEY • HAMBURG
STOCKHOLM • ATHENS • TOKYO • MILAN
MADRID • WARSAW • BUDAPEST • AUCKLAND

First edition November 2012

ISBN-13: 978-0-373-62159-0

CITY OF SWORDS

Special thanks and acknowledgment to
Jean Rabe for her contribution to this work.

Printed in U.S.A.

The
LEGEND

...THE ENGLISH COMMANDER TOOK
JOAN'S SWORD AND RAISED IT HIGH.

The broadsword, plain and unadorned,
gleamed in the firelight. He put the tip against
the ground and his foot at the center of the blade.
The broadsword shattered, fragments falling
into the mud. The crowd surged forward,
peasant and soldier, and snatched the shards
from the trampled mud. The commander tossed
the hilt deep into the crowd.
Smoke almost obscured Joan, but she continued
praying till the end, until finally the flames climbed
her body and she sagged against the restraints.

Joan of Arc died that fateful day in France,
but her legend and sword are reborn....

1

His arrow struck deep in the deer's chest but missed the heart. The animal struggled to get up, tangling itself in the tall grass and making a painful mewling sound that caused his throat to tighten. Dragging one leg, he limped toward it. Though always a heavily built man— sturdy, he preferred to think of himself—he used to get around effortlessly. But age had taken its toll, coupled with the fevers that had plagued him these past few months.

His doctors demanded he avoid roast meat. Who were they to tell a king what to do? Boiled venison was not so tasty, and he intended to savor a properly pre-pared roast tonight.

Charlemagne drew his sword, the blade catching the late-afternoon sun and taking on a molten cast. He couldn't stand to see the animal suffer. One slash across the throat finished it.

"Cette épée, ma chère amie, a déjà tué," he said. *This sword, my friend, has already killed.* A great many men. He spoke French to accommodate his aide, his

tongue halting around the words. He much preferred the Germanic dialect of the Ripuarian Franks, or Greek or Latin, or even the exotic-sounding Arabic that he fancied. But his aide was not well versed in languages.

The two men dragged the deer back to Charlemagne's home.

He cleaned his blade first, then bathed and dressed for dinner, wearing a linen shirt against his skin and matching breeches. Over this he wore a dark tunic trimmed with a pale silk fringe—the one bit of finery he allowed himself. He preferred to dress like a commoner, leaving all but one jeweled ring in a chest by his bed. Lastly, he put on ivory hose and comfortable shoes. He left the room, but returned to check himself in the mirror. There were guests to consider tonight, and he wanted to appear well-groomed.

Despite his years he remained good-looking, tall but not overly so, with a thick, squat neck and a nose that belonged on a bigger man's face. His hair was white, but there was an abundance of it. He arranged the curls with his fingers, squared his shoulders, pronounced himself acceptable and went downstairs.

Among the dinner guests he was about to greet was his son Louis, whom he had recently crowned. It would be good to see him again and to speak of politics and alliances. No doubt someone would ask to hear tales from one of his great battles. Charlemagne had been engaged in one clash after another throughout nearly all his reign, usually at the front of his scara bodyguard squadrons. But sometimes alone when there was no one to bear witness.

Always with Joyeuse in hand. *Mon épée.* He patted the scabbard. Three decades of fighting, more than a dozen wars, and now this sword was relegated to putting a deer out of its misery.

Perhaps he would regale those gathered with that final push he'd orchestrated to conquer Saxonia and to convert the barbarians to Christianity. It was a good story, and he didn't mind retelling it. Then he would excuse himself and retire early, as he planned to venture out again at first light. A few more days of hunting, then he would travel to Aachen, given the onset of November. He'd come to enjoy hunting animals far more than he'd ever enjoyed hunting men.

THOUGH HE WOULD WORK at it doggedly for those few days, fate would grant him only one undersize buck. Charlemagne's plans to return to the hunt in the spring would never materialize, as he would fall ill with pleurisy.

"Joyeuse," he said, as he took to his bed a final time. *"Mon épée."*

A servant placed the sword at his side.

Charlemagne wrapped his thick fingers around the pommel. This sword, his one constant companion, gave him some measure of peace.

"Joyeuse, *ma très chère amie.*" He took one more breath, and died.

2

The sword was her one constant companion. It was a yard of double-bladed steel, honed impossibly sharp. Though a priceless relic, it was not a showpiece suited to a museum. It was a dealer of death—her servant and master, good fortune and wretched curse. Once belonging to Joan of Arc, shattered and mysteriously re-formed, it had come to her…along with a destiny to wield it wisely.

The lights from the train station were diffused by the thin fog and distorted the blade so it looked like a ribbon of darkened silver. Annja swung it above her head in a flashy move meant to rattle her less-skilled opponent.

"Eh…à armes égales!" he cried.

French was one of the several languages Annja knew. *Fight on equal terms, with equal weaponry.*

He wielded a switchblade, which was no match for her sword. He should have fled as his two companions had moments ago, but he stood there, puffing himself up with the bravado of youth. The night and the mist hid some of his features, but Annja could tell he was probably still in his teens, given the acne scars on his face. He stank from going too long without a bath and wearing clothes tinged with the grime of Paris. His breath smelled of vodka, which meant he'd consumed a generous amount, likely adding to his courage. His hair stuck up at all angles, held in place by something that smelled vaguely sweet.

"All right," she said. "I'll fight you on equal terms." With a thought, she dismissed the sword, relegating it to the otherwhere where it hung, waiting for her to summon it again.

He glanced quickly at the ground and into the shadows. Not spotting the sword, he returned his full attention to her. *"Pute!"* he spat.

With a clipped laugh, Annja crouched to meet his charge. He didn't disappoint her, darting in and slashing forward, a quick jab typical of street brawlers. The tough lacked finesse, but he was burly and mean, and those traits helped compensate for his deficiencies.

She sidestepped and brought up her foot, catching his ankle. He stumbled, but managed to keep his balance. He whirled toward her, eyes narrowed.

"Espèce de pute!"

"Quite the limited vocabulary," she taunted, again waiting for his rush.

"De merde," he replied. *"Putain de merde!"*

Annja made a tsking sound and waved her finger at him.

"Livrer aux chiens!"

"No," she said. "I'll throw you to the dogs. Actually, the police."

She'd come here looking for a fight. She'd needed the exercise and a distraction, from an assignment she had no interest in—a two-part segment for *Chasing History's Monsters*. Her TV show's producers were really reaching into the bottom of the barrel for legends to sensationalize. Familiar with Paris, she knew to avoid Les Halles, Le Châtelet and Gare du Nord this late at night, when the crowds had disappeared. So that's precisely where she'd ventured. Les Halles and Le Châtelet had yielded no opponents, but Gare du Nord and its shadowy side streets had brought out this fellow and his now-absent friends.

Tourists traveling alone around the old train station were warned to keep a low profile and to avoid wearing jewelry that might entice thieves. But Annja had done the opposite. In the sequin-trimmed cocktail dress she'd worn earlier to dinner, emerald necklace dangling in the low V of the fabric, she'd trolled back and forth like a fisherman after bass.

This fellow's fluid, if vulgar, French was tinged with some kind of accent. Probably from one of the Roma camps, she guessed. France had declared war against the illegal encampments that had sprung up around Paris, evacuating many of the immigrants living there. But pockets still persisted. Paris news agencies had been reporting on the Romany gangs preying on travelers arriving from London on the high-speed trains. Now Annja was preying on one of those gang members.

He shuffled to his right, putting his back to an old stone wall and tossing the knife into his other hand—trying to rattle her. His breath was slow and even, and his crouch was similar to the horse stance of the swordsman. Annja waited for him to make the next move, knowing full well he was weighing her with anger in his eyes.

A moment later he came at her, this time stabbing at her side, then wheeling and darting at her again. The move was unexpected, and he managed to slice her dress. Annja cursed herself for underestimating the youth. A street brawler, yes, but somewhere along the line, he'd had training. She appraised him more carefully. The sleeves of his shirt were tight around his biceps, suggesting muscles. His calves were thick, too. Certainly not the common ruffian she'd originally considered him to be. As he came forward and jabbed at her, then shuffled back, she realized his moves were those of a boxer.

"You might make a better opponent than I thought," she told him. By the look on his face, he didn't understand English. She repeated the sentence in French.

"Marie-salope!"

"I've been called that before," she returned.

He pointed the knife tip at her throat and made a gesture with his free hand.

"Yes, I gathered that you want my necklace." When

the corner of his lip turned up in a snarl, she added, "I'm rather fond of it. A gift from an old…friend."

He continued to come at her, jumping in and back, swinging his knife and alternately punching with his free hand. He didn't connect with anything, but he didn't give up. She moved out of his way each time, but kept him close, not wanting to discourage him. She was in heels, and the spikes caught in the cracks of the brick and threatened to topple her. It would have been easier to slip out of them, but she didn't want easy tonight.

"Tu peux crever, connasse!"

"No, I'm not going to die tonight," she said. "But neither will you. We're just playing, aren't we? Like children looking to run off a little steam?" *And in the process teaching you a lesson,* she thought. *"Ducon la joie,"* she called him, half surprised at herself for stooping to his level.

The words enflamed him and he sped up his rushes, sweeping the blade in a wider and wider arc, his anger making his moves more erratic and easier to dodge.

"Du-te la dracu!" he shouted.

It was Romany now, not French. And though Annja knew only a smattering of the language, she figured out that he'd just told her to go to hell.

"Not tonight," she repeated.

The exertion felt good, like the welcome burn from a long jog through Central Park. She kept her breathing steady and deep, drawing the smells of the place into her lungs. Oil from the trains, a trace of exhaust from cars that trundled by on the main street nearby, urine, and dampness and mold; it had rained here a few hours ago. And there was the smell from her assailant, stronger now because he'd been working up a sweat. She picked up a trace of cigarette smoke, which she hadn't noticed before. The kid had that addiction, too.

"Maybe a stint in jail will help you with some of those bad habits. Clean you up a little, eh?"

He jockeyed for position, which allowed her to step onto the sidewalk. Easier on her heels. He cursed again, a mix of Romany and French this time. Annja surprised him and took the initiative, stepping in and thumping him on the chest with her open hand. Finally he was showing signs of fatigue, but he still wasn't giving up, his predatory gaze lingering on the emerald necklace.

"The man who gave me this said it was four hundred years old, give or take a decade. Worth as much for its historic value as for the gems." She knew he couldn't understand her. "You'd probably fence it for a few cases of Alizé Bleu."

The dance had managed to wash away her fatigue. The past four days had taken her under the city, to the famous Paris catacombs stretching back to Roman times, when they'd been excavated in the harvest of limestone. Annja had been there before, to tunnels that served as the meeting ground for secret societies, the birthplace of spooky legends. Even into the chambers where long-buried skeletons were stashed to make room for more bodies in the city's overcrowded cemeteries.

She'd walked through halls lined with bones and ancient graffiti, helping her cameraman figure out which angles to shoot from—no doubt beneath the spot where she and her opponent stood now. As many as six million dead were believed to crowd the labyrinthine network, some of them killed during the French Revolution.

The tunnels had been covered on television before, sometimes from a historical perspective or a military one; German soldiers had used a chamber during World War II as a bunker, she knew. Programs had aired about the reported ghosts, disembodied voices and shadows that followed tourists. Annja's assignment had been to find something fresh, and so she'd interviewed tour guides, as well as several workers who'd hauled away rubble from some of the collapsed areas. The floating, hazy orbs they'd recently spotted seemed to be the fresh take she was looking for.

As always, she found the place fascinating. A skilled archaeologist, she had an affinity for ruins. But she also believed the tunnels had been done to death. She hadn't wanted to come to France, anyway—it was a place of nightmares for her.

Joan of Arc had been lashed to a pillar in the Vieux-Marché in Rouen and burned at the stake in 1431. After her horrible death, her body was burned a second time and then a third, the ashes scattered into the Seine. Annja was somehow connected to the holy martyr, and her sleep on occasion was cut through with fiery images.

But while France held nightmares for her, it was also a paycheck. At least this week. She'd finished her work shortly before five today, showered, dressed in the only couture outfit she'd brought to the city and took her cameraman to Pierre Gagnaire's in the eighth district for fish terrine. She was certain her little dance here had worked off the calories from the rich and expensive dessert. Maybe it was time to call it a night.

Her opponent took a few steps back and cocked his head, listening. She listened, too. There were the muted sounds of the city: cars trundling past on the main strip, the clacking departure of an aging train, the soft strains of a Thierry Cham zouk R & B tune that dissipated to nothingness, and a syncopated slapping that grew louder and announced the return of the hood's companions. They'd brought help. Altogether there were seven of them.

"Chamelle vérolée!" the one she'd been fighting shouted. He grinned widely, revealing his crooked teeth and a stud through his tongue.

Annja felt for the sword in her mind, but waited. She delivered a roundhouse kick to her dancing partner, her pointed heel jabbing his stomach. His breath knocked out of him, he doubled over and dropped the switchblade. Without pause she kicked him once more, angling higher and pounding her foot against his chest. He slumped to his knees, cursing. To make sure he wouldn't be entering the fray again, she administered a quick neck chop, which rendered him unconscious.

Then she devoted her attention to the remaining six.

"You will die for that," the tallest said in English, his Romany accent apparent. He brandished a gun and pulled the trigger.

3

The bullet came close, passing where Annja's head had been a heartbeat before. There must have been a silencer on the gun; its spitting sound was barely audible. On reflex she'd ducked just as he'd reached into his jacket pocket, and she rolled forward, losing her shoes on purpose and coming up in a crouch.

Don't bring a knife to a gunfight, they said. Or in her case, a sword. Still, in her mind she touched the blade, seeking its reassuring presence. One glance at the gang, then she slipped to where the shadows were thickest along the wall.

The patchy fog and the darkness made the men seem even more menacing. The tallest was well over six feet, thin but with broad shoulders. Like a dagger that had been jammed tip first into the street. He was in the front, two each to his right and left, back a few feet. So the guy she'd fought moments ago hadn't been the gang leader, she decided. The others were all of similar build to the tall one with the gun, and all with the oddly cropped and spiky hair their unconscious fellow sported. A sixth held back. He also had a gun with a silencer, but she couldn't tell its make for certain. Maybe an old French-made MAB PA-15. The guy up front had a sleek SIG Sauer. That they had guns, particularly a SIG Sauer—with silencers—marked them as a notch above a common gang. Probably stolen.

They were close enough that she could smell them; they had the pong of the streets. They talked softly in Romany as they scanned the area, taking in the guy she'd knocked out.

Well, she'd craved an adrenaline rush. Selfish.

One of the men moved his arms to his sides, showing that he had a length of chain for a weapon. The other three produced switchblades, one in each hand.

"Girl, girl, girl," the tall one in the lead said. "Come out where we can get a better look at you." He held his free hand high. "We won't hurt you."

"Much," said the one with the chain.

Annja felt their eyes on her—they knew exactly where she was. She also sensed other eyes on her. Another gang member?

"Come out, girl." The tall one again. "Girl, girl, girl. Come out. Come out."

"Come out, come out, wherever you are," Annja whispered as she did just that. In a blur of taupe taffeta, chiffon and sequins, she sprinted forward, surprising both gunmen, who couldn't draw a bead. She slammed into the lead one, striking his throat with her elbow and grabbing at his gun with her other hand. She threw the SIG Sauer behind her, listening to it clatter on the street. She pulled her second elbow jab to avoid killing him and stepped back as he dropped, crouching below the chain that cut through the air.

Five left standing.

Four after she shot toward one of the switchblade wielders, kicking him in the groin, then following through with a punch to his jaw that sent a few teeth and a spray of blood flying. Almost too easy.

"Scroafă!" the other man with the gun hollered. He was considerably older than the others, maybe thirty, with a short beard and a dead eye. He fired, missing her again as she dived, the bullet striking the pavement behind her. *"Scroafă!"*

Annja didn't know the word. He fired again, and this time the bullet grazed her arm, feeling as if an open flame had been put to her skin. She slipped by the three men surrounding her and raced toward the one-eyed gunman, darting left when he brought the gun up again. The sword was in her hand; she hadn't realized that she'd reached for it. The pommel felt good against her palm; its presence cut some of the burning sensation from the graze. She turned the blade vertical to the street and then brought it around like a batter would swing at an incoming ball. The flat of the sword connected with the man's hand and caused the gun to fly from his grip.

"Bisturiu!" one of the men behind her shouted. *"Spada!"*

"Yes, it's a sword," Annja said. It had taken the wound to her arm to make her realize how stupid she'd been, looking for a fight just to get in some physical activity. Annja had been thrust into more than enough fights through the past few years. She didn't need to go trolling for them.

"Idiot!" She cursed herself as she spun on the ball of her bare foot, a painful sensation on the rough pavement, and brought the flat of the blade around again, striking him in the arm. At the same time she kicked at his knee, hearing a discomfiting pop.

"Scroafă!" The one-eyed man repeated it like a chant before Annja cuffed him on the neck and rendered him unconscious. She turned to face the remaining three just as the one with the chain lashed her chest.

The air rushed from her lungs and she doubled over, still managing to point the sword at him. Determined, he whipped the chain at her again, as if it was a weightless thing in his hands. It caught the blade, but only for a moment.

"Infern!" the chain wielder gasped.

Annja took advantage of his momentary surprise to slice down with the sword. She pulled her punch, using just enough force to wound him, but not cut off his arm. The pain made him drop the chain. Some of it landed on her bare feet, adding to her aches.

"Ceda," he said, grasping his bleeding arm and holding it close. Behind him, the others took off running. Annja realized they'd been the same two who had run

away at the beginning…and come back with reinforcements. Would they return with still more? *"Ceda."* He bent over, his back rounding and making him look like a turtle. *"Ceda."*

"I suspect that means you surrender." Annja willed the sword away and, despite her pain, shoved the man toward the wall.

In the shadows there, Annja found her purse, which she had dropped when she'd picked the fight with the first youth. She grabbed it, took her cell phone out and called the police, quickly explaining in French that she'd been accosted by a Roma gang and that some vigilantes came to her aid. The tale was half-true. Prodding the man to stay ahead of her, she nudged him toward her shoes, which she gingerly put on. Then she directed him to sit near one of his fallen fellows.

"Wait," she told him. "Do you understand English? French?"

He nodded.

"Wait for the police."

When she could hear sirens, she returned to the shadows, following the wall back to the old train station. And toward where she had earlier sensed someone else watching her.

"Roux."

"You're hurt."

"I'll heal."

"Rather quickly no doubt."

The wail of the sirens grew louder. Annja glanced toward the men, making sure none of them had bolted.

"And what was all of that for, Annja Creed?"

She touched her arm, feeling the sting from the bullet and the warmth of her blood. There was a first-aid kit in her suitcase at the hotel; she always traveled with one.

They kept close to the front of the massive Gare du Nord. The original train station had been demolished a century and a half ago, deemed too small. This huge affair, built in its place, had been recently added to. Designed by French architect Jacques Ignace Hittorff, it was one of Annja's favorite places in Paris, the facade created around a triumphal arch, the main cast-iron support beams supplied by an ironworks in Glasgow. In daylight, you could see eight statues along the building's cornice, each representing international destinations—London, Brussels, Vienna, Warsaw, Frankfurt, Amsterdam, Berlin, Cologne. Annja and Roux passed beneath the one representing Vienna.

The station served all of northern Europe, so was a beehive of activity around the clock…though not so much outside the building this time of night. Well past midnight now, there were a few souls about, some gaping down the street in the direction of the downed gang.

From the cover of their vantage point, she and Roux watched as a police car arrived, its flashing ice-blue lights cutting through the thinning fog. A van pulled in behind it and policemen spilled out. Like swarming ants, they took control of the Romanies, lifting the unconscious forms and handcuffing the older one. Annja couldn't hear what they were saying, but the older man pointed with his head toward the shadows and the train station.

Annja started to move again, as fast as she dared without drawing attention. She pulled Roux along with her.

They reached the far end of the station and turned the corner.

"Didn't want to stick around and explain yourself to the police?"

"I'll be in France for the better part of another week," Annja said, changing the subject.

"Certainly enough time for you to pick another fight with the Romany gangs."

She didn't bother to answer that.

"More of the underground? For your television program?"

How did Roux know—? Stupid. Somehow he always knew where she was. Part of his shtick. One of Joan of Arc's knights, he had been unable to save the crusader when she was burned at the stake. And, it seemed, he'd been cursed to live until her sword—shattered by the English—was reassembled. He'd spent more than five centuries searching for the pieces of Joan's sword. But the sword was whole now, resting in the otherwhere until Annja needed it, and Roux was still around. Just how old he'd live to, nobody could predict. She looked upon him as a mentor of sorts. A mentor with an agenda. What had brought him out here in the early-morning hours?

"I'm done in the catacombs," she said. "I leave tomorrow—later today, actually—for Avignon."

"A vacation? Certainly long overdue."

She shook her head and let a silence fall between them. She heard a bus chug by on the main street and a few cars motor past. From somewhere came faint music. She focused on it, trying to place it, finally coming up with Ange's "Le Cimetière des Arlequins," a progressive rock song from the 1970s.

"Working on another episode of *Chasing Historical Monsters?*"

"*Chasing History's Monsters,*" Annja corrected. "And, yes, that's why I'm going to Avignon. My producer is being cost conscious. He figures if he's sending a crew to France, he might as well get several segments out of it. So we did the tunnels under Paris…."

"And what lies under Avignon?"

She wondered why Roux was curious. If he could somehow always tell where she was, why would he bother to pry?

"Just making conversation, Annja."

Was he privy to her thoughts? No, she knew that was beyond him. She smiled wistfully. "The cynocephalus and Saint Christopher."

In the haze from a streetlight, Annja saw Roux's eyebrows arch. In the light he appeared old, as if in his seventies, though he was considerably older than that. His white hair caught the light and he'd trimmed his beard since she'd seen him last. His skin was like worn leather, but he didn't look older than when she'd met him.

"Old man, you don't know about Saint Christopher and the legend of the cynocephalus?"

His grin revealed white, even teeth. "Sorry, no."

"Cynocephali are said to be dog-headed men who serve like the Benedictine monks. Centuries back they supposedly sent a delegation to the pope in Avignon. Some of the medieval legends paint Saint Christopher as one of the cynocephali."

"Fascinating."

She doubted Roux was fascinated by the trivia. "In any event, my producer found a posting on the internet that some dog-headed men were spotted by tourists in Avignon a few weeks ago."

Roux tipped his head back. "Probably some costumed youths."

"Or real dogs transformed by Photoshop."

"Beautiful place, Avignon. The City of the Popes in the thirteen and fourteen hundreds."

"During the Catholic schism," Annja added. "I've been there before. And I don't get tired of it. One of the few cities in France to have maintained its ramparts and Rocher des Doms."

"And the bridge of Avignon." Roux's face took on a vacant look, as if he was lost in some long-ago memory. "On the left bank of the Rhône." He paused. "And the place where Annja Creed will chase her next historical monster."

He pivoted to stand in front of her, his pale blue eyes peering into her green ones.

"Be careful, Annja, that a historical monster does not come chasing you."

4

She drove a 2005 Peugeot 607, four-door, gunmetal-gray. It didn't look like anything special. Because it was a manual, she was at the wheel rather than her passenger—who was in charge of this foray. The Peugeot handled a little stiffly. She preferred smaller, splashier sports cars, but they'd needed something as nearly invisible as possible. Her window was down, and she had the vent going full blast to cut the reek of smoke left from previous drivers. Her passenger didn't seem bothered by the smell.

"Do you smoke?" she asked.

"Slower," he warned. "Wouldn't want to get in an accident." He paused. "Or get a speeding ticket."

"Of course, Archard." She edged her foot off the gas. "But next time, we rent an automatic and you drive. I am tired of your constant directions." He had been at her since they'd left Paris, suggesting when she should change lanes and which turnoffs to take. He'd picked the route. He was more familiar with this part of France, but that didn't mean his constant corrections were any less annoying. Bad enough that she sometimes heard voices in her head. Voices that had told her to take this trip with Archard. She didn't need him talking, too.

It was nearing noon when they reached Rocamadour. She'd wanted to stop well outside of the town and come in after dark, but Archard had insisted they arrive early. "Being ahead of schedule is always best," he'd said. She enjoyed his accent, rich and typically French, but he rarely said anything she cared to listen to. "It allows for the unexpected and it lets us look around."

She knew better than to argue. He was one of Lawton's senior knights, and at the moment she was just a lackey. With luck, though, and a good performance today, that would change.

"Park in the lower city," he instructed. "You—"

"I've been here before," she interrupted. A lie, but what did a little one matter? Besides, the place had a population of well less than a thousand, so how hard could it be to find her way around? "Give me a minute and I'll find a good spot."

"When were you here?"

She ducked the question by pulling into a small lot and getting out. "Quaint." Or worse than quaint, she thought. She loved Paris—so busy, lively, colorful, loud. This was anything but. Perched on a rocky plateau that overlooked the Alzou valley, the town was known for its incredible views and historical religious sites.

"So why way down here?" she asked. "We have to—"

"For a handful of hours, we are sightseers, Sarah. Enjoying the weather, taking a tour, stopping for lunch."

She let him steer her to the second floor of the Envies de Terroir, where she was happy to discover a handsome waiter who spoke English. They took a table by the window, one a little large for just the two of them, but it was away from the other diners and they could talk without being overheard. Archard ordered the lunch special for them: ventrèche and tomato tartine, and glasses of wine.

"I'm surprised you're drinking," she said. "More, that you're letting me drink."

"We'll walk it off long before tonight." Later, he ordered a second glass, and she was quick to ask for a raspberry-and-almond tart from the cart the waiter was pushing.

"Since you're buying," she said, as she took a bite and savored the rich dessert. "Good food. Place is a little quiet, but it'll do." Everything was a little quiet here.

He finished his wine, paid the bill and led her out onto the street.

"More than a million tourists come here every year, Sarah. Some for the wine, most for the buildings. Pilgrims, too."

"Were you one of them? A pilgrim?"

He nodded. "That was many years ago."

"How many?" Archard wasn't *that* old. In his late thirties, maybe forty tops, Sarah guessed, which put him at about twice her age.

"I was young," he answered. "Let's ride the elevator from the lower town, Basse Ville. We'll take the stairs tonight."

The architecture was amazing, and Sarah wished she really had been here before, so she could have taken time to properly explore. She had been enrolled as a European history major when she'd dropped out of the University of Provence Aix-Marseille a month ago, in her second semester. Her current career path was more interesting.

Archard remained silent while a few more tourists boarded the elevator and it started its ascent. A young woman in a low-cut shirt was pressed against him, but he showed no reaction. "When you were here before, Sarah, did you come for the Black Madonna? The centerpiece of Chapelle Notre-Dame?"

"Sure. A casual tourist, you know." She had to stop lying in an effort to impress this man.

Sarah watched as the cluster of churches and chapels came into view, and then quickly stepped out of the elevator when it reached the top. She and Archard pretended to browse the souvenir shops before taking a walking tour of the Basilique St-Sauveur.

The hours ticked by and she found herself actually enjoying the day. Until the sun started to set and they took the last elevator ride back down to the lower town, and anxiety set in. Archard noticed.

"Are you certain you're up for this, Sarah?"

"It's what we came here for, right? And you can't do it without me." She thrust out her chin and exhaled, fluttering her curls against her forehead. "Yes, I'm up for this. I've been looking forward to this since Dr. Lawton lectured about it."

"Dinner first."

"But—"

"We need the night, and a good meal will help pass the time. Aren't you hungry?"

Dinner was at the Beau Site Jehan de Valon, and she ordered for herself this time: an omelet with truffles, one of the most expensive items on the menu, and a salad. Archard opted for the duck-steak carpaccio with sliced cantaloupe. They both had a liberal amount of coffee.

"So you were a pilgrim…." She didn't know much about Archard other than that he was divorced.

"I studied with the Benedictine monks here, and I had the good fortune to scrub the floor of the Chapelle Miraculeuse, where the tomb of Saint Amadour is located."

"And he is—?" Sarah sucked in her bottom lip, angry with herself for letting slip her ignorance.

"No one to concern us tonight."

She shrugged and looked out the window, watching four women carrying lit candles.

"So the Chapelle Mirac—"

"Is not where we are going."

"I know. I took courses from Dr. Lawton first semester and—"

"That makes you an expert, eh?" Archard's eyes twinkled in amusement.

"Dark enough yet?"

"Yes, but not late enough. Patience, Sarah. Patience is—"

"A virtue."

They got candles out of the trunk of the rental car and joined a small procession climbing up the Grand Escalier, a weathered stone stairway to the chapels they'd toured earlier in the day. Sarah counted the steps: two hundred sixteen. No wonder they'd taken the elevator the first time, she thought. The climb wasn't taxing to her, though. In fact she wished the people in front of them would walk faster. They paused at each of the fourteen stations of the cross until they reached the Cross of Jerusalem, at the top.

She thought Archard would be winded, given the years he had on her. But he surprised her, showing no sign of fatigue. The same could not be said for some of the tourists who'd ascended with them.

"When you came here on a pilgrimage—" she started to ask.

"I took the stairs on my knees, as is customary when seeking penance."

"Tough on your pants, I'll bet." And penance for what?

His eyes narrowed. "This is a holy place. Your footsteps will fall on stones touched by Zacchaeus of Jericho, Saint Dominic, Saint Bernard—perhaps even

Charlemagne, when he prepared to fight the Spanish Moors. Miracles happen here, healings, conversions. Do not mock this place."

"Sorry."

The buildings looked different in the dark, the Romanesque-Gothic style made eerie in the flickering light from the candles and the pale glow that spilled from a few windows.

Sarah and Archard mingled with the tourists, many of them praying softly, their voices lost in the strains of a chant coming from the nearest chapel. Archard prayed, too, though she couldn't hear him. She just noticed his lips move and his thumbs rub against the base of his candle. She hadn't been to church since she'd lived with her parents in Delaware, but she wasn't irreligious. Deciding that it would be appropriate to copy the others—and that God might actually pay attention here—Sarah bowed her head and prayed that she wouldn't screw up.

An hour later, she and Archard tossed their candles and hid in an alcove of the Basilique St-Sauveur, where they waited until the last tourist left. Sarah guessed that it was early morning, maybe two or three, judging by how tired she was. The buzz from the coffee had worn off a while ago, and now she had an urgent need to find a bush to squat behind.

"I'll see to security," Archard whispered. She had to strain to hear him. "In a few minutes I'll meet you inside the Chapelle."

She watched him leave, and then slipped outside to pay the rent on the coffee. There was no one milling around—a good thing. But she knew the place would be bustling in a handful of hours…especially if she and Archard succeeded.

Sarah returned to the alcove, counted to one hundred, then glided next door to the Chapelle Notre-Dame. Archard said there was security, and she had no doubt it was high-tech, though decidedly out of place in the old buildings. The Black Madonna, which she'd read about in a tourist pamphlet in one of the souvenir shops, was the focal point of this building. Hopefully, the bulk of the security efforts were tied to the Madonna. Sarah waited a second count of one hundred. Still no Archard.

"Great," she breathed. So far she'd done nothing illegal; she could hightail it out of here and go back to her studio apartment on Avenue Georges V. Instead, she sucked in a deep breath and went through the arch. When she didn't hear any alarms go off, she let her breath out. She pulled a tiny flashlight out of her pocket, cupped her hand over the top and aimed it around until she found what she was looking for. Then she switched if off, tiptoed to the wall and took off her shoes. She didn't want the hard rubber soles marring the wall or squeaking. She tugged a pair of tight-fitting gloves out of her pocket and wiggled into them, though she wasn't especially worried about leaving fingerprints. She'd never been in trouble before. Still, it was a precaution.

Where was Archard?

She felt along the wall and found the natural cracks in the stonework. Wedging her fingers in, she slowly and quietly pulled herself up. The muscles in her arms bunched and her chest tightened. Nerves. Sarah thought of the chant she'd listened to earlier. The sound had been soothing. *Relax.* She pulled herself higher, relying only on her handholds, her feet spread in a ballet dancer's second position against the stone.

Relax.

Sarah felt a ledge and gripped it. The pain in her fingers helped her focus. A little higher and there was a second ledge, which she pulled herself onto, resting her knees. Finding a good handhold, she leaned backward, one arm outstretched, fingers searching…searching… finding a beam. She wrapped her arms and legs around it and inched out upside down. If she fell, she might break a leg or something. It probably wouldn't kill her but would get her in a world of trouble, and Dr. Lawton would be furious.

Where in the hell was Archard?

Farther. A little farther. It was so dark in here. She was on the underside of an overhang, and the shadows were making this more than a little difficult. The flashlight wasn't an option. It had been risky using it the first time. A dozen or so more inches and…there! Her eyes managed to distinguish the blackness just enough. She clamped her legs tight on the beam, stretched out and wrapped her fingers around the pommel. The sword was suspended from the ceiling just beyond the archway. Sarah cursed herself for not looking closer when they'd taken the tour this afternoon. Maybe she could have asked one of the monks what was holding it. She tugged without success.

"Dammit!" The whispered word bounced off the stone and came back at her.

She inched out farther, pulled harder, ground her teeth together and gave it one more yank.

She heard a loud snap.

A little too loud. Sarah wished she hadn't drunk so much coffee. The voices in her head encouraged her. *You can do this. You can do this now.* The sword still wasn't free, just loose from one of the cords. How many were holding it? Didn't matter. She'd come too far to stop. She pulled again, as hard as she could, and was rewarded with a second snap and the sensation of falling. She managed to catch herself with her legs, but was dangling, her free arm flailing, the sword grasped in the other. Made of iron, the weapon was heavy. She squeezed the pommel tight so she wouldn't drop it.

"C'mon. C'mon." Sarah drew herself up, wrapping her free arm around the beam and wedging the sword against her chest. Getting back to the wall took what felt like an eternity, and then another long stretch of time passed before she reached the floor. She laid the sword down very slowly so it wouldn't make a sound against the stone, then put her shoes back on and picked the blade up again.

She plastered herself against the wall, taking even,

shallow breaths and listening. No footfalls. Nothing except her heart pounding thunderously. Her back against the blocks, she crept along the alcove, stopping every few steps to listen again.

Now to get out of here.

The sky was lighter outside than when she'd gone in the Chapelle. No, she decided, the inside of the building had just been dark in contrast. Only minutes had passed, not the hours it had felt like. Light from the scattering of streetlamps in the Basse Ville, the part of the town below the cliff, seeped up like the glow from a halo.

Sarah pulled in a sharp breath when she heard a footfall against gravel. A monk! No, not one of the monks. It was Archard. He came around the side of the Chapelle and headed toward her.

"Where the hell were—"

He set his finger to his lips and took the heavy sword from her. Then he nodded toward the stairs. "Hurry," he whispered in her ear.

"Where were you?" she persisted in a murmur.

"A little more security than I expected." He pulled her into a niche between the buildings and then grabbed her hand, tugging off her glove and touching her fingers to the tip of the stolen sword. It was broken, jagged. "So it is real. See? The genuine one. You did great. Now get the rest of it. I'll meet you at the car." He reached into a pocket and handed her a small GPS device. It blinked softly with her coordinates. From another pocket he produced a chisel. "And, Sarah, speed would be good."

Getting "the rest of it" proved much easier said than done.

They motored out of the village at dawn, her bleeding fingers gripping the steering wheel of the Peugeot, her clothes torn, her knees badly scraped and every inch of her throbbing.

5

Annja couldn't sleep.

She sat up and swung her legs over the edge of the bed to pull on a pair of sweatpants. Her stomach churned and a bitter taste settled in her mouth. She'd had another nightmare—images of fire swirling all around, bright red and orange, hurtful in their intensity. Like before, there was a face in the flames. Sometimes the face was her own, and she woke up from those nightmares sweating.

She was drenched in sweat now.

Slipping on the athletic shoes that had set her back half a paycheck, she stood and stretched, stuck her hotel key card in her pocket and reached for a fresh T-shirt.

She wanted to be home, curled up on her bed, shutting out the god-awful blare of the Brooklyn traffic. She could sleep through that ruckus, somehow even found it comforting. But in France she often had nightmares. Not always, but enough that she wondered why she bothered to come back. Why hadn't she told Doug to get someone else for these segments?

She looked at the clock on the nightstand. One forty-five.

A quick run. That ought to get her through this. Certainly safer than picking a fight with a gang of punks outside one of the city's old train stations.

She made sure the door clicked shut behind her, and then padded past the bank of elevators to the security door at the end of the hall.

She eased that shut behind her, too, wincing at the grating sound it made, and jogged down from the eighth- to the seventh-floor landing, turned and headed toward the sixth. The air was fusty and stale.

The stairwell, dimly lit with energy-saving spiral fluorescent lights, probably wasn't intended to be used by hotel guests. Emergencies and power outages, Annja figured, and for guests like herself who couldn't sleep. The walls were painted a hospital-green, reminding her of avocado dip. They and the security doors were thick enough that she shouldn't disturb anyone's beauty sleep.

She laughed as her feet hit the fourth-floor landing and she picked up speed. She loved to run.

Annja felt the beginning of an exercise burn in her chest as she reached the first floor and wheeled around to start the jog back up. The smell of cleanser lingered like a thick fog. She thumbed the button on her iPod and then inserted the earbuds, not once missing a step or losing her cadence.

Wagner's *Ride of the Valkyries* played just loudly enough to muffle her breathing and her slapping shoes.

Kill da wabbit, kill da wabbit. As much as Annja loved Elmer Fudd, she flipped the button to bring up another piece. Balakirev's *Islamey.* She set her feet in time to the beat and felt the piano riffs travel up and down her spine. The music swelled as she again neared the eighth-floor landing.

Up twelve more floors, to the top of the hotel, before returning to her room for a welcome shower and a few hours of good sleep. That was the plan. She felt wired, as if she'd just thrown back six cups of coffee. Maybe she'd do two circuits instead. That'd be enough. Yeah. Better than a sleeping pill.

As she hit the tenth floor, Balakirev reached a man-cando section. Over the whisper of the piano, Annja heard the scrape of a door opening somewhere above her. A snippet of conversation drifted down, and then she heard the pounding of feet. Two more insomniacs.

Annja pressed herself against the wall of the eleventh-floor landing as they thundered toward her—two young women she'd seen in the restaurant during dinner. They sported hot-pink Wales Wrunners T-shirts. They smiled as they bounced by. She recalled reading about a marathon in town in another day or two. These were no doubt entrants.

At the sixteenth-floor landing, Annja nudged the button on the iPod again, wanting something a little livelier. Mikhail Glinka's *Kamarinskaya* blared, and she ran faster.

The burn in her chest had spread to her neck. Her

face was flushed from the mild exertion and her heart rate was up. The stale air reached deeper into her lungs, and she felt a sensation in her legs that wasn't quite an ache, but was telling Annja that her muscles were stretching from the climb. It was a good feeling.

She turned her head and blew a hank of hair out of her eyes. She set her feet to the beat as she neared the uppermost landing. Annja brushed the door to the roof with her fingers, leaving four thin streaks of sweat, then spun on her heel and started back down.

She passed the Wales Wrunners again on the sixth-floor landing. They were coming up this time and pressed themselves against the wall to let her continue. Common runner courtesy. One of the girls said something, but Annja couldn't hear her over the Glinka.

At the bottom the cleanser scent again assailed Annja—bleach or floor polish or both. She touched down on the landing, brushed her fingers against the first-floor door and then started up. She took fuller, even breaths now.

She spotted two more insomniacs when she turned on the seventh floor and started up the next flight. They stood shoulder to shoulder on the eighth-floor landing, blocking her path. Dressed in dark pants and jackets, they reminded her of the Blues Brothers. One was tall, the other shorter and stocky with a pockmarked face. The stocky one wore sunglasses, despite the stairwell's dim lighting; that fact set her nerves tingling. Annja

jogged in place on the stairs, halfway between land-
ings, and plucked out her earbuds.

She waited for the men to move or to say something.
Neither did.

"Excuse me," she said as she reached the step just
below them. They backed up, but not enough for her
to reach the landing door. She didn't like the looks of
them, and hackles rose on her neck. "This is my floor,"
she said, a little louder. She thought about reaching for
the sword, but they hadn't threatened her. Maybe they
were with the Wales Wrunners.

The stocky one tilted his head to the side, as though
he didn't understand what Annja was saying, and so she
repeated it in French. He nodded in comprehension and
smiled, took a step back to accommodate her. Without
warning, the tall one's fist shot out like a piston, striking her on the shoulder. There was considerable force
in the blow, and it caught her off guard.

Annja fell, arms flailing. Her legs struck the stairs
and her back slammed down as she bumped and slid
to the lower landing. Her head bounced hard against
the tile and her vision swam. Her right ankle hurt like
hell—definitely sprained, maybe broken—and she felt
as if a truck had fallen on her.

She tried to get up, but her head was spinning, making the stairwell's hospital-green paint a sickening swirl
of color. As Annja retched, the tall man clomped down
the steps and grabbed her by the waistband.

The sword! She felt for it with her mind, but everything was out of sync and she raced toward merciful unconsciousness.

"Where is it? In your room?" the stocky one asked in perfect English. He had the gravelly voice of a smoker. He'd taken off his sunglasses, revealing little black pig eyes. He heaved Annja around the corner to the next set of stairs and shoved. She was pitched down another flight and then another.

The tall one continued talking, but Annja was beyond making out the words. The sounds mingled with the crashing in her ears and the shock as her body hit each step. Blood filled her mouth. The sword hung beyond her reach in an otherworldly space her mind was too muddled to access.

Bending over her on the fifth-floor landing, the stocky one took Annja's iPod and stuck it into his pocket, pausing only long enough to turn the device off. He found the hotel key card in her pants. "Let's check her room."

The tall man grunted in agreement as the blackness reached up to claim Annja.

6

Archard placed the sword on the altar, first the large section and then the smaller one that Sarah had prized out of the cliff. In the gap between the two pieces, the black velvet looked like oil in the dim overhead light. A yard long, the section near the haft was jagged and reminded him of a bolt of lightning.

He bent over the blade, seeing his gray eyes reflected back at him, with faint lines visible at the corners. The years were starting to show.

"Durendal," he said.

"Durendal," one of two men behind him repeated in awe. "Durlindana. Durandarte. God-touched. Dr. Lawton will be pleased."

"Indeed." Archard pressed his fingertips to the pommel. "Most pleased." But he couldn't imagine that his employer's pleasure would exceed his own. "The sword of Charlemagne's paladin Roland."

"Destined to be yours now," the other man added. "You are the doctor's lead knight."

"I read about Roland," Sarah said slowly. "In Dr.

Lawton's textbook. Some called him Orlando, and the sword—"

Annoyed glances from all three men made her stop.

Archard closed his eyes and prayed over the weapon. He heard the soft hiss of his own breath, faster than normal because of his excitement. The walls of this building were thick, but still the wail of a siren managed to find its way in, crescendoed. Another joined it, and then both faded to nothing. He continued to pray.

The other two tugged Sarah back to give him time alone with the sword.

"You endure," Archard whispered, when he had finished his prayer. The name Durendal was believed to have come from the French word *durer,* meaning "to endure." Despite Roland's attempt to destroy it to keep it out of enemy hands, the blade had survived. Damaged, but it still endured....

In Italy it was called Durlindana, and in Spain, Durandarte. Just as Charlemagne had presented it to Roland, Dr. Lawton said it was to be Archard's now. Once said to belong to the fabled Hector of Troy, it was supposed to have been forged by a mysterious Berkshire master blacksmith named Wayland. Its origin was murky, but according to the *Song of Roland,* somehow an angel had got hold of it and given it to Charlemagne. Did it truly have a tooth of Saint Peter inside its golden hilt? Roland touched the hilt again, holding his fingers against the warmth of the metal. A hair from Saint Denis, a piece of cloth from the Virgin Mary's cloak and a drop of blood from Saint Basil—all those things were said to have gone into its making.

"God-touched," Archard whispered.

And now it was his.

But was he worthy of it? And of being Dr. Lawton's "Roland"?

Archard had memorized the *Song of Roland,* perhaps the oldest surviving French manuscript of any consequence. He'd been with Dr. Lawton for the past five years, coming to the scholar in much the same way Sarah had, through the university. He hadn't been a student at first, but rather a teacher, one relatively fresh from his doctoral degree and entrenched in the religious studies department. Archard's wife, in the history department, had suggested they attend one of Dr. Lawton's lectures after dinner one night. He'd agreed to go because it would gain him "wife points," which usually translated into out-of-the-ordinary sex.

The topic—religion's influence on medieval European conflicts—held enough of an interest that Archard had stayed awake through the entire presentation. He was more fascinated by religion in its permutations in present-day society, but was nonetheless captivated by Lawton's intensity and the way the man could hold a crowd on such an otherwise dry topic. Archard had recognized the charisma and power in Dr. Lawton, and had started attending more lectures, some with his wife, most without. Drawn like a moth.

Had he traded one addiction for another?

Archard smiled at that thought. If so, it had been a more than fair trade. A far better addiction, this.

His interest in religion had begun in high school, when his parents sent him to Avignon to seek penance for his obsession with girls. He'd gotten two pregnant before his sixteenth birthday—three, but one he'd managed to sweep under the carpet on his own. His father was well-off and paid for his indiscretions, after eliciting a promise from him to study with the order in Avignon. Archard spent the summer among the monks before deciding their lifestyle was a little too austere for his tastes. Especially since he couldn't tamp down his interest in women.

And so come the fall he'd mixed his two fields at the university, delving into religious studies while pursuing as many girls as he could manage, given his academic work. Eventually he tried to settle down with a beautiful history major, who agreed to share a flat with him at the edge of campus. In time they married. He knew she was aware that he sometimes stepped out on her, but he wondered if she knew just how often.

And then Archard's promiscuity became an issue with Dr. Lawton. The more time he spent with the professor, and the more he opened up about his life, the more Lawton beseeched him to change.

"Choose your penchant for flesh or choose salvation for your soul," Archard recalled his mentor telling him after one lecture. "There isn't room in my company for both." Archard had attended it with a visiting student from Ireland who'd caught his fancy. Dr. Lawton said no more on the matter for several months.

The more lectures Archard attended, the more he fell under the professor's spell. He even enrolled in some classes as a student himself, and the professor took him under his wing.

"You are my Roland," Lawton told him on a weekend trip to the Imperial War Museum and the Tower of London in England. That night over dinner, the professor had outlined his plan, and Archard bought into it. But Dr. Lawton worried that "his Roland" could not wholly focus on their mission.

Women had always been the one chink in his armor, the one distraction that kept him from a perfect life. So Archard found a doctor in Paris who cured his sexual appetite with anti-androgen drugs. In some circles it was called chemical castration, though that was a misnomer, as he remained intact. It was a treatment the courts sometimes imposed on molesters or rapists. The drugs reduced his libido by suppressing his testosterone. Women no longer aroused him.

His wife left him…and left the university.

He'd chosen this chaste, important life over the bawdy, selfish one he'd left behind.

A good trade. A more than adequate trade.

"Much good will come of this," Archard recited. In the *Song of Roland,* the paladin had used Durendal to hold a hundred thousand Muslims at bay until Charlemagne and his army could retreat into France.

Archard turned and regarded the two men and Sarah. "Recovering this sword, embarking on Dr. Lawton's quest. Nothing but good will come."

The men nodded. Sarah wrung her hands together.

"So…who's gonna fix the sword?" she asked. She shifted her weight back and forth on the balls of her feet and dropped her hands to her sides. "I mean, it's not really much use with the end of it broken like that, is it?"

Archard growled softly in his throat. "Let Dr. Lawton know we're ready, Sarah."

She thrust out her chin at the order. A year ago he would have found her attractive and probably lured her into bed. Now she was only irritating. "Sarah…"

7

The largest oil painting on the wall—lit museum-style in an ornate gold frame above the wainscoting—was a portrait of a well-dressed man with an abundance of black curls that fell past his shoulders. His face was all angles and planes, his eyes hooded and intense. There were other paintings, too, and all of them looked as if they'd been rendered by the Old Masters.

The room they were displayed in was opulent, the furnishings new, but not modern. Brocade cushions on white high-backed chairs. Settees, low tables, candelabras, a thick rug on the floor shot through with metallic threads. It all looked to be a carefully arranged tourist exhibit. There was even a velvet rope stretched across one section of wall to keep people from getting too close to the paintings. But this wasn't a public exhibition. It was simply a favorite spot in Dr. Lawton's warehouse in Paris.

He nudged back a heavy drape and peered out the window, looking down on the loading dock and at another warehouse across the street. The neighboring structures were busier—one supplied grocers, another automotive dealers. In reality the automotive supplier was a front for stolen cars coming into Europe from the United States. Dr. Lawton found the operation distasteful and intended to turn them in when he wrapped up his own business in this area.

His antiques storage warehouse was a front, as well. He cluttered the lower level with all manner of objects he purchased legally. Some of them were even rare finds. Although one object that had arrived a short time ago couldn't fit into that category....

He heard a sound behind him.

"Dr. Lawton," Sarah said, "we're back."

"I know. I saw the car and the van arrive."

"It took longer than I thought it would, going to that dink-burg of a town, and—"

"And?" He didn't bother to turn around.

"It's downstairs. Archard has it. Do you want to—"

"Of course."

"Should I have him bring—"

"No. I'll come down."

He stepped away from the window and let the drape fall back, paused and then turned to see the girl. Woman, he corrected himself. But just barely. She was young. Beautiful, though he had to really look to see it. She unwittingly dimmed her loveliness by wearing baggy shirts spouting slogans and pictures of whatever rock band she was into. This evening she sported a white skull and crossbones with bat wings and A7X in big block letters. Her makeup did nothing to improve her appearance. She wore thick eyeliner and layered on the mascara. Smudges of shimmering green and blue paste covered her lids and tapered to points. Her lipstick was dark. Unnatural. Never red.

"We got into Paris a few hours ago," she said. "But I needed to clean up and change. My clothes got pretty well shredded."

He raised an eyebrow, inviting her to explain.

"It was worse than those rock-climbing walls at the gym," she began. "Not the big part of the sword. It was just hanging out there in the open…right where your research said it would be. But the tip of it…" She held out her hands so he could see all the cuts and broken fingernails. "It was exactly like the legend you taught in class. Roland had tried to throw the sword away, off the cliff, so the enemy wouldn't get it. But the blade hit the stone, and a piece of it broke off and stayed there."

"And the monks displayed the point that fell."

"Yeah." She paused. "They never bothered to go get the other piece. I had a hell of a time in the dark, finding the spot where that little shard was in the cliff. Then I had a hell of a time getting it—"

"God guided your hands," Dr. Lawton said. "And brought the pieces together so that they could be reforged."

"Uh, yeah." She waited, fidgeting in the ensuing silence.

He watched her for several moments, knowing she couldn't keep her tongue from wagging.

"So…who's going to get this one? Archard? I figured it would be Archard because of Roland's significance. He thinks it's going to be his sword. He's down there drooling over it. Are you—"

"Yes, Durendal is to be Archard's sword." A longer silence settled over them.

Finally she broke it, stuttering, "Am I going to… Are you going to—"

"If there are enough, Sarah. I do not intend to leave you out."

He turned his back to her and faced the large portrait. "He died on the twenty-eighth of January. It was the seventh day since he'd taken to his bed and after his final Holy Communion. Did you know that?"

Sarah shook her mass of short blond curls. "I'm not much of an historical scholar," she admitted. "I tried to be. Loved your courses. Maybe I shouldn't have quit like I did, but—"

He gruffly cleared his throat. "He was seventy-two years old, forty-seven years into his reign. Twice my age when the pleurisy killed him." Lawton slowly paced in front of the painting. "Buried the same day, in Aachen Cathedral. The rush wasn't necessary—it had been so cold and the disease hadn't touched his outward appearance. A count in Aachen claimed to have found and opened the tomb, finding the corpse inside sitting on a throne, decked out with a crown and scepter, the tight flesh over the bones incorrupt. God-touched."

Sarah appeared to be in awe, but the professor suspected it was for his benefit.

"He died depressed. He hadn't been afraid of death coming—that comes to all men. But he was afraid of being incomplete."

She tipped her head in question.

"There were things left undone," Lawton explained.

"But you will finish those things," she said, squaring her shoulders.

"Together, we will finish those things." He paused and turned to regard her again. "If your belief grows stronger. If I can sense in you an honest interest and desire. If you shed your youthful curiosity. If you follow me honestly."

"I do. I—I will."

He grabbed her by the shoulders. "If you are to be one of my twelve, you must convince me, Sarah."

"Anything," she said. "I'll do anything."

"Then prepare for another foray. Now, shall we…" He glided past her toward the stairs, inviting her to follow. "Shall we see Roland's Durendal?"

The big staircase was a wrought-iron, circular one he'd imported from an ironworks in Scotland. It ended in the center of a massive room filled with crates and forklifts—the trappings of a warehouse. An illusion he found satisfactory.

Dr. Lawton approached Archard, who was kneeling

in front of one of the smaller crates, now draped with a length of velvet. It was as close to an altar as could be arranged here. The lighting was poor, which helped hide the true nature of the building, but the makeshift altar was directly beneath one of the fixtures.

"Dr. Lawton," Archard stated solemnly.

"Durendal," Lawton said. "Our mission has begun in earnest."

8

"I thought it was a wrap, that we were done. You sent the rest of the crew home." Rembert Hayes was Annja's photographer for the dog-men segment in Avignon. He'd worked diligently with her on the project for the past three and a half days, and now he nudged his wheeled suitcase with his foot, jiggling it just enough to make a soft clacking sound against the marble floor of the Hotel Danieli lobby. He'd been her cameraman in the catacombs under Paris before that, never complaining, happy to get the work, in fact, as he was a hungry freelancer. But he'd just gotten a text from his daughter, who was on her way to the hospital to give birth. He was obviously going to miss the event, but he wanted to get back home to New York as soon as possible, and Annja sympathized. His daughter would be a first-time mom with single-parent responsibilities.

"I thought it was a wrap, too."

"May I call a car to take you—" the bellman began, but Annja's scowl cut him off.

"Rem, I'm very sorry, but—"

"Plenty of footage, Annja. We have some great color work." He drummed his fingers on the concierge counter and jiggled the suitcase again. "I called. We can catch a flight in two hours at the Caumont Airport, just outside town. It'll take us to Manchester, and we can connect to New York and—"

"Be home sometime tomorrow," Annja finished. She studied him and offered a sad smile. "I thought your daughter wasn't due for another two weeks."

"The baby had other ideas, I guess."

"Look, your wife's with her, right?"

He nodded.

"Then she'll get your daughter through this. We've got one more interview." She waved a sheet of paper at him. She'd had the concierge print out an email off her phone. "Some tipster named Gaston claims to be one of the dog-men."

"That's...what Doug Morrell's call was about?" Rembert sputtered. "One more interview? We don't need it."

"I might not have liked this whole assignment, Rem. But I'm not going to do a half-assed job when this could add something to an otherwise mediocre piece. And that's what our dog-men story is right now...nothing special."

"Damn, Annja."

"I'm not going to argue with Doug about it. We're doing this."

"Doug doesn't have a pregnant single daughter."

"Doug's twenty-two."

"My point." Rembert made a face. "All your beloved producer cares about are ratings."

"Let's go see this guy and get it over with. Then we'll take the train back to Paris and get a direct flight. We might still make it home sometime tomorrow." She told the bellman to store their suitcases.

"Damn, Annja." He held the door for her. "A dog-man, eh?"

"A cynocephalus."

"Yeah. Yeah. I know what he's called. I just hope he's had his rabies shot."

Annja shot him a look. "We'll walk. It's not far from the hotel. The Centre Historique."

"Our old hotel was closer."

"You're going to complain about everything today, aren't you, Rem?"

He said yes one block later, when the gray afternoon sky opened up and drenched them.

Their previous lodgings, the Avignon Grand Hotel, had been much closer, practically across the street from their meet at the Palais des Papes. But their stay there hadn't sat well with Annja, after the beating she'd taken in the stairwell and the theft of her laptop from her room. She'd told Rembert about the theft, but didn't mention the beating. After she'd come to at the bottom of the stairs, picked herself up and staggered back to her room, she'd discovered that all her things were just where she'd left them, but there were tiny differences that raised the hairs on the back of her neck. And there was the missing computer. So she'd relocated the crew to the Danieli and reported the theft to the police. Again, she didn't report the beating. Annja healed quickly—a strange phenomenon somehow linked to the sword—and she didn't want to explain that particular quirk to her photographer or the police.

They were soaked by the time they reached the cluster of centuries-old buildings at the edge of the Rhône. It looked as if the walls of the medieval structures might tumble down the bank and spill into the river. The grandest, the Palais des Papes, was considered one of the most important Gothic buildings in Europe. Annja had been through it twice in the past.

They shook themselves off just inside the entrance.

"The palace of popes, eh?" Rembert mused. "And the place of dog-men. Hope our fellow has been nice and dry in here."

Annja cocked her head.

"You never had a dog, did you?" he pressed.

Annja had been raised in an orphanage in New Orleans. There was a resident cat, but she'd never caught more than a glimpse of it—the thing always fled from the children. Her life had been too crowded for pets, and now she traveled so much. She envied people who had such companionship. "No. No dogs."

"Well, they stink to high heaven when they get wet."

"I like you better when you smile."

"That doesn't mean I think this interview is a good idea." Rembert brushed the water drops off his camera, then dug a dry handkerchief out of his pocket to wipe it. "So, what's with this place? Enlighten me a little. Only got an outside shot of it two days ago for color on the city."

"Gascon Bertrand de Goth—Pope Clement V—moved the papacy here after his election in 1305. This building went up after his death. Terribly expensive…"

"You'd think religious people would spend the money on the poor. It'd be the religious thing to do, wouldn't it?" Rembert panned the camera around the interior and then got a shot of Annja with her wet hair plastered against the sides of her face.

"This was fortified to withstand attacks, expanded over the years, the wings flanked with high towers. Adjoining buildings were added to enclose the courtyard."

"Beautiful, but excessive," Rembert said.

Despite the archaeological significance of the place, Annja agreed with him. A dozen tourists wandered in the cloister, and they looked so tiny under the high, arched ceiling. Like ants. No doubt the rain was keeping the bulk of the tourists away. She tried to imagine what the place had looked like when the popes walked these chambers, before it had been seized and sacked. Before it became the setting for a massacre of revolutionaries in the late 1700s and was turned into a barracks and prison. Frescoes had been obliterated, the interior woodwork used to build stables. But in the early 1900s, when it became a museum, restoration began, and the renovation work still continued all these years later.

The place carried the smell of old stone and cleaning products, and through the open front door came the smell of the wet city and the Rhône. Rembert focused his camera on the tourists.

"So what's our dog-man look like? A Great Dane? Boxer? A bitzer?"

"Bitzer?"

"Ah, that's right, no dogs. A bitzer...bits of this and bits of that. A mutt."

Annja studied the tourists. "No idea. Doug's note said Gaston would find us. We just have to be visible and wait for him."

"Wait. That's great." Rembert edged farther in, dribbling water on the stone. Annja followed him, looking down corridors that led to other wings. "So we wait. How long? Let's give him an hour, tops. Would maybe still give us time to catch that plane, and—"

"Mrs. Creed?"

Annja and Rembert whirled around to face a wiry youth standing just past the entrance, squinting against the rain. His oversize pants and jacket made him look small.

"Miss. Miss Creed." Annja stepped closer. Rembert began filming. "Are you Gaston?" For some reason she had expected someone older.

"Gaston? No. Not me." The rest of his words were in French. "My brother's name is Gaston." He twisted the ball of his foot against the stone. "I am to bring you to him."

"This isn't the guy," Annja whispered to Rembert. "This is his brother."

The air hissed out between her cameraman's teeth. He looked at his watch.

"We don't have time for a scavenger hunt. Gaston was supposed to meet us here. That was the message, right, Annja? That was the deal. We—"

"He doesn't like to be seen in public, Miss Creed," the kid interrupted, still speaking French. "He's only doing this because of the money. You promised money for the interview."

Rembert recognized the word for *money*.

"We're paying for an interview, Annja?"

It happened sometimes. She nodded and said in English, "According to Doug, we're paying this guy."

"This just gets better and better."

Annja almost called it quits, between Rembert's attitude and the fact that Gaston wasn't here. But her gut told her to pursue it. "Is he close, your brother? Nearby?" She repeated the questions in French.

The kid nodded. "Under the bridge. Away from the rain and people. He hides there and…you will pay him to talk to you, right? He said he would only talk for money."

"He talks, and then I make arrangements to pay him. I didn't bring the money with me." Annja had not wanted to set herself up for a mugging. "I'm not carrying cash." She pulled her pants pockets inside out to show him they were empty. "The money is at the hotel.

He talks to me, you come back with me to the hotel and get it. I promise to pay."

The nod became vigorous. "All right. That is all right, I guess. You come now, and then you give me money."

He turned and tromped out into the rain, Annja and a reluctant Rembert following.

"Wait!" Annja called. "What's your name?"

Without stopping, the boy replied "Jacques" over his shoulder.

"It'll be a bitzer, that's for sure," Rembert grumbled.

The bank was slick, but Annja navigated it. Her cameraman was not as sure-footed and slid halfway down on the seat of his pants, cradling his camera to his chest and cursing when he bumped across rocks. The city above was clean, but the riverbank was another matter. Plastic foam cups, crushed cigarette packs and other assorted garbage pooled in low spots. The stink of refuse and sodden earth was strong.

"Let's wrap this up," Annja said, extending a hand to Rembert.

"I second and third that." He checked over his camera and wiped at the water again, a futile gesture, as it was raining harder. "Doug's bad idea is getting worse and worse and worse."

"Miss Creed." Jacques slogged forward, pointing to a recess under the bridge. "My brother waits there."

"Now *I* have a bad feeling about this," Annja whispered. The whole thing hadn't felt quite right, not since she'd read the note from Doug about this interview. Actually, not since she'd set foot in Avignon... But she needed to pursue this. Something niggled at the back of her mind. "Gaston?" She raised her voice to be heard over the running river, the drumming of the rain and the slapping of Jacques's footsteps ahead of them.

A figure emerged from the shadows. He had a build similar to Jacques's, but she couldn't make out any details other than that he looked bedraggled and rumpled.

"I am Gaston." He spoke English, but his accent was thick.

Annja paused, but Rembert, camera to his face, crunched forward over broken glass and gravel. His backside looked like a mud slick.

"She said she would pay us," Jacques announced. "Miss Creed has money and—"

"So you're a cynocephalus?" Rembert asked. He paused and stood directly in front of the man, blocking Annja's view of him. "One of the dog-men of France? You look pretty human to me. In fact...hey, what are you—"

It happened fast. The two grabbed Rembert and spun him around, the taller putting a knife to his throat, the other producing a blade and holding it to his stomach. Rembert dropped the camera, his arms flailing, but stopped moving when the one named Gaston drew blood.

"Stay still," Gaston said. "If you want to live."

Annja had been reaching for the sword with her

mind, had felt the sensation of the pommel forming against her palm, but didn't take it. The blade hung in the otherwhere, waiting.

"I told Jacques the money's at the hotel." She peered through the driving rain, eyes locking onto Rembert's panicked stare. "I've only got a few euros with me. You can have them, but—"

"We don't want your money, Annja Creed. We want your sword."

The accent. It wasn't French. Close, but there was a difference.

Gaston nudged Rembert farther out from under the bridge.

"You." Annja recognized Gaston. He was one of the gang she'd fought in Paris, outside the train station. He was one of the Romanies who'd fled before the police arrived.

What was he doing here?

Had Gaston overheard her talking to Roux, telling him she was coming to this city for another episode of *Chasing History's Monsters?*

"The sword! If you hand over the sword, Annja Creed, we'll let your friend live."

9

"Annja!" Rembert's face was pale. "What do they want? Money? I've got euros. Give them our money!"

Although Rembert didn't know much French beyond asking where the nearest restaurant and bathroom were—and though he was oblivious to what the pair were really after—he recognized their intent. Annja saw his lower lip quiver. He had broken out in a sweat. He clumsily tried to reach into his pockets, maybe to pull out a wallet, but the Romanies snarled and poked him with their knives. Rembert stood still. Her photographer was not a physically weak man, but neither was he a stupid one.

"The sword, American archaeologist!" the taller of the two shouted. He pressed the knife harder against Rembert's skin, which was white around the tip of the blade, with a splotch of red showing. "It was not in your hotel room. At either hotel. Where is it? Where is the old sword?"

"I don't have a sword," she snapped. Only the two of

them, right? Not much of a threat… No threat at all, if Rembert wasn't in the equation. "Do you see a sword?"

There could be more, hiding behind the embankment or up on the bridge, maybe behind her. She couldn't hear any other people talking, no crunch of shoes over the gravel and glass at the edge of the river. She wasn't going to risk a glance over her shoulder—not yet.

Her mind raced. They'd followed her from Paris.… Was it possible that night outside the old train station, when she'd been looking for a fight to ease her soul, they'd actually been looking for her? Her, specifically? That they were the ones doing the stalking? Had they known about her sword before the street fight? *Was* that possible?

Annja had always tried to be circumspect when she called the sword. She'd never been caught on tape wielding it. She would know if that had been the case; she had contacts all over the world who followed her interests on the internet and who would have notified her. If nothing else, Roux would have said something.

"The sword! Hand it over! Hurry!"

"I've got no sword here. No gun. No knife. You can see I have no weapon." She paused. "But I have money. Euros. We were going to pay for an interview. We've got money for that. We can go back to the hotel, all of us, Gaston, and—"

He laughed. "A ruse to get you here. Dog-men." He spat.

"Look, whoever you are—" She stopped when she heard the cry of some large bird passing low over the river, followed by the noise of a siren, which quickly receded. What sounded like a boat behind her on the river… She doubted anyone on board could see into the shadows under the bridge, but maybe she could do something to get their attention.

"We don't want your money, American." The tall one spat again, as if the notion of cash left a bad taste in his mouth, and drew the knife down Rembert's throat. The pressure was enough to produce a line of blood, but not enough to cause the photographer serious harm.

"Annja!" Rembert howled. "Give them what they want."

"I do not think you worry about your friend, American archaeologist. I do not think you consider us serious. I can promise you, we are serious. We will kill if we have to."

His companion laughed and jabbed Rembert in the stomach, again enough to draw blood. "She should take us serious, eh, Dimitru?"

The tall one scowled.

So she had one piece of information, a name: Dimitru. Definitely Romany.

"Dimitru!" Annja had the thug's complete attention. "You say you want a sword. I could—"

"No. Not *a* sword. *Your* sword. The one you flashed

in Paris, that night so late. Before the police came and took my brothers."

"I'll have to go get it for you." She extended her arms to her sides and opened her hands as wide as her fingers would stretch. "I'm not carrying a sword." She turned slowly, taking a deep breath, glad for the opportunity to look behind her. She saw the ship, a barge. Not yet close enough. It didn't look as if anyone was on deck. She hadn't heard anyone come up behind her. Other than the threats of the Romanies, she'd heard only the sounds of traffic across the bridge and past the embankment. Finished her circle, she faced the Romany again. They'd pulled Rembert a little deeper into the shadows under the bridge. "It won't take me long."

"You think me simple," the tall one hissed. "You have the sword, Annja Creed. You have it with you. Maybe it is invisible. Maybe it is a ghost thing. But I know you have it."

"We are done talking to her, right, Dimitru?" The other guy poked Rembert again. "A boat is coming. Someone might see us."

"They see nothing," Dimitru said softly. "This rain."

"Annja," Rembert pleaded. "What do they want? We can give them money, can't we? My camera…I dropped it there. They can have that. Annja, tell them they can—"

"We do not want your money," Dimitru said in English. "We want the woman's sword. I am done with this."

"Stop!" Annja cried. "Leave him alone. Let Rembert out of here, let him leave, and you can have the sword. Let—"

"Rembert is our insurance, Annja Creed. Is the sword worth more than his life?"

"Of course not." She nodded. "Let him go."

"The ghostly sword for the photographer, then," Dimitru said. "Now. Make it appear now. Like before."

Annja felt the pommel touch her palm, and she wrapped her fingers around it.

"What the hell?" Rembert said.

"This what you want?" she asked.

"Drop it and back away," Dimitru ordered her.

Annja set it gently at her feet in the scrubby weeds and the remains of someone's fast-food dinner that had been tossed off the bridge. From the Romanies' vantage point, they wouldn't be able to see the sword. Annja stepped back and sent it into the otherwhere. Dimitru's expression didn't change.

"Let him go. Rembert is not a part of this," she said. "There's the sword. We had a bargain."

Dimitru hurled Rembert behind him, and the shorter Romany kicked the photographer in the back of the legs, dropping him to the gravel. At the same time, Dimitru shot toward Annja, knife slashing to keep her at bay.

"Get back!" he hollered to her. "Get back and no one has to be hurt!"

A dozen steps and he was at the spot where she'd dropped the sword.

"Trick!" he screamed. "Where is it? Petre...she tricked us. Kill the man! Kill him—" The Romany's voice caught in his throat.

10

Instantly, the sword was in Annja's hands again and she was bringing it around, aiming to strike him in the arm with the flat of the blade. She'd hadn't meant her blow to be a killing one, but she'd put all her strength behind it, and Dimitru somehow turned into it and rushed her in a crouch. She tried to pull her swing in that last second, but he was too fast and caught himself across the throat. At the same time he managed to stab her in the thigh, but his knife didn't sink deep.

The knife wound hurt, but worse was the sting of death she thought she could have avoided. *Dwell on that later,* Annja told herself. She kept hold of the sword with her left hand, and with her right tugged out the knife and dropped it next to the body.

Annja stepped around Dimitru and headed toward the other man. Petre. The wiry Romany emitted a high-pitched wail. He'd been bending over Rembert, one hand grasping the back of his head, the other readying to slice his throat. But at the sight of Annja advancing on him, he bolted, angling up the steep, slick embankment.

The photographer stayed down, wrapping his arms over his head.

Annja glanced at him as she charged after the Romany, dismissing the sword and pumping her fists to speed her feet. Rembert didn't appear to be badly hurt.

And she desperately needed to find out why they wanted her sword. How they knew about it.

She followed the youth up the bank, sliding once and hitting a chunk of concrete that sent daggers of pain into her knees, almost as bad as the knife wound in her leg. She picked herself up, catching sight of him cresting the top and sprinting into traffic.

Horns blared, tires squealed and someone rolled down his window to spew a stream of curses. Annja dodged the cars, taking only a little more care than her quarry had, which cost her precious seconds.

The rain made the city a blend of blue-grays that caused the buildings and people to look almost surreal—a muted watercolor painting dripping all around her. The storm had increased in intensity in the minutes since she and Rembert had slipped down the bank for the ill-fated interview. Fat drops hammered the pavement and splashed back up like ricocheting bullets.

Her quarry was easy to make out from the other pedestrians braving the weather. None of them were running and pushing people out of their way, and nearly all of them had umbrellas or hats. She was about a block and a half behind him, gaining a little.

"Hé! Que faites-vous?" a pedestrian shouted at her as she nearly tipped him over.

"Sorry," Annja called over her shoulder.

"Qu'est-ce que tu fous là, toi?" This from a young man not quite as polite as the first.

She tromped through a puddle, sending a spray of water at a stooped woman with a large blue umbrella.

"Appellez la police!" the offended woman hollered. *"Appellez les flics! Elle m'a poussé, c'te vache!"*

Annja grimaced. She hadn't pushed the woman. No doubt the police would be arriving soon, anyway, especially if Rembert had called. Lord, what would he tell the cops? Would he mention her sword?

The buildings she thundered past were dirty from age and darkened by the storm. Everything seemed ancient compared to her neighborhood in Brooklyn. Signs on the sidewalk were a blur of colors; she was going too fast to read them.

She lost sight of him when he rounded a corner. When she skidded around it after him, the Palais des Papes loomed into view, the place where she and Rembert had first met "Jacques." There! She snarled when she spotted him dash through the entrance. It was a beautiful building, holy in its original intent, and she disliked the notion of the Romany punk hurtling through it.

Petre, that was what the other man called him.

"Petre!" she shouted. "Stop, Petre!" The sirens were growing louder. If Rembert hadn't summoned the police, someone on the sidewalk had. "Stop, Petre! I only want to talk!"

Annja raced through the entrance, barreling into a pair of women who were opening their umbrellas as they left. She knocked one woman flat. The other dropped her umbrella along with something she had purchased, and that broke with a resounding crack against the stone floor. Annja paused long enough to help the one up and spit out an apology. Then she was running again. She didn't see her quarry, but there were signs to mark his passing—another visitor picking himself up, a man retrieving papers and other objects that had been scattered. Not to mention the trail of wet footprints.

The slapping of her shoes on the stone floor echoed.

"Where are you going?" an American tourist asked as she passed. All the other words shouted at her were in French. There were more people around now than when she and Rembert had been here minutes before. Perhaps a tour bus had dropped them off, or they had come in to escape the storm.

The wet trail led into one of the wings. Annja spotted her quarry just ahead, where a hand-holding couple stood looking at something in an alcove.

Petre grabbed the woman and flung her to the floor. Her companion hollered and bent to help her.

Annja leaped over them like a racer jumping hurdles

on the track. Then the Romany gypsy was out a side door, and she followed.

The rain pounded her once more. Not an inch of her was dry, and now she was feeling chilled. The guy was back on the sidewalk, never pausing to look behind him, obviously knowing Annja was still on his tail. He pushed an old man waiting at a bus stop, then grabbed a woman getting off a bus and threw her behind him— obstacles to slow Annja down.

He skidded around a bench and vaulted a large cement pot filled with flowers, landing like a cat before cutting across the street. And then he disappeared behind another bus.

"No you don't," Annja growled. She wasn't about to let him elude her. Not now. The bus pulled away from the curb just as she reached it. But a quick scan through the windows didn't show any panic or jostling. The passengers looked calm. "So where?" She took in everything lightning-fast. "Where did you go, Petre?"

She studied the entrances to the old buildings, the shops with awnings sagging low from the rain, the people huddled beneath them.

Nothing.

He hadn't come this way.

Wait. There was a gap between two buildings near where the bus had stopped, not wide enough to be an alley. Without thought, Annja plunged down it, the stone wall grazing her shoulder as she went.

As she hurried past a boarded-up recess, Petre

jumped out at her, shoving her against the opposite wall. He had a knife in his hand, but not enough space to use it effectively. Annja grabbed his wrist and pressed it against the stone, squeezing until he dropped the blade and wedging herself against him. He struggled, but she held him hard and brought her face to his ear.

"Don't move, don't barely breathe. You know what I'm capable of."

He stank of sweat and the grime of the city and of fouling himself.

"You're going to talk to me now. Understand?"

He nodded.

"The sword. Why do you want my sword?"

His answer was halting. "Paid…to get it."

"Who paid you?"

He shrugged. His eyes looked dead.

"Who?"

"A collector."

She dug her fingers into his arms with enough force to make him wince. "Let's try this again, Petre, right? Who paid you to steal my sword?"

"Dimitru knew a man. Did work for him in Paris. He paid Dimitru, and Dimitru asked me to help. In Paris and here. This collector—Dimitru said he was rich."

Annja let out an exasperated sigh. Dimitru was gone, and so, apparently, were the answers she wanted.

"You didn't know this man he did work for?"

"I told you no. Never saw him. But Dimitru said he collects swords."

"And how did he know about mine?" Annja didn't expect him to answer that.

"Old swords, that's all I know. Special swords. Dimitru was to get yours and then another. Swords of history."

It was a start, Annja thought. Maybe if she did a little digging, called some—

A commotion back on the sidewalk brought her out of her thoughts. Through the haze of rain she saw flashing blue lights.

"Through there!" she heard someone shout. "They went through there."

Annja squeezed by Petre, putting distance between herself and the police.

Historical swords, the Romany youth had said.

She suddenly recalled something Roux had told her days ago. "Be careful, Annja, that a historical monster does not come chasing you."

11

Dr. Lawton stood at the podium of the lecture hall. The room could hold three hundred, but he filled it only during his special evening lectures, and he hadn't offered any this semester. Today he had one hundred students, impressive given what many of his colleagues considered a dry subject with no practical application for the real world. *Fools,* Dr. Lawton thought. He was practicing the applications beneath all their upturned noses.

"What do you see?" he asked his students.

He'd rigged a laptop to a projector, and an image of a man in armor shone larger than life against the wall.

"A knight," a girl in the front row volunteered.

It was the typical answer he pulled from freshmen.

"A Templar," another suggested.

"A suit of armor from a museum," a rail-thin woman said. "It doesn't look like there's anybody inside it."

Dr. Lawton surveyed the room in silence. In the back row, a few students were texting. Their loss.

"What do you see?" he repeated in his deep voice.

"Can you look past the armor, the metal? Can you look past the centuries?"

No answer. But he had their attention—most of them, anyway.

"I see blood." Dr. Lawton knew he was a striking man. Tall, always impeccably groomed, well dressed in clothes that were both fashionable and a little out of fashion. He stood out. He wore his hair long, as he believed a history professor should. His spectacles had a nearly invisible frame, so as not to obscure his face, which was all angles and planes. "I see a lot of blood."

He waited. Sometimes a student would pipe up, saying, "I don't see any blood" or "Blood, my ass." This time there was nothing. The ones in the back row had stopped texting.

"I see the blood of a thousand warriors who dressed like this and who gave their last breath in defense of their beliefs. I see a thousand warriors striding to their deaths so the meek and innocent could live without fear. I see valor and love and sacred honor. I see sacrifice and respect, unyielding courage and unwavering faith.

"This is the armor of a paladin," he continued. "If a man dressed like this came into a village, peasants and gentry would drop to their knees in respect. Today's soldier gets a pat on the back for his service in Afghanistan, a thank-you for his tours in Iraq and Iran, perhaps a slight edge over some chap competing for the same dead-end job. But today's soldier is not held in the same regard as these men." He gestured to the image.

"These paladins were put on a pedestal by society, elevated because they were better than the men around them. They embodied patience and dignity, grace in the face of impossible odds."

He touched a key on the laptop to start the slideshow. More suits of armor, woodcut images from history texts, photographs from reenactments.

"The paladin. Ms. Jensen, do you know his origin?"

"You're referring to the Knights Templars, right?" She tapped her finger on the edge of her iPad. "The Knights Templars are considered the very first order. God and duty, right?"

Dr. Lawton touched another key and a stock image of a Templar Knight appeared. "No one coerced a man to join the Templars. Their devotion, righteousness and ideals came from within." He noticed the slightly smug look on Ms. Jensen's flawless face. "They had no expectation of reward, though they gained considerable wealth for their order." He paused. "But they were not the first paladins. That honor is due men five hundred years earlier."

Ms. Jensen looked surprised. "But the textbook—"

"You're not reading from *my* textbook."

"Then who were the first paladins?" This from a hawk-nosed young man in the middle of the lecture hall. "If it wasn't the Templars, then who—"

Dr. Lawton was pleased he'd managed to stir their interests. "Surely you're familiar with Charlemagne."

There were nods all around. A few tapped on their

iPads and netbooks. Ms. Jensen leaned forward in her seat.

"I mention him today only because we are covering paladins, and he birthed them."

He noted a few raised eyebrows. "The paladin traces his roots back beyond the establishment of knightly orders," he stated calmly.

"Isn't that a contradiction?" the hawk-nosed man asked. "Didn't the knights create paladins?"

Lawton grimaced. "In the eighth century the Twelve Paladins of Charlemagne came into being. They were a dozen powerful soldiers put in charge of his armies. Those twelve protected him and pledged their lives to him."

"Roland," one of the older students offered.

"He was Charlemagne's first paladin, yes. If you are curious—" Lawton searched his memory "—Mr. Tarrington, the *Song of Roland* is in the public domain. A poem of epic adventure and unmatched heroism." He flipped through the next several slides. "I recommend reading it…though it is by no means required for this course." He couldn't help but smile when he saw students taking that down.

"Roland was the first, but there were others. Can you name them?"

A hand shot up toward the back. "Ogier the Dane."

"I commend you, Ms. Appleton." He had no trouble remembering her name. She was one of his brightest students. He already had his twelve assembled, but if one of them fell, she was a replacement candidate. Worth grooming. "Yes, Ogier the Dane was one, as well. They carried special swords. Durendal for Roland, Sauvagine and Courtain for Ogier."

"They named their swords. Ha."

He couldn't pick out where the affront had come from.

"Like naming a pet dog or something."

That's when he saw the speaker, wearing a retro Rolling Stones T-shirt. He suspected he'd have to fail him.

"The three swords were forged by Munifican," Dr. Lawton said. "Each taking three years to make, so fine and divine the blades were. And," he added softly so none of the students could hear, "soon all three of Munifican's prized swords will be mine."

12

It looked as if the earth were flipping a defiant finger at heaven, Archard thought as he studied the monument. The stone tower stretched upward, with the top made to resemble a king's crown. But it looked like a middle finger gesturing skyward.

He'd done his research. The monument was built in 1869, very near the spot of William Wallace's victory at Stirling Bridge. It wasn't a particularly pretty setting, but the stone structure loomed over the Scottish countryside.

He nosed the rental Fiat into one of the few empty spots in the lot, turned off the ignition and pocketed the keys. "Are we ready?" he asked.

Sarah nodded. "Yep, let's do this."

The man in the backseat didn't reply, but got out, rotated his neck and reached down to touch his toes, working off the cramp from sitting in the small car. Ulrich was a tad over six feet tall and very lean. The German's skin looked as if it had been stretched too tight over his frame, his wrists so bony they looked painful.

Gaunt was the word Archard ascribed to the man. Pale, unhealthy. But Ulrich, in his late fifties, was fit enough for this particular task and actually was in deceptively good shape. Archard watched him walk to the trunk.

"Well?" the German asked.

Archard thumbed a button on the key chain and the trunk popped open. "We don't need the…supplies… until tonight."

"I want to check on them, the ride and all. And I want my camera." Ulrich's accent was more American than German. He'd spent nearly twenty years in the United States, managing an art gallery in Atlanta, Georgia, and lecturing at the university there about ancient art and artifacts. A contemporary of Dr. Lawton's who met the professor when they were working on their advanced degrees, he'd been a part of this group since his return to Europe in January. Archard liked him. He was a good conversationalist and his intellectual equal.

It was Saturday, the weather was good and tourists waited on the curving walkway to the monument. It was easier to go unnoticed in the middle of a crowd, which was why he'd picked this day. Archard led the way, pausing near two horse-faced women, probably related, who were reading a plaque. He waited until they were finished before stepping up. Sarah and Ulrich joined him. The German aimed his digital camera at the plaque, but no telltale green light came on. Ulrich was only pretending to take pictures and likely didn't even have batteries in the camera. Archard hoped no one else noticed.

At the gate the German paid cash for their admission.

"First visit to the Wallace Memorial?" the girl behind the counter asked.

Ulrich nodded, and they fell in line behind the horse-faced women.

Archard heard her ask the next group the same question.

More than half the assembly was female, a mix of ages and beauty. A large-breasted woman on the shy side of thirty looked his way and smiled. She had dyed red hair and too much mascara. Her companion was thickset and roughly the same age, trying to cram too many pounds into a pair of jeans. Her legs looked like English bangers.

The reason for the visit was on the first level, and Archard went there straightaway, Sarah and Ulrich a few paces behind. The Wallace Sword was displayed point down in a thick Plexiglas case that was roped off.

Archard leaned against the wall, admiring the ancient claymore. The cool stone was rough against his fingertips and had a scent to it that he found preferable to the perfume Sarah had used too liberally this morning.

A guide entered and gestured to the sword. "The Wallace Sword was kept in Dumbarton Castle for many years before being removed to this monument. Wallace wielded it in the Battle of Stirling Bridge in 1297 and then a year later in the Battle of Falkirk."

"Was this the only sword he used?" a tall woman with wire-rimmed glasses asked.

"The only one of note. What do you see when you look at it?" the guide asked the assembly.

"I see blood," Sarah said. "Blood and death, and Wallace responsible for it all. I see courage and sacrifice. I see men slogging across a battlefield, not knowing if the day will be their last."

"Uh, yes. Interesting," the guide said. "According to English records, the governor of Dumbarton Castle was given the sword in 1305. More accounts of the sword are found two hundred years later. Then, King James of Scotland was said to have paid two dozen shillings to an armorer to give the sword a new scabbard, belt and pommel, necessary alterations, as the original scabbard and hilt were supposedly covered with the skin of the English commander Cressingham. There are no more records of the sword until the 1800s, when it was sent for repairs to the Tower of London. Toward the end of that century, it made its way here to the Wallace Monument." The guide regarded the sword, beaming. "Now, if you will follow me, I'll take you through the rest of the monument."

Archard, Sarah and Ulrich fell into the middle of the group, which started wending its way up a circular staircase. In the Hall of Heroes, there were busts of middle-aged and old men, noble and aristocratic.

Archard's interest in history hadn't included Scotland, but he was nonetheless familiar with Robert the Bruce, Robbie Burns and, of course, William Wallace. Sarah was intently studying the visages, brow knitted. Archard knew better. She wasn't interested in the displays, but was doing a good job of looking as if she was.

"Though Wallace is a true national hero, there were men in his company of equally strong character." The guide pointed out busts of several who'd lived during that time. "The men following Wallace beat back the armies of the Earl of Surrey and Hugh de Cressingham, treasurer to King Edward."

"The guy whose skin was on the scabbard," a man at the edge of the crowd interjected.

The guide cleared his throat. "Scottish forces were considered disorganized before Wallace whipped them into shape. The English hadn't been prepared. Wallace directed his spearmen to advance on Stirling Bridge from the high ground. The English cavalry became cut off from the rest of their soldiers and were quickly slain. Hugh de Cressingham? They flayed him, and historians claim that Wallace indeed took a broad piece of Cressingham's hide and used it as a baldric for his claymore. It wasn't an unheard-of practice."

"Ghastly," said the sausage-legged woman.

Her friend giggled.

The guide raised his voice to continue his memorized speech. "Wallace showed England that infantry could defeat cavalry. Though Scottish casualties weren't recorded, the English claimed to lose one hundred cavalry and five thousand infantrymen. Unfortunately, Wallace didn't get to keep his title of Guardian of Scotland for long. During the summer of 1298, King Edward brought his army north from Flanders. On the field of Falkirk, Wallace was defeated. He eluded capture, however, for a few years."

An elderly man raised his hand. "I watched *Braveheart*," he said in a British accent. "Saw it twice. How close was it to—"

"Not close," the guide said. "But it was far from a terrible movie."

"They gutted Mel Gibson," said a middle-aged woman in a short skirt, heels and tight sweater. She was someone who would have aroused Archard a few years ago. "Well, they made you think they were cutting him open and pulling his innards out."

"His character," the sausage-legged woman corrected. "They gutted his character."

The guide eyed the assembly. "Ah, there are no wee babes here today, and so I will add this bit. Wallace was captured in August 1305, taken to London and tried for treason. Finding him guilty, they put a garland of oak on his head…pronouncing him king of outlaws. History recorded his response—'I could not be a traitor to Edward, for I was never his subject.' Wallace called the absent John Balliol his king."

There was a wave of murmurs from the Scots in attendance. The woman with the sausage legs said, "And the real Wallace looked better than Mel Gibson."

"Wallace's death was prolonged," the guide continued. "They stripped him and dragged him through London behind a horse. Then he was hanged, strangled but not yet killed, taken down, castrated, gutted and his intestines burned while he still breathed. Quartered, his head was cut off and put on a pole on London Bridge."

The large-breasted redhead made a choking sound.

"Then they beheaded Wallace's brothers and put their heads on display, too," the guide finished.

Archard stepped inside the small gift shop. On the lowest level, the crowd began to break up. He selected a key chain with a replica of the Wallace Sword, and moved to the counter. One of the horse-faced women was there with a stack of postcards. Out of the corner of his eye, he saw Sarah hold up a rose-colored T-shirt with a picture of the Wallace statue on it. "Whatcha think?" she asked Ulrich. Archard didn't hear if the German replied.

"Can I help you?" The horse-faced woman had left, and the employee at the register was reaching for Archard's key chain.

"This…and a pack of gum," he said. "Any flavor."

"Any?"

"Which one do you like?"

Her eyes twinkled. "The cinnamon. It has a bit of a bite to it. Tickles my tongue."

"A pack of cinnamon, then." He paused. "No, make it two."

She grinned and rang up his sale. A few years ago he would have asked her out after her shift ended, and he had no doubt that she would have accepted.

"Thank you," he said, moving away and making room for the elderly man who was buying a postcard.

Ulrich was studying the door frame of the gift shop, eyes drifting up to the security camera. The German had been taking note of all the cameras in the tower and how they were wired. Of course, the devices would be operated from some tucked-away office.

Archard had noted a camera near the display of the Wallace Sword, one more in the stairwell and then one near the top, where the most elaborate statues were arrayed. If there were more, he trusted Ulrich had noticed them. However, he suspected there wasn't a lot of security here, the statues being too big to easily haul away. The gift shop was likely a target because of the cash register and some of the pricier souvenirs. And the sword, of course. He considered that the Wallace Monument's greatest treasure.

Archard left the gift shop and headed outside, glad when Sarah and Ulrich followed a few minutes later. He didn't want to linger at the monument too long, certainly didn't want to do anything to stand out. He chastised himself for the cinnamon gum; the clerk would remember him for that. But that wouldn't link him to the upcoming theft.

They spent the rest of the day in town, playing tourists up from Paris and eating a lengthy dinner that the German paid for. They returned to the Wallace Monument shortly before midnight, seeing only one other car, no doubt belonging to the security guard. One car. Probably just one man. Archard suspected the watch would be doubled after tonight.

"Shall we?" He got out of the car and waited until Sarah and Ulrich retrieved backpacks from the trunk. They walked around to the far side of the monument, to the door used by staff. Sarah set to work on the lock, while Ulrich clipped the wires on the outside security camera and alarm.

Slipping inside, Archard paused and let his eyes adjust to the dim lights of the corridor. He motioned to a door marked Office, and Ulrich went inside. Sarah stayed in the hall, head cocked, listening. Archard heard what she was paying attention to: footsteps. Going up, from the sound of it. Maybe the security man was on a regular patrol. It was a good distance to the top, so that would buy the German time.

Ulrich knew security systems even better than Archard. At the art gallery in Atlanta, he'd constantly updated the monitors and added upgrades to the video feeds. He'd also learned how to disable them. Archard brushed past Sarah so he could watch Ulrich disable the system of the Wallace Monument. Everything Archard knew had come from questionable sites on the internet. Sarah's burgeoning skills were mostly internet acquired, too.

Next, they went to the sword room, and Ulrich disabled an independent security sensor affixed to the back of the Wallace Sword display. While Archard and Sarah stood watch, listening for the guard, the German produced a thin cutter he ran down a seam of the Plexiglas. Within a handful of minutes, he'd opened the case.

The metal blade was more than four feet long, nearly two and a half inches wide at the thickest part and tapering to three-quarter of an inch before the tip. After holding it for a few moments, Archard decided it felt heavier than the six pounds the display plaque claimed. He passed it to Sarah, who held it in front of her with both hands. Blade and pommel together made it taller than she was, and she lowered it quickly. "Only six pounds, eh? I don't think so."

"Shh." Archard took it from her and held it out. "It's where the weight is distributed," he said softly, "that makes it difficult to hold for any amount of time. I'd say this was quite lethal on the battlefield."

Sarah retrieved a length of folded canvas from her pack and laid it out on the floor. He set the sword on it and wrapped it up.

"I've made an error." He smiled ruefully. "This won't fit in the trunk of the Fiat."

"I'll be cramped in the backseat, then." Ulrich sighed.

"No, I think it's Sarah's turn to be cramped." Archard picked up the bundle. "Time to leave."

They were at the back door when they heard footfalls coming back down.

And they were in their car and pulling away when the security guard saw the opened, empty case in the Wallace Sword room.

13

The drizzle painted everything gray. Annja thought it suited her mood.

Despite the weather, tourists were out, making the walk up the long flight of steps, although more than a few were grumbling about it. There was an elevator, but a sign indicated the power was out. At least the rain was gentle, not like the storm that had drenched Avignon—and her and Rembert—two days ago.

She'd said goodbye to him last night. It was more than twenty-four hours after the flight he'd wanted to take back to New York. But he'd been treated at the hospital and then quizzed at length through a pair of interpreters at the police station. About the death of the Romany under the bridge. They made it clear that Rembert wasn't a suspect, but he was apparently the sole witness—even though someone on the barge had reported seeing two people running up the bank. Rembert hadn't said too much about the incident.

He had mentioned her, of course, and that they'd been lured to the river with the promise of an interview for a TV show they were working on. Then the Romanies had tried to mug them, figuring them to be rich Americans—Annja especially, because she was a television personality. Rembert said everything went fuzzy after that because of the beating he'd sustained.

Annja had arrived later at the police station and backed up his story. She admitted to leaving the scene, but only to chase the other Romany, whom she said she lost sight of downtown. A few shopkeepers corroborated her report.

There was no mention of a sword.

The police were left mystified about who actually killed the Romany, though the officer in charge speculated that perhaps the partner who fled was responsible, not wanting to share the Americans' money. Both Rembert and Annja swore the two Romanies had knives and bad tempers, which was the truth. Perhaps if the dead man hadn't been Romany, if he hadn't had a switchblade, the officials would have looked closer into the case. But the police weren't heartbroken over this guy's death. And so Annja and Rembert had been cut loose.

Rembert vowed never to come back to France.

Annja stopped at one of the stations of the cross, standing behind a middle-aged woman. She offered a brief prayer for Rembert and his family, hoping that everything would turn out well for his daughter and the baby. Rembert a grandfather? She smiled. A rather young grandfather.

When she returned to New York, she'd have to look

him up. *Dear God, let him keep his mouth shut back home about the sword...*.

Two hundred and sixteen. She wondered if there was some significance to the number of steps. They were so worn in places, some in desperate need of repair and a potential hazard to the people using them. But she hoped the town officials wouldn't touch them; let them be, let the years and the constant tread of feet continue to wear them away.

At the top she stood quietly and took in the ancient buildings. There were no historical monsters here to document for her producer, but the archaeologist in her would love to do an in-depth special about the oldest of the cloisters—and the monks who continued to live here. Too bad there was no tie-in for her program. It smelled fresh, in part because the drizzle washed everything clean, brightening the aged stone. The air was so clear this high up, with no trace of exhaust or other pollutants, just a hint of a campfire and something roasting. Wildflowers grew in patches of dirt between the slabs of rock.

Annja hadn't asked Rembert about the baby's father, and he certainly hadn't volunteered anything. His daughter wasn't married. They'd set up a nursery in what had been Rembert's office. The daughter—Jane?—was going to keep the baby. Even without it having a father, Annja envied the infant. She'd grown up in an orphanage in New Orleans, and though her childhood hadn't been horrible, it had been horribly empty. Rembert's grandchild would at least know one parent. Annja decided to find a baby gift in France before she left.

Her producer hadn't been happy about her decision to take a week's vacation rather than return with Rembert. Doug had argued with her, but then backed off. He always backed off.

A week, she'd told him. She would give herself that long to delve into this stolen-sword mystery.

She passed the final station of the cross and stepped out onto a path of wet clay. Following it, Annja came to an arch too low for a car to pass under, though she saw depressions from repeated traffic by carts and bicycles. A small group of tourists were huddled under it. One of them held up against the drizzle a windbreaker that read Rocamadour Rocks. It displayed a picture of one of the abbeys poised on the edge of the cliff as if about to dive into the sea.

Annja spotted a tall monk standing under an overhang a dozen yards away. He had his cowl pushed back, and she recognized his face from a picture she'd seen on the internet: Brother Maynard.

Thrusting her hands in her pockets, she headed his way. She walked quietly, but he either saw or heard her, and turned. He had a long, handsome face and kind, sad eyes.

"Miss Annja Creed? The television archaeologist? The one who inquired about our stolen sword?" His English was perfect. "I have watched some of your programs. Ancient Egyptians in Australia and teakwood coffins in caves in Thailand. Very interesting."

She nodded. "Yes, those segments would be mine." Out of the corner of her eye, she noticed thick wires running along the tops of a few of the buildings, some coming down to lights above doorways. The modern convenience of electricity and phone cables looked incongruous up here. "But the Australian segment was quite some time ago."

"I rarely see anything first-run," he said. "Please, come inside and dry off."

She followed him through a tunnel that opened into a room filled with polished walnut benches. Electric lights shaped like candles hung from the center on iron chandeliers, leaving everything appropriately dim. The place was a little deceptive. From the outside the building didn't look so deep. Some of it must have been carved into the mountain itself.

"So it was stolen from this room." Annja looked around, trying to see where it might have been displayed.

Brother Maynard gestured toward the archway they'd come through. "It was hanging there. We removed the cords, but Brother Viland intends to replace the sword with a replica."

"I thought it was a copy that hung there."

"Ah, yes, the mayor was on record saying that the sword we displayed was not really Roland's, that it was a replica. I think he honestly believed that. But it was genuine. Unless it can be recovered, the one that will replace it will be whole."

Annja studied the archway, noticing the hooks the sword had hung from. She heard music coming from somewhere below. Soft conversations in French drifted in through the entrance. Someone laughed. The woman Annja had stopped behind at one of stations of the cross came in. Annja and the monk remained silent until after she left.

"Whole? The sword you had was broken?"

"Legend had it," the monk explained, "that Roland was on the cliff, helping to hold off an army so that Charlemagne and his men could retreat. He'd intended to destroy the sword so it wouldn't fall into enemy hands, but the blade proved indestructible. He hid it beneath his body, some say. Others say he threw it off the cliff."

"And you support the cliff version."

"High in the stone, there is a gash where part of the sword remained for centuries."

"Part?"

The monk smoothed a fold in his robe. "Roland inadvertently broke his 'indestructible' sword when he threw it off the cliff. The tip lodged in the rock and the blade snapped. The sword that hung from our ceiling over there had a section missing."

"Don't you have—" Annja grimaced "—security?" It was a shame that such a sacred place needed it.

"Of course, but apparently it wasn't adequate, and

Brother Viland discovered that the system had been dismantled. It wasn't an expensive system, and it was old. We had little fear of thieves." He waved his hand to indicate the wooden benches and the iron lights. "What is there here that someone would want to steal?"

"The sword."

The monk scowled. "I wish the thief had believed it was a replica. A shame and a sin…"

Annja padded over to stand beneath the hooks. "They would have needed a ladder."

She didn't hear the monk come up behind her. He touched her shoulder. "I don't think so." He stepped to the wall next to the archway and pointed to a spot in the stone that was shiny, as if it had been polished. "There and there and there."

"Someone climbed the wall." Annja reached for one of the handholds the thief had used. She could have managed it, but it would have been difficult. "Impressive."

"A shame," Brother Maynard repeated. "And a sin."

"Very much a shame."

"It's unfortunate we didn't sell the sword last year."

Annja glanced at him in surprise. "Someone tried to buy it? Maybe that's who stole it."

The monk shook his head. "It was an older gentleman, a doctor from the south. He offered a good price, and Brother Viland considered it. Perhaps we should have accepted."

"This doctor—"

"I don't recall his name, but he couldn't have climbed the wall."

"A doctor."

The monk scratched at his chin. "He was polite and didn't press us."

She walked out through the archway and again stood in the drizzle. The monk joined her. "Thank you for taking the time to meet with me, Brother Maynard."

"The pleasure was mine, Annja Creed."

14

The power had come back on and the elevator was working, but Annja took the two hundred and sixteen steps back down, not minding the drizzle and enjoying the solitude, as no one else was using the stairway. She'd booked a room in the Grand Hôtel Beau Site, a Best Western in the lower part of town. On the way to it, in one homey, sandalwood-scented shop, she found a small crocheted throw with the image of the Black Madonna and the main station of the cross. It would make a lovely baby blanket, a memory of Rembert's visit to France.... On second thought, she put the throw back on the shelf and decided a U.S. savings bond would be a more welcome gift. Rembert might not want to remember anything about France. She picked out a few postcards, and also bought a soft drink and chips, which she made quick work of devouring under an awning. Then she walked around the lower city until even the tourists who didn't mind the weather disappeared for dinner.

She settled into her room at the Beau Site, taking a hot bath to chase off the chill and snuggling into a voluminous robe the hotel provided. She moved her laptop from one corner to the next until she finally found a spot where the Wi-Fi worked well and she could get on the internet. She paused in her search about Roland and Durendal long enough to answer the door for room service: giant prawns, duck foie gras with strawberry chutney and chocolate mousse on a cookie covered with mint ice cream, as well as an iced parfait with almonds and caramelized apricots. The waiter rolled in a small table with service for two; she'd certainly ordered enough for two people. But Annja hadn't eaten a full meal since breakfast and was famished. She had an unreal metabolism that resulted in high restaurant tabs. But she made enough with her *Chasing History's Monsters* gig to more than cover her appetite.

Annja surfed the internet while she ate, washing everything down with a large chilled bottle of Perrier. She started with the theft reports from the cloister here in town. Nothing new since she'd looked yesterday and nothing that Brother Maynard hadn't revealed, except for attesting to the sword's authenticity.

Durendal had been taken after her fight at the train station in Paris, but before the Romany pair had come after her and Rembert under the Avignon bridge. Were the incidents related? Was the same gang involved? Annja didn't believe in coincidences. Avignon, Rocamadour and Paris…the targeted swords were the common factor. But Brother Maynard hadn't remembered seeing any Romany tourists the day Roland's sword was stolen.

On a whim, she checked eBay. There was an assortment of old swords listed for sale, but nothing matching Durendal's description. Definitely old stuff, though, some of the swords pretty valuable. A few offered proof of authenticity. She was familiar with other internet sites that dealt with antiquities whose origins were murky. Some of the relics stolen from the Egyptian museum in Cairo in recent years were sold this way. A few of the items were recovered in bidding wars, but the thieves were never apprehended. Tonight nothing caught her eye. Durendal—or anything that looked like it—was not for sale online. The oldest authentic piece was a saber from the Civil War.

The hours melted away as Annja lost herself in historical tidbits in the various electronic nooks and crannies of the World Wide Web. One link led to another and another, tugging her along.

"Nothing. Nothing. Noth—"

Something. Here was a news report, an entry just posted, several minutes ago, about a theft of an old sword from the Wallace Memorial near Stirling, Scotland. It included a picture of the Wallace Sword, a massive claymore meant to be wielded two-handed, once owned by the Scottish martyr.

Durendal.

The Wallace Sword.

And the attempt on her sword.

"A collector," the Romany youth had said when she'd pressed him up against the wall in Avignon.

No coincidence. The incidents were indeed all related. Someone was collecting historical weapons. Had there been more thefts?

It was midnight. She'd intended to turn in early so she could return to Paris first thing, to find leads there. Instead, she ordered another plate of giant prawns from room service and kept at it.

Durendal.

The Wallace Sword.

She posted questions on some of the chat sites frequented by archaeologists and treasure hunters. Had anyone heard of ancient weapons gone missing? Stolen? Sold?

She was about ready to give up when she got a nibble from a Ph.D. student in Sendai, Japan. The university there was back in session. He was an American studying for his doctorate in astronomy, but all things Japanese intrigued him, and he'd come across a recent report of a historical katana that had been sold for a ridiculously low price. He referred her to a story covered in the English edition of a local paper.

Annja emailed him her thanks and clicked open the link.

Honjo Masamune was the name of a sword sold to a French college professor visiting Tokyo last month. She clicked one link after the next, pulling up file after file, settling on one at a Japanese museum's website that seemed to have the most complete account. She searched until she found an English translation. Masamune had been a celebrated swordsmith, considered Japan's best weapons maker. He'd fashioned many blades, ones in collections throughout the world worth small fortunes. One sword in particular was famous—the Honjo Masamune, passed down throughout the shogunate period.

Records claim that Masamune had lived in the mid-1200s to early 1300s. He'd been trained by Masters Saburo Kunimune and Awataguchi Kunitsuna—names that meant nothing to Annja—and was known for making exceptional blades at a time when steel was usually riddled with imperfections. Some of his swords, called *tachi* in Japanese, were laced with a pearly substance that made them shimmer. They were noted for having gray shadows on the front of the blade and clear lines on the leading edge. Annja's own sword had similar lines and shadows. The Masamune Prize was presented at Japanese sword-making competitions to this day.

The Honjo Masamune was considered his greatest creation, possibly the finest sword ever made in all of Japan. It was likely named for General Honjo Shigenaga, who'd acquired it during a battle. Annja dug deeper, finding the history fascinating. Shigenaga had been attacked with the blade, which split his helmet. Though injured, he survived and claimed the sword as a prize. After that, it passed from one hand to the next, sometimes sold, sometimes inherited. It was declared a national treasure in the 1930s. The last Japanese owner was a Tokugawa Iemasa, who gave it to the Mejiro police station in December 1945. A month later that sword and fourteen others were given to Coldy Bimore, a sergeant in the U.S. 7th Cavalry.

From there the sword was sold to various foreign collectors, first in the United States, then Europe, returning to Japan, where it was sold again, just a month ago. Its owner had lost practically everything in the 2011 tsunami. Japanese museum officials were horrified that it only went for a million dollars. It was worth far more, but the museums were in no position to outbid the collector.

The name of the buyer, a college professor, was Archard Gihon. The academic world wasn't known for exorbitant salaries, so Annja figured he likely came from money, to be able to afford something like this. And he was French. She started searching for information about him and came up with frustratingly little. A professor of religious studies born in Nice, currently on sabbatical, married once and divorced. The only name listed for his ex-wife was Beatrice. He'd written a doctoral thesis on comparative religions in modern European society and published several related articles. Nothing here indicated he'd have the money to buy an expensive sword, let alone afford a lengthy trip to Japan. No mention of inheritance, no address listed. She was intending to return to Paris tomorrow—later today, she amended, when she saw that her laptop read 3:12 a.m.—

and a visit to the university to discover more about Archard Gihon was in order.

She bookmarked a few sites, then set her laptop up to recharge. Crawling into bed, she fell asleep quickly... and slipped into a dream.

In it, Annja walked barefoot down a street paved with bricks. Her breath puffed out in little clouds. She saw goose bumps on her arms and frost on the roof of a house, but she wasn't cold. The buildings were old, like the ones in Avignon, but not as large. The windows were shuttered, but soft light spilled out from cracks in some of them. She tipped her head back, seeing a great display of stars.

Annja continued walking. The place looked familiar, comfortable, and yet she couldn't name it. Roux would know. He was here at her side. But she didn't want to break the silence.

A signpost loomed into view, but she couldn't read it. The stars provided enough light, but the letters were a jumble, shifting in and out of focus and rearranging themselves as she stared. Annja looked away and spied a face peering at her from the lone open window. It was a young woman, her hair pulled back severely. A plain woman, but the more Annja looked, the more she realized it was a singular face, beautiful in its simplicity and purity. Roux saw the woman, too, and nodded as if he knew her.

Who is she? Annja asked. She felt she should know

her. But the question was in her head; no sound came out to break the perfect silence.

Who is she? And who am I?

Her hands looked different to her. And she wore a silver ring on one finger and a twine bracelet on her wrist. There was a scar on the back of her right hand that she couldn't recall.

In her dream there wasn't a single car in sight. Only hitching posts and a water trough. The air was fresh, as it had been on the Avignon cliff outside the cloister where Roland's sword had been stolen. She suddenly realized she had a sword, too. It materialized in her hands.

Joan of Arc's sword.

Annja swallowed hard, her throat constricting and a rock forming in her stomach. She'd had dreams like this before—nightmares. This time she was Joan. Roux took the sword from her grasp, kissed her cheek and melted into the bricks. Men sprang up where blades of grass had poked through the cracks near her feet, some in armor, some looking determined and angry. There was pity on the faces of others.

Shutters were thrown open, and more faces appeared, all of them young and unlined, women with their hair pulled back tightly. All staring at her with unreadable expressions. All the same women. All Joan.

Annja didn't need the men prodding her; she knew where she was going. It was falling into place now. Rouen, May 1431. She—Joan—had been tried for heresy, condemned and sentenced to die. Annja quickened her pace, leaving the men behind as she headed toward the center of town, toward the pillar. Time to end this nightmare. She climbed up and stood against the tall wooden post, accepting a cross made of twigs that someone thrust into her hands. Usually in the dreams she was bound there, but not this time.

Annja hadn't felt the cold, but she felt the heat as flames started crackling all around her. The clean air was fouled by the burning wood and the stench from her flesh as it was charred. One of the soldiers raised his sword, and through the smoke she saw the blade transform into hers—Joan's. Other hands were raised, swords appearing in them, too. One soldier held a great two-handed claymore…the Wallace Sword. Another sword had a broken tip…Durendal. It was a veritable city of swords, so many she couldn't count them. One blade was a katana…the Honjo Masamune?

The closest sword was familiar, too, but the flames were growing wilder and it was hard to see the details. That sword was held by Geoffroy Therage, Joan's executioner. "I greatly fear I will be damned," she heard him say. Then Geoffroy took the familiar blade and thrust it through the flames at her, piercing her heart.

Annja awoke sweating profusely, the damp sheets tangled around her.

That was a variation of the dream she'd never had before.

Her laptop chirped to announce an incoming email.

One of her contacts had sent her a notice about an historic sword going up for auction tomorrow. In Spain. Annja was quick to book a flight out of France.

15

The place had been a boutique at one time, one of those pricey little consignment shops filled with designer clothes and painted a mix of pastels. The original name could be seen faintly in bleached green paint: Seconde Fois—"second time." But over that in eggshell-white was its new name in block letters, TOMES TRAN-QUILLES.

Tranquil Tomes was a bookstore of sorts, three doors down from Les Nymphéas Review, where they'd eaten dinner, a restaurant that borrowed the name of one of Monet's most famous paintings. Sarah had hardly touched her wild-duckling Rouennaise; she was anxious and didn't want a heavy meal to dull her senses.

This was all on her.

She'd found Tranquil Tomes after a lot of research. Lawton had been pleased with her find. Her mission to be in charge of. This was a real chance to prove herself.

And it was smack-dab in the middle of Rouen, Dr. Lawton's city of choice.

He'd sent two men with her, twins—Luc and Gaetan

Neveu. Of his associates, they were the closest to Sarah in age. Though black, they had been adopted as infants by a rich white couple north of Paris, friends of Dr. Lawton's. Sarah was glad to have the two with her. Their company was a nice break from Archard's. If he'd been along, he would have taken charge.

This was *her* mission.

The bookstore posted evening hours, and the three of them went in shortly after eight. It smelled of something she couldn't place, some musky scent that hung heavy in the air, so sweet she almost gagged. Probably an incense stick…. Ah, there it was, smoldering in the cupped hands of a ceramic Buddha. Sarah hated incense. She noticed Luc wrinkling his nose, and was pleased it wasn't just her.

The books, displayed on two walls, were sparse compared to most bookstores. Sarah took the shelves to her right, the brothers the ones to the left, their long raincoats swishing around their calves. She watched them pick up one thin book after another, reading the titles. Luc started to page through one, as if he was actually interested.

Sarah nodded to the salesclerk at the back and picked up one of the thicker books. She watched the black-haired shopkeeper out of the corner of her eye, trying to decide if it was a man or woman hunched over the counter, staring at an iPad. The clothing could have passed for pajamas.

Creating Values was the title of the volume in Sarah's

hands. Half the books appeared to be in English. She glanced at the table of contents and the foreword, which mentioned Nichiren Shōshū, a Japanese Buddhist denomination dating back to the 1200s. "'Sōka Gakkai means the "society for creating values," founded in 1937 by Tsunesaburo Makiguchi and Josei Toda.'" She struggled with the pronunciations as she read aloud. "'Derived from Nichiren Shōshū, it has recently spread into Europe and the United States.'"

Sarah's research had revealed that in the past five decades, the sect members had been aggressively proselytizing, using a strategy called *shakubuku,* or "break and subdue."

"Happiness is the primary goal of life, eh?" Gaetan flapped a thin book in his right hand. He had a small ceramic Buddha in his left, a price tag plastered on its bulbous stomach. "I can get into happiness, but this place gives me the creeps." He placed the book on a shelf.

Sirens blared and lights flashed as an ambulance and two fire trucks sped past the shop window. The sounds receded and she heard chanting. It was coming from the back room behind the shopkeeper.

"So, these claim," Gaetan continued, "that happiness is gained through goodness, prosperity and beauty. Well, the guy back at the counter is no beauty. Says, too, that it relies on the teaching of the *Lotus Sutra.* Wonder if that's anything like the *Kama Sutra.*"

Sarah's face colored. She knew Gaetan was just trying to get a rise out of her.

sonal fulfillment, which leads to a better society.... How did you learn of us?"

Sarah craned her neck so she could see the shop-keeper. "I got one of your pamphlets. That's why we came."

The man appeared even more pleased.

A bell tinkled, the door opened and a woman came in, tugging a young boy. She went straight to a shelf with incense burners. "Which one should we get Aunt Vicki for her birthday?"

Her son didn't answer; he was watching Gaetan and Luc.

"You discuss what?" Gaetan asked.

"The *Lotus Sutra*. An important passage stresses that every one of us has a latent Buddha nature. All of us can attain Buddhahood."

The chanting grew louder, and Sarah could pick out the words—*nam-myoho-renge-kyo*.

The shopkeeper was saying something else, but Sarah had missed part of it, caught up in the mesmer-izing sound of *nam-myoho-renge-kyo, nam-myoho-renge-kyo, nam-myoho-renge-kyo.*

"—the divine life state, the true path of enlight-enment. We read in the doctrine of *Three Thousand Realms in a Single Moment of Life,* by Ichinen San-zen, that—"

Nam-myoho-renge-kyo, nam-myoho-renge-kyo, nam-myoho-renge-kyo...

"—Buddhism is practiced here, in the back room, in

the shop, out on the streets of Rouen. It is practiced everywhere in daily life. It is not relegated to some mystical place high on a mountaintop."

Nam-myoho-renge-kyo, nam-myoho-renge-kyo, nam-myoho-renge-kyo...

"We overcome all of society's obstacles. We defeat, spiritually and intellectually, those things that—"

Nam-myoho-renge-kyo, nam-myoho-renge-kyo, nam-myoho-renge-kyo.

Sarah replaced the book she was holding and drifted closer, her feet moving in time to the chant.

"I think this one will do nicely for Aunt Vicki, don't you?" the customer asked the little boy, who was still watching the twins. It was a rosy-pink Buddha incense burner with a grin spread wide across its fat face. "And I suppose we should get her some incense to use with it."

Nam-myoho-renge-kyo, nam-myoho-renge-kyo, nam-myoho-renge-kyo...

The shopkeeper looked around the twins to the woman and her boy. "May I recommend the Auroshikha varieties? The cones of lemongrass, French lavender and ylang-ylang are especially pleasing."

Nam-myoho-renge-kyo, nam-myoho-renge-kyo, nam-myoho-renge-kyo...

"So global warming would be history if everyone was Buddhist, right?" Gaetan said, drawing the shopkeeper's attention again.

"I suppose you could look at it that way." The man nodded thoughtfully. "Here we teach our members how to apply Buddhism to their daily lives and to promote its spread through society."

"That's exactly why we showed up," Luc said.

"To join us?"

He shook his head.

Sarah walked over to the customer. "Lovely little boy."

The woman looked up from the incense assortment. "Michael. His name is Michael, and he just turned three."

"American," Sarah said. "Sounds like you're from Boston."

The woman smiled. "New York, actually. My husband is teaching a semester at the business school in the city. He wants to live here full-time." She paused. "You're American, too."

"From Boston."

"Visiting? Studying…"

"Are you a Buddhist? One of these sect members?"

"Not exactly," the woman answered, surprised at the change in their conversation. "But I come here a lot. I like the way they think."

"You would do well to leave now," Sarah said.

Nam-myoho-renge-kyo, nam-myoho-renge-kyo, nam-myoho-renge-kyo…

The woman gave her a curious look. "See here. I'll shop where I want, read what I want, and I'll—"

Sarah pulled out the SIG Sauer she'd concealed beneath the flap of her jacket. She pointed it at the woman's forehead and pulled the trigger. It made a spitting sound with the silencer. Blood and brains splattered out the back of her skull, dotting the array of incense burners and some of the books. The woman's body dropped and the boy started to cry.

Nam-myoho-renge-kyo, nam-myoho-renge-kyo, nam-myoho-renge-kyo...

"Casse-toi!" the shopkeeper hollered, his mouth dropping open. He wasn't able to get anything else out—in one fluid movement, Gaetan reached into the folds of his long raincoat and pulled out a saber, raising the blade and slicing through the man's throat. The twins jumped back to avoid the spray of blood.

Sarah stepped around the wailing boy to the front door, locked it and flipped the sign around to read Closed.

"What about the boy?" Luc asked.

"He's three," Sarah said. "Too young to read."

Nam-myoho-renge-kyo, nam-myoho-renge-kyo, nam-myoho-renge-kyo...

The people chanting in the back room must have been able to hear the boy, but were too caught up in their chanting to come check.

"Let's move." Leading with the gun, she stepped through the curtain and started firing. Gaetan was next in and rushed a tall Japanese man who looked to be making a martial arts move. Gaetan finished him in two swipes. Luc joined them a heartbeat later, drawing a saber with his left hand and an antique katana in his right.

"May we finish this for you?" Luc asked Sarah as he slashed a young woman, who dropped to her knees and clutched her stomach, as if trying to hold herself together. But Luc swung at her again, cutting off her head with the katana.

"Certainly." Sarah thrust the SIG Sauer back in her waistband and watched the twins appreciatively. She counted twenty-eight people in the room—she'd taken out five right away, which left twenty-three for the twins. The ones who lived past the first few seconds were still screaming for help and mercy. One old Japanese man rocked back and forth on a rug, continuing to chant. Gaetan finished him.

The sabers and katana glistened in the light of a few dozen candles. They seemed to whistle as the twins continued to slay the people assembled. The brothers were fencers who'd competed at the 2008 Olympics in Beijing. Gaetan had narrowly missed medaling. Now they ran a small fencing school near Dr. Lawton's warehouse. Sarah knew they favored foils, but sabers were more effective for killing, because they had a slashing edge.

"That didn't take long," Luc said. He looked at his watch, then knelt and wiped the blood off the blades. "In and out in less than a half hour. Honjo Masamune served me well."

"Hopefully, I will gain my named sword soon," Gaetan said.

"Hey, me, too," Sarah said.

"Security camera," Gaetan pointed out. "Got to find the feed." He returned to the front room.

"Make sure they're all dead," Sarah told Luc. "No one except that little boy gets to keep breathing." Then she followed Gaetan. He was rummaging around under the counter.

"Found it."

"Can you erase us?"

He was fiddling with some of the controls. "Oh, hell," he said. "I'm not familiar with this model." He yanked at the machine and pulled it loose. "Let's just take it with us."

"Computer?"

Gaetan shook his head. "Primitive operation. Just a calculator, cash box and ledger. Oh, and the iPad. Looks like he was playing solitaire." He slipped the ledger and iPad under the same arm as the security-system hardware. "Might have some links saved on it, find some other Buddhist hot spots in Rouen."

"Finished, Luc?" Sarah fixed her gaze on the boy. He'd stopped crying. He was sitting next to his mother, patting her hand and asking if they could go home now. "We need to get out of here, guys. We've got more stops to make tonight. And you've got a chartered flight to catch before sunup."

"It's a shame you won't be coming with us, Sarah."

She shrugged. "I guess Dr. Lawton's got other plans for me. That's okay. But before we do anything else…

my stomach's growling and I've got a hankering for a foot-long. There's a sandwich shop the next street over. A cold-cut combo would do nicely."

She grabbed the cash box on the way out.

16

Annja passed the taxi stand and got on the public bus after landing at the airport in Burgos. The Spanish city was colorful, and she took it in as she watched people get on and off at the stops: Belorado, Segovia, Avenida de Castilla y León, San Roque. She stepped off at Glorieta de Logroño, as it was the closest to the hotel she'd booked.

She'd never been to Burgos before, but she'd done her research. It had less than two hundred thousand residents and was a principal city in the northern part of the country. If she could manage it, she hoped to take in the cathedral of Burgos, Cartuja de Miraflores and Huelgas Reales Monastery while she was here. And she intended to visit the new Museum of Human Evolution, expected to become one of the most-visited museums in the country. She might as well see something more than the inside of an auction house.

Annja left her suitcase at the hotel and took off shopping. She needed something appropriate for tonight's event, and nothing she'd brought to France for her shoot would do. After the fight at the train station in Paris, the cocktail dress needed some repairs. This "vacation" was getting expensive.

She started with a pair of bronze leather shoes, four-inch heels designed by Sergio Zelcer: the equivalent of two hundred American dollars. The dress, one of Cristóbal Balenciaga's designs, was four times that amount…on sale. It was a soft print of buttery shades with dark brown accents. Annja didn't need to be extravagant, but others at the auction would be wealthy, and she had the role of a well-to-do American television personality to play.

A ballroom near the civic center had been set up for the affair, with high-backed velvet chairs arranged around the stage near the center. Annja managed to get in by plying her celebrity status, and the attendant at the door gave her a paddle with a number on it. She was guest 181, but didn't care about the other one hundred seventy-nine—she was looking for only one name on the list. Archard Gihon, the man who had purchased the rare Japanese sword. But the attendant held the sheet too closely for Annja to see more than a few names on it, none of which she recognized. She selected a seat toward the back, where she could get a good view of the people trickling in.

She'd discovered that most of the bidders would be from various parts of Spain, with others invited from France, England, Sweden and the United States. They made an elegant crowd in their tuxedos and designer dresses, with a smattering of mink wraps thrown in. The majority were in their sixties, Annja observed.

A waiter moved through the aisles, offering white wine and champagne. She took a glass and pretended to sip at it, eyeing people over the rim.

"Bidding is to be in euros," an owl-faced man in a burgundy tuxedo announced as he strode to the podium. "But accommodation will be made for those preferring to deal with pesetas."

Another waiter came by with more drinks, but Annja nodded him politely on his way. Alcohol clearly loosened purse strings.

"Lot number one is an oil painting from the Cuzco School," the auctioneer began in Spanish. A man to his right repeated everything in English. "Spectacular in its condition." It featured cherubs placing a gilded crown on Mary.

Annja's attention drifted from the rest of the auctioneer's description. She concentrated on the people who continued to dribble in. She was glad she'd spent the money on her new clothes; the designer outfit helped her blend in.

There didn't seem to be a particular theme to this auction. Every kind of object was being put up for sale, mostly from museums that were cleaning out their displays, the announcement had read. Making room for more acquisitions and raising funds for renovations.

Next up was something fairly recent: a twentieth-century bronze garniture and candelabras, gaudy and gold and pulling in only a few hundred euros. It was followed by a set of French commodes, which set an elderly woman in the third row to tittering. Her companion bid the toilets up to four hundred eighty thousand pesetas—three thousand euros—before the auctioneer gaveled it *vendido,* sold.

A variety of French furniture came next, and Annja saw that a few French bidders—one who ran a string of hotels, she heard whispered—competed. Antique tables and chairs, consoles, sofas. She shifted in her chair, half bored, half anxious, picking up a few names here and there when the auctioneer identified the bidders. No Archard. If this was all for nothing… Annja gritted her teeth.

Wall hangings, antique mirrors, tapestries, sketches and watercolors were paraded before the guests, not a piece going unsold.

"¿Por que estás aqui?" The man next to Annja leaned over. He was in his late forties, tanned and solidly built.

"Espadas," Annja answered. "I am interested in the swords."

His eyes widened. "Ah, American?" he said quietly. "You are the American television archaeologist. Miguel said you had asked to attend. I am Fernando." He extended his hand, and she took it, feeling calluses that didn't suit his refined attire. "I dabble in digging, a hobby."

His smile was warm and beautiful. "Pleased to meet you," she murmured.

"Shh!" A reed-thin man in front of them drew his finger to his lips.

Sorry, she mouthed.

Bidding was heated for a selection of fifteenth-century Spanish pottery and Alcora ceramics. Conversely, an array of nineteenth-century glass pieces, including two *boules d'escalier,* went for very little.

Among the odder pieces were a child's "rocking boat" that dated to 1910, a pair of mid-eighteenth-century Spanish fauteuils with provenance, an art deco bronze lantern and a set of Royal Doulton tobacco jars from 1900.

"For those with military interest," the auctioneer's translator said next.

Annja sat up, glancing around the room.

"Now we will get to your swords, yes?" Fernando said. "Perhaps you will let me buy one for you?"

"Shh!"

Annja was glad the reed-thin man kept him from saying anything else.

"First up is this German breastplate circa 1580." It was pitted, as if it had taken a lot of blows in battle. It went for three thousand euros. Annja doubted it was worth nearly that much, especially in that condition, but the bidder had been enjoying several glasses of wine.

"A sixteenth-century sailor's knife," the auctioneer's translator continued. "Fine condition, if simple. See how it is pierced so it can fold, yet it could also function as a deckhand's tool." It brought only one hundred euros. Annja nearly raised her paddle, knowing it was a very good price and thinking she could donate it to a museum in New York. But better to not draw attention.

She took another sip of her wine, waving away a waiter who came to offer her a fresh glass.

The next item came with a lengthy explanation. The more elaborate the presentation, the higher the bids tended to range.

"In the second half of the nineteenth century, change swept throughout the world," the translator droned. "Industries, including for Toledo etched cutlery, came to the fore and brought out a renewed interest in arms and armor. Some artisans rendered masterpieces that rivaled the sword makers of the Renaissance. Anton Konrad of Munich, Germany, was one such designer. We have for your bidding pleasure one of his more noted works."

Annja leaned closer to Fernando so she could see between the people in front of them. It was a broadsword from the sixteenth century. A monitor overhead magnified the lavish embellishment of mulberry motifs in relief. She put it at a little more than three feet long.

"Would you like that one?" Fernando whispered, drawing another quiet reprimand.

Annja shook her head. A portly man named Javier won the bid at sixteen thousand euros.

Another sword was brought out, a rapier with shell guards etched with classical figures and foliage in a

Brescian pattern. The work ended in fleur-de-lis motifs on the guard's quadrants.

"This blade is Spanish," the translator said. "Signed by Francisco Ruiz. From 1650."

Bidding closed at one hundred forty thousand euros.

"Ah, Miss Creed, I fear this next sword is beyond even my price range," Fernando said.

"I present a sword of El Cid," the translator proclaimed. The auctioneer launched into a lengthy explanation, reading from a series of cards.

"Rodrigo Diaz de Vivar, better known to the world as El Cid, was born into a small village not very far from Burgos. A knight, a warrior, educated and brave, he was the right hand of Don Sancho and fought battles in Zaragoza, Zamora and Coimbra. He was exiled in 1081 from Castille, but returned to Burgos six years later. He was exiled again in 1089."

A handful of bidders got up to leave, including the couple who had purchased the collection of French commodes.

"El Cid is credited with furthering the Christian religion. He surrounded himself with poets, living magnificently in Valencia."

The sword was brought out to a subdued murmur of appreciation.

"On the tenth of July, 1099, El Cid passed from the world, and the Christian community mourned him. He is buried in the cathedral in Castille. One of his swords is here today."

A blade that was more a work of art than a weapon was placed on a table covered in dark red velvet.

"Tizona," the auctioneer said. "A sword important enough to have a name."

Annja wondered if her own sword was named.

"In the poem *El Cantar de Mio Cid,* we learn that the sword Tizona frightens unworthy opponents. It is said to have a divine power. Though forged in Córdoba, it has Damascus steel in its blade and bears two inscriptions. The first reads *'Io soi Tisona fue fecha en la era de mil e quarenta.'* 'I am Tizona…'"

Annja lost the rest of what he said when she heard someone whisper, "Archard." She looked for the speaker.

"The second inscription reads *'Ave Maria, gratia plena. Dominus tecum,'* which is Latin for 'Hail Mary, full of grace. The Lord is with you.' We will start the bidding at five hundred thousand euros."

Fernando stretched an arm behind Annja, and she got up and moved to the back of the room near the door, leaving him openmouthed and staring after her. She stood next to the attendant who had checked people off the guest list. She studied each man who raised his paddle and bid.

"One million euros."

The auctioneer nodded and then announced, "One million euros to Archard Gihon of Paris." She saw him then.

"Do you know this Archard Gihon?" she whispered to the attendant.

He shook his head. "First auction I have seen him at. I understand he and his associate are collectors of antique weapons. They requested invitations."

"They?"

The attendant sighed. "A professor Charles Lawton of Rouen."

"One-point-five million euros to William Sandoval," the auctioneer announced.

"A professor?" Annja pressed. The monk in Avignon said a "doctor" had offered money for Roland's sword. Dr. Lawton?

"I do not know what he teaches."

She could tell he was tall, judging by how he sat in the chair. Gray tuxedo jacket, long white hair pulled back in a ponytail. She couldn't see his face, Archard's, either, but she would. They would have to walk by her to leave the room. She thought about bidding against them....

"Two million euros to Archard Gihon," the auctioneer announced.

It was far too rich for her.

Bidding continued in incremental jumps of a hundred thousand.

Fernando craned his neck around, saw her and winked. She pretended not to see him. Annja figured he knew better than to raise his hand, lest the auctioneer take it as a bid.

"Two million five hundred thousand euros."

There were small waves of hushed chatter. Everyone in this room was rich, but apparently even by wealthy standards this was getting a little pricey for one piece.

"Three million euros."

The attendant leaned close. "It has now exceeded anticipated figures. The museum was reluctant to put it up, but they will be quite pleased."

"Four million euros to Archard Gihon."

The room fell silent. Four million euros for one sword. Annja held her breath.

"Vendido!" Polite applause followed the signal of the sale.

Another small table was brought out, filled with an assortment of jewelry, with a large tiara sparkling in the light. Annja ignored the spiel and the starting bids. Her full attention was on Archard Gihon and Dr. Charles Lawton, who had gotten up from their seats and were bent over a desk at the side of the room, no doubt making arrangements to pay for Tizona. There was a door nearby, and for a moment Annja was fearful they would slip out before she could catch up.

But they headed down the far aisle toward the back of the room, where she was standing. She decided she would follow them out, rehearsing how she would introduce herself.

They stopped directly in front of her.

"Annja Creed." Archard took her hand, bowing and

lightly kissing the back of it. "I am Archard Gihon, and this is—"

"Professor Charles Lawton," the other man said. His voice was rich and melodic, and Annja studied his striking features. There was something vaguely familiar about him. "Good to finally meet you, Miss Creed." His French accent was heavy, but he spoke perfect English. "I have heard a great deal about the famous American archaeologist."

"Ah, she is from…" Archard pursed his lips, as if searching his thoughts. "Ah…the program called *Chasing History's Monsters*." He gestured for her to precede them. "Shall we? So we don't disrupt the others?"

She stepped outside, and they joined her after saying farewell to the attendant.

"What brings you to Spain, Miss Creed?" Archard asked. "And what brings you to this auction?"

Annja met his gaze. His emotions were unreadable. He remained politely detached. She looked at Dr. Lawton, who appeared to be studying her.

"Actually, I came looking for you," she said. "Both of you."

Dr. Lawton clapped his hands. "Excellent," he said. "A coincidence, Miss Creed, as I have been searching for you, too."

"You have something we need to acquire," Archard explained.

"A special sword," Dr. Lawton said. "Did you bring it with you?"

A shiver passed down Annja's spine.

17

Gaetan parked in front of a narrow, three-story house on Rue Lefort Gonssolin and turned off the lights, but he left the motor running. Sarah opened the glove compartment and took out a small flashlight, flicked it on and held up a piece of paper.

"Yeah, right address." She crumpled the paper and dropped it on the street as she got out of the car. "Last stop. Listen, Gaeton…Luc and I will take this, but keep a close eye out, 'kay?"

He raised an eyebrow.

"Eye out. You know, watch the neighbors. If it gets a little loud, we don't need anyone coming over or calling the police." One of the voices in her head told her not to call Gaetan an idiot.

"I will keep both of my eyes out," he said.

"Just honk if there's a problem," Luc told him. He got out of the backseat and drew his katana, leaving the saber behind. "We will be quick. We're due at the airport in an hour."

Sarah didn't expect trouble. It was after eleven, and

while there were a few lights on here and there down the block, more than half the houses, including this one, were dark. People had to get up early for work in the morning probably, she thought.

She crept toward the house, crouching like a secret agent from a B movie. Luc followed a few yards behind, checking left and right, then waited while she went around to the back. After a few moments, he slipped to the side door and put his ear to it.

Sarah came back and whispered, "No electronic security on the outside, anyway."

He pointed up.

"An open window?"

"And the room looks dark. Maybe he isn't home."

"Car's in the garage. Boost me."

Luc set the sword on the ground and laced his fingers together. Sarah stepped into his cupped hands and he raised her so she could grab on to a decorative piece of brickwork. Her wall climbing at the gym had served her well. She scrabbled up and slid through the window, poking her head out and giving Luc a thumbs-up.

Several minutes later, a light came on toward the back of the house, and Sarah opened the side door. "Easier than I expected," she told Luc. "I'm getting good at this." She motioned him inside and closed the door behind him. "He had a security panel in the front hall, but the idiot didn't bother to turn it on."

Sarah had stuck her gun in the waistband of her pants, but pulled it out and waved it at the home's occupant, now tied to a kitchen chair. "Make sure he can't get loose."

Luc tightened the knots. "Where did the rope come from?"

"Pull cords from a drape upstairs. So I did good, huh?"

He nodded and stepped back so he was shoulder to shoulder with her, studying the captive. "I'm impressed, Sarah."

The man in the chair looked terrified, with sweat beading on his forehead and his lips working around the wad of paper towels Sarah had stuffed in his mouth. The front of his jeans was wet; she'd literally scared the piss out of him.

"He was real cooperative when I showed him the gun," she told Luc.

The man mumbled in an attempt to speak.

"Luc, meet François Lebeal," Sarah continued. "He manages one of the smaller banks in Rouen. Fifth on our list. Last target tonight." She leaned close to François and pushed the end of her silencer into his chest. "He thinks we're here to rob him." She paused. "Idiot."

"Oh, we will rob him, Sarah."

"Eventually." She made a show of pacing around her captive. "If I take the gag out…and you talk above a whisper…it'll be the last sound you ever make. Got it?"

He nodded.

She waited another moment and took the gag out.

François whispered, the words coming rapid-fire in French.

"English," she warned. "If you're going to talk that fast, make it in English."

"What do you want? Money? I have money upstairs. More. I can get you more. From my bank. I can—"

She waved the gun under his nose. "We don't want money."

"Jewelry," he said, still whispering. "You said you were going to rob me. Gold. I have a gold ring with diamonds. On the bureau in the bedroom."

"We don't want jewelry."

He stared at her, wide-eyed. "Then what?"

"What do we want?" She looked up at Luc, then back to François. "We want to save your soul, but I don't think that's going to happen. I saw a cross hanging upstairs. Another one here." She nodded to the wall, and Luc followed her gaze.

It looked like a Christian cross, but with four more points coming out in a starburst pattern from the center.

"That's a Scientology cross," Sarah told Luc. "The other targets didn't have them displayed quite so prominently. Eight points represent their so-called eight dynamics of existence." She tsked as she turned back to the man in the chair. "Scientology. What an absolute mindless idiot."

"I...I don't understand."

"What's not to understand? You're a Scientologist, François. You follow a religion made up by a science-fiction writer. Made up. L. Ron Hubbard probably meant it as some joke, and you and a couple hundred thousand others bought into it. I've read all about you." Sarah spat in disgust. "If old L. Ron found his way to heaven, I bet he's laughing his ass off at the lot of you."

"Please."

Sarah glared at him. The voices in her head told her to finish this up. She pushed the gun at him again. "We'll see if the handful of other known Scientologists that I killed tonight are being reborn."

François screamed and Sarah stuffed the paper towels back in his mouth. He nearly choked on them as he struggled in the chair, threatening to tip it over. Luc raised his katana, and François sat still, whimpering around the gag.

"Like I said, we'd give you the chance to repent, but—"

François nodded his head vigorously.

"I'm doing you a big favor. You're an alien, right? One who'll get reborn, your literature claims. If you think about it, you should be grateful. We're giving you a chance to start over." She put the gun to the side of his head and pulled the trigger.

Brains and blood exploded across the kitchen countertops and stove.

"No need to make this one look like a robbery," Luc said, staring at the mess.

Sarah wrinkled her nose. "Well, this is the sixth Scientologist we got tonight. Police will figure out

the connection." She laughed. "Hey, they might think there's a serial killer on the loose targeting Scientologists."

"The Buddhists—"

"Well, yes, them, too. Serial-killer bait, Buddhists and Scientologists. And that's just the tip of the religious iceberg. Dr. Lawton said once this started, the cops were going to go ballistic."

"We are not serial killers," Luc insisted.

"No, we're crusaders."

"Paladins."

"Yes, paladins. And tonight...tonight, Luc, the cleansing has begun."

The voices in Sarah's head congratulated her on a job well done.

18

"I will offer you a more than fair price for your sword, Miss Creed. As you saw from the auction, I am willing to spend considerable money to acquire fine things."

"Swords. To obtain swords."

"Particular swords," Dr. Lawton replied. His eyes narrowed, as if she'd affronted him. "Ones with an important history."

A handful of women in long dresses and capes left the auction, one complaining that she wasn't willing to pay "those prices for that sort of jewelry."

Annja watched them make their way down the hall toward the front door. "El Cid's sword, for one."

"Tizona," Archard said. "This was only one of El Cid's swords."

"The most important one," Annja added.

"Miss Creed, I am interested in discussing your sword, not one I have already acquired," Lawton stated. "I am a busy man, and idle talk doesn't fit into my schedule. Shall we begin with a price?"

Annja locked eyes with his. She still couldn't figure

out why he seemed familiar, couldn't place where she might have seen him before. Her temper might be getting in the way. She felt heat rising to her cheeks and considered denying the sword's existence. "I don't have the sword with me," she finally said.

"But you can get it."

"It's not for sale." She would have loved to leave now, get out of this building and Spain, go back to Brooklyn. She could consider this mystery closed; she'd found the collector. But why was this man collecting swords? To what lengths had he gone to get them?

"The Japanese katana," she said. "You bought that and—"

"Honjo Masamune." Dr. Lawton shook his head, strands of hair coming out of his ponytail like threads of a spiderweb loosened by a puff of wind. "Archard purchased that one," he said. "I was committed to a series of lectures."

"So Mr. Gihon bought it for you."

"Again, I am not interested in talking about blades I have already acquired."

"Just the ones you've yet to collect," she said.

Dr. Lawton smiled, his expression smug and reptilian. "About your sword."

"It's not for sale."

"Everything has a price, Miss Creed."

She was growing warmer, her temper simmering. This was not the time nor the place to confront this man. Now that she'd seen him, had his name—names had power—she could research him. Every good hunter knew to learn about her prey. She didn't know enough about him…only that he had money, an associate named Archard Gihon, was a native Frenchman—that she could tell by his accent. Not enough information.

"Shall we say one million euros?"

She brushed by him, but a hand clamped on her arm. Her surprise held her in place. It was Archard's hand, and his strong grip tightened for a moment before he released her.

"What right do you think you have…" Annja let the sentence go unfinished.

Archard took a step back.

"Miss Creed, you talk of rights," Lawton said. "By right, your sword should be mine, anyway. It should have passed to me."

Her mouth dropped open, but she instantly recovered. "If you'll excuse me, Dr. Lawton, Mr. Gihon." She managed a half-dozen steps before his next words stopped her.

"Joan of Arc's sword. Truly, it should be mine. I should have inherited it."

She whirled around, a thousand thoughts spinning in her head.

"I know the sword you wield once belonged to Joan of Arc. It is a singular sword, with five crosses etched on the pommel. I know singular swords." Dr. Lawton paused as a trio emerged from the auction room, two middle-aged women escorted by a considerably younger man. They were laughing at a joke he'd just told.

"I know your sword's history."

He couldn't know how she'd acquired it, that it had been shattered and re-formed, that it hung suspended in the otherwhere, waiting for her to summon it. She wasn't even sure how it had all come to pass. She sensed the sword now, waiting, felt her fingers start to curl instinctively around the pommel. *No!*

"Dr. Lawton, Mr. Gihon—"

"Dr. Gihon," Archard stated.

So he was a full professor. "*Dr.* Gihon. This is neither the time nor the place."

"So you will not consider selling it to me?" Dr. Lawton said. "Pity. Unfortunate for both of us." His expression lost its smugness and he seemed genuinely sad. "I have more money than I need. You could be set for life."

This time when Annja walked away, Archard didn't reach out to stop her. "Neither the time nor the place," she repeated.

"Then I will call on you later at your hotel," Dr. Lawton said. "Perhaps I can convince you to change your mind. I can be quite persuasive. Do not dismiss me so lightly. Archard, shall we retrieve Tizona?"

Annja set her feet in step with her pounding heart. It was late, but the city still bustled, with cars and horse-drawn carriages passing by, and lights from clubs, restaurants and other hotels looking like fireworks come to ground. She headed south, toward her own hotel.

Why had Lawton upset her so much? He'd offered to buy her sword…which she couldn't sell even if she wanted to. At least, she didn't think she could. So why was she upset? He couldn't get her sword.

That he knew about it… She'd been so careful, or thought she had. Roux and his nemesis, Garin—another man helplessly tied to Joan of Arc's story over the centuries—would not have told a soul.

Five crosses on it. How had Lawton known that?

The sword had a name. Or at the very least a title. What was it?

A man stuck his head out a car window and whistled. Annja walked faster. The air was still and warm and felt good against her face even though it smelled of automobile exhaust so close to the street, of spoiled food from garbage near the curb and the stink of blacktop from a parking-lot paving project. Her senses were acute, and she siphoned through everything to the scent of flowers. She spied them in baskets hanging from street poles. And something else… The hair on the back of her neck rose. She spun around, peering into the shadows.

Was she being followed?

She turned back around and kept walking, her pace slower and determined, her feet aching from the new shoes that would eventually be comfortable.

She *was* being followed. She just couldn't see the watcher. Lawton lacked the speed to have kept up with her. Archard Gihon perhaps, as he seemed younger and more athletic. Lawton had the money to employ a lot of people. Like the Romanies.

So he was collecting named swords. The Wallace Sword and Durendal were two, but they'd been stolen. Did Lawton believe the ends justified the means?

She was certain the answer was yes. He wanted to purchase her sword, and she'd said no. He'd tried to have it stolen from her in France. Would he try the same here in Spain?

When she reached her hotel room, she locked the dead bolt, set a chair in front of the door and tried to dull her concerns in a hot bubble bath. It was futile.

Annja had intended to spend what was left of the night on her laptop, researching Charles Lawton, but sleep beckoned.

She settled into the bed and pulled the covers up, seeing her sword hovering in the otherwhere. "What are you called? How can he know your name, and I don't?" Annja forced herself to employ meditation techniques, finally drifting off.

She found herself on a dirt road. The setting sun was warm on her back.

She didn't know where she was going, only that it was someplace at the same time important and peaceful, grandiose and humble. She—or whoever she was in the dream—was anxious about something and had the feeling of being followed.

Pursued?

She wasn't running, but traveling at a steady tempo,

glancing over her shoulder every once in a while. She wore loose pants, cinched tight at the waist, and a shirt that was thin at the elbows and ragged from age and washings. Her hair was cut short. At a distance she could pass for a boy, but not up close. She got a good look at her face when she stopped by a stream for a drink, and found her features were delicate, her skin smooth, her cheeks red from the exertion.

How long had she been walking? Where had she come from?

Her eyes sparkled. Everything about her was young. She felt strong.

It was Joan. Annja was dreaming of Joan again. She'd thought she could escape the dreams, having left France behind.

A church came into view, and Annja recognized it. She'd visited it once before....

The Church of Saint Catherine de Fierbois.

Annja cooled her face with the stream water, stood and smoothed her clothes. She ran her fingers through her hair.

The church wasn't far from Chinon, and she'd journeyed there after being validated by the dauphin, but before she—Joan—was to go to Orleans. She'd been listening to voices inside her head. They'd told her to go to this church.

The voices guided her inside. She paused to pray in the quiet, simple beauty of the sanctuary. Finished, she went behind the altar and seemingly easily unearthed a sword from beneath the dirt floor. It had five crosses etched on the pommel and guard, and was Annja's now.

Joan hadn't known where it came from; Annja had learned that later through study. Charles Martel, grandfather of Charlemagne, had left the sword there to commemorate his victory over the Saracens.

"I loved that sword because it was found in the Church of Saint Catherine, whom I loved," Annja said. Joan's words at her trial of condemnation.

The sword was coated with rust. It had not been buried deep, but the elements had eaten away at it. Still, the rust rubbed off easily.

A flash of fire blotted out the church. Through it Annja saw a man raise Joan's sword. Through a wall of red, she saw other swords raised, among them Tizona.

She awoke, sweating, tangled in the sheets, the breeze from a window she hadn't opened drifting in with the scents of the city.

"Good morning, Annja Creed."

She sat bolt upright. Two men stood at the foot of her bed.

19

Morning? It still looked dark. But just enough light came in through the open window to reveal the men to be twins.

She slammed her hand down on the light switch on the nightstand. The lamp flicked on and they blinked.

She took their measure in an instant: lithe, athletic, muscles tensed beneath their tight-fitting pants and short-sleeved shirts, their clothes the color of shadows. She reached for the phone.

"Don't."

She reached for the sword, felt it with her mind, but decided not to call it. That would be what they wanted, wouldn't it?

"Dr. Lawton sent you." She didn't mean it as a question.

"You are a beautiful woman, Miss Creed," the one on the right said in a velvety voice. He sounded like a well-educated man, from Paris. "If you want to keep being beautiful—"

"And keep breathing," the other one said in a tone a tad higher and breathier, "you should surrender—"

"My sword." She swung her legs over the side of the bed. She'd worn a pair of flannel shorts and a loose T-shirt to bed. Sometimes she didn't wear that much, and was glad she'd opted for something last night. "I thought Dr. Lawton wanted to buy it."

"And I thought you had declined to sell it," the one with the breathy voice said.

Confirmation. They worked for Lawton. Had they stolen Durendal from the monks in Avignon? The Wallace Sword from the monument near Stirling?

"I don't have it with me." Annja nodded to her suitcase, a soft-sided duffel on the luggage stand. "You're welcome to search my bag, not that any decent-size sword would fit in it. I've got nothing in the closet but an expensive dress."

They stood silent for a moment. She heard a door open and close down the hall, followed by the sound a rolling suitcase makes. She knew better than to call out; she might put the other hotel guest in danger.

She hadn't noticed any weapons on the men; their hands were out to their sides, fingers spread in a non-threatening gesture. But their very presence in her room was a threat, and that they'd come in through the window. She was on the eighteenth floor, and not near the fire escape. There was a soft chime as the elevator arrived. A glance to her door showed the chair she'd set in front of it was still there.

"We think you do have it with you," the breathy one said.

"Get up." His twin reached behind him and pulled a sword from a sheath at his back. It was a pitted katana.

"Honjo Masamune," Annja said.

"Perceptive. Now, get up."

Annja felt for her sword. It waited for her, but she sensed a pervasive anxiety. Her mind churned. She could call the weapon, fight them here. She had fought in close confines many times before. The noise would bring security, other guests.

One of the twins tossed her a pair of shoes—the only tennis shoes she'd brought with her. Thank God they hadn't made her put on the new leather heels; she had blisters.

"Put them on. Hurry." This one pointed to his waistband. The handle of a SIG Sauer protruded.

For the moment, she'd play along

20

Glancing at the nightstand, she saw it was 5:00 a.m. Her wake-up call was coming in a half hour. Would someone check if it went unanswered?

"Where are we going?"

"To get your sword, Miss Creed," the twin holding the katana said.

"I'm not dressed to go anywhere." The one with the breathier voice seemed the more anxious of the two, the muscles of his arms quivering ever so slightly. The other one had steadier eyes, and she guessed he was in charge. Associates of Lawton? Hired thugs like the Romany gang members? "Don't you think I'll raise some eyebrows in the lobby?"

"Move. We are not going out that way." He pointed his sword toward the window. At the same time his brother fitted a silencer on his gun. "If you don't cooperate, we'll end this now."

The gun was aimed at her. For a moment Annja felt the pommel of her sword against her palm, but she pushed it away.

She padded to the window and looked out. "Eighteenth floor," she said. The roadway below was shiny, the glow from streetlights reflecting off the pavement; it must have rained a little while ago. The sky was only now starting to lighten. "Do you expect me to jump?"

"There is a ledge." This came from the one with the gun, who had moved up behind her. "Step out onto it. Be careful."

"You can't be serious. You want me on the ledge?" It wasn't her best performance. "We're eighteen stories off the ground."

"It should be no difficult matter for you. Step out onto it," he repeated. "Walk to the fire escape on the corner, and we will follow you."

She opened her mouth to protest again, but then decided against it. The ledge was certainly wide enough. It was how they'd reached her room. Someone on the street, or in one of the few passing cars, might see her and call the police. But did she really want that? She slipped out the window and walked east, the ledge a balance beam. She moved quickly, thinking she'd put some distance between them, get up to the roof, where there was more room to fight, or at least where she'd have more options. Annja was certain they wouldn't kill her. If she was dead, Lawton wouldn't be able to get her sword.

Not that he was going to get it with her living, either.

"I thought your boss was willing to buy my sword. He made an opening bid last night."

She wrapped her fingers around the iron of the fire escape and started climbing, not giving them a chance to tell her what direction she was supposed to go.

"You refused. Have you changed your mind?" She wasn't sure which one had spoken.

"No. I haven't changed my mind." She glanced down. Both men were close behind her. The one with the sword had sheathed it to have his hands free to climb, and she saw that he had a second sheath and a smaller blade below it. From her vantage point, she also saw a sheath on the other twin's back. Both were swordsmen.

What the hell was this all about? Buying and stealing ancient swords?

"So if I'm not willing to sell," she mused, "you're going to try to steal it from me?" Like these two had stolen the Wallace Sword and Durendal. Maybe.

"Climb."

She was doing just that, and not too long after reached the top. "Now where to?" She stood a yard in from the edge of the roof. Her hotel was the tallest building on the block, at twenty-two stories, and it gave her a remarkable view of the city. The sky was lighter up here, the air cooler and cleaner. A half-dozen pigeons eyed her from their perch on the service exit to the roof.

"Your sword. We have come to—"

"Yes, I know. You've brought me up here because you want my sword. You have me at more than one dis-advantage," she said. "I'm practically in my underwear. I've no idea where we're going—"

"To get your sword," they said practically in unison.

"And I have no idea who you are."

The one with the gun grinned. "Gaetan," he said. "I'm Gaetan." The other shot him a withering look, but he only shrugged. "It doesn't matter that she knows my name."

Because you intend to kill me after you have my weapon.

The velvet-voiced man didn't introduce himself, but he drew the sword again. The hiss of the blade coming free from its scabbard sounded like a cat's purr. A heartbeat later, he pulled out the other, a saber—relatively new, from the looks of it.

"Honjo Masamune," Annja observed of the katana. "A fine weapon." So the professor wasn't putting it up on a shelf to gather dust, she thought. "Dr. Lawton gave it to you."

"To use," Gaetan said. "Only for my brother to use. But not so fine a blade as yours. Now, your sword, please."

She walked backward.

"That's far enough," Gaetan said. Annja judged that she was roughly in the middle of the roof, where it would be harder for anyone below to see her. In truth, she didn't want the police to come; she wanted to handle this on her own. The cops would only make it more difficult for Annja to get to the bottom of the mystery about Joan's sword.

She held her arms out. "You think I'm going to

take you to some locker at the airport where I have it stashed? What sword?"

"Joan of Arc's," said the man with the two blades. "Produce it now."

"I don't know what you're—"

"You know exactly," Gaetan declared. "You can produce it out of thin air."

"How do you know?" she asked. "Just tell me. How do you know about my sword?"

Sirens cut through the stillness, several of them heading west. Fire trucks off to fight a blaze. Cars started honking.

"Tell me how you know," she said. "Give me that much."

"A fair request," No-Name said.

That was double confirmation that they intended to kill her. She'd seen enough movies to know that if the villain started to talk, there was lethal intent. So Lawton wasn't as civilized as he'd appeared at the auction.

"In researching swords online, Miss Creed, your name came up. There were no pictures, but what there was was intriguing," Gaetan said.

Certainly enough people in the years since she'd first held Joan's sword had seen her wield it, but—

"When you came to France, publicity of your filming preceded you," Gaetan continued. "It saved us a trip to your country. Convenient that you came to us."

"In Paris it wasn't difficult to have you followed," the other said. "And provoked."

Annja gritted her teeth. The gang she'd fought outside the train station—each man there had seen her with the sword. If she hadn't picked that fight, this might not be happening. But then she might not have learned about the theft of Durendal or the Wallace Sword, either, and certainly she'd know nothing about Dr. Lawton or Archard Gihon.

"And what makes you think my sword belonged to Joan of Arc?"

"A portrait," Gaetan said.

Annja had read extensively about Joan. "Only one portrait was painted of her and the famous sword, and history records it as being burned."

"History is not always right," Gaetan countered. "I have seen it."

"That's enough. We've told her more than necessary. Wasted minutes. The sword. Now."

"I hand it over and you let me walk away?" Annja had been judging how far they could reach, guessing at their speed, wondering how much training they had. Some of the Romany toughs had exhibited a measure of skill, but most were just thugs. These two wielded swords of their own. A different kind of challenge.

"Of course," Gaetan said.

"You've told me your name and I've seen your faces."

He pushed the SIG Sauer into the waistband of his pants. "The sword and you walk. Easy. My word and my honor."

Annja concentrated, and in the same breath her fingers wrapped around the pommel. She held it with both hands, up and ready, but made no move on them.

"Set it down," Gaetan instructed.

Annja almost did…as she had under the bridge in Avignon. "Joan of Arc had two others, you know. Swords." She could trick these men, let them think they were going to simply take the sword and then have it disappear on them.

"Not as important as your sword, those other two Joan used." Gaetan took a step closer. "And they were easily obtained, purchased. I've seen them, too."

"That's enough." His twin shot him a look.

"Fine. Now, do not make this too difficult, Miss Creed," Gaetan said. "Surrender the sword—"

"Surrender it now," the other cut in, "or I will lop off your hand to get it."

Annja crouched. "Come and get it, then."

She'd known from the moment she saw them in her hotel room that it would come to this and that she would win. The thing left undecided was whether she would have to kill them. Annja detested killing. The sword she wielded had not been entrusted to Joan of Arc for that purpose. At least, Joan had not used it that way. The Frenchwoman had led an army and fought bloody battles, certainly slaying men along the way, but she'd used her other two swords for the grisly work. This special sword, the one the voices in her head had told her to claim at Saint Catherine's Church, Joan had considered a divine relic. Historical records stated that she'd used it to chase whores out of her army's camp, turning it sideways and swatting them with it. In the fourth session of her trial, she was quoted as saying the blade was "excellent for giving hard clouts and buffets."

Annja, however, had used it to kill…but only when she believed there was no other choice. Each death weighed heavily, and in the back of her mind, she could see the face of each person she'd cut down.

The man with two blades came at her first, and in the same instant Gaetan pulled a sword from his back, a saber. They separated, coming at her from each side, flanking her. A part of her felt the welcome rush of adrenaline, and her heart started beating faster. Roux had called her an adrenaline junkie once, and though she'd scoffed, she had to admit it was a valid assessment. She spun to parry Gaetan's lunge. He was using the flat of his blade, not trying for a lethal strike.

The other twin? He intended to hurt her. Annja jumped back and pulled her arms in tight. He'd led with the katana, and the air whistled as he brought it down where her arms had been. She felt the breeze from the blade, the swing had been that close.

He had just tried to cut off her hands.

21

Annja shifted her weight to the balls of her feet and reassessed her situation. The pair exhibited considerable skill, having the moves of fencers.

When they came at her again, she twirled away, nearly slipping when her foot touched a slick spot on the roof. The recent rain had puddled, and she skipped over a patch of water outlined by pigeon droppings. Annja crossed her feet, right in front of left, pivoting as she crouched, coming up and kicking out, catching Gaetan on the jaw. She heard a crack and saw him spit out blood and a tooth.

In pain and anger, he swung faster, turning the blade. He was no longer trying to hit her with the flat of it. But his temper made him sloppy and his rhythm was off. She dropped under the swinging weapons of both men, spinning toward the roof access door. Annja kicked out again, missing her target and again nearly losing her balance on the slick surface. But she regained her composure quickly and darted closer to Gaetan, who appeared only slightly less adept than his brother. Ducking again, she brought her elbow up when she straightened this time, jabbing him in the stomach.

Gaetan stumbled backward, and she followed, keeping a wary eye on the other one, bringing her sword up to knock away the saber and barely managing to avoid the swipe of the katana. Actually, not entirely avoiding it, she realized, noting a line of red forming on her arm and registering the sting. He stabbed both weapons at her, nearly connecting again.

She decided to pursue Gaetan first, get him out of the way, so raised her leg at a high angle and kicked at his head. The move succeeded in catching him off guard. She turned into him and jabbed him in the stomach again, at the same time avoiding the katana by a hairbreadth.

So far she hadn't resorted to a lethal move against either of them. Killing them wouldn't help get her answers. Neither man spoke, concentrating on flanking her. She raised her sword toward Gaetan, avoiding another blow from his twin.

They both wore chest protectors, a piece of fencing gear made of thermoplastic or Kevlar, the latter from the looks of it. In her T-shirt and flannel sleep shorts, she had no such advantage.

The breath rushed out of Gaetan as he lunged, and she parried with her own thrust. He circled her like a cat, his twin mirroring the move to retain the flank, both stepping back beyond her reach. Then the unnamed twin darted forward and almost managed to hit her twice. He would have—scoring himself points in an épée competition—if she hadn't blocked him. Points instead to Annja.

Gaetan stomped his foot in a puddle, startling her. She sidestepped, at the same time feeling the other's katana rip her T-shirt.

"Last chance," Gaetan said. "Hand over the sword."

"Is the sword worth your life?" his twin asked her.

It wasn't.

"Is it worth yours?" she replied. They weren't giving her much of a choice. She changed her grip on the sword, noticed Gaetan registering the move. She wasn't using the flat of the blade any longer.

He smiled slightly as he lunged and retreated, changing the tempo of his swings. Annja recognized the balestra maneuver, a French fencing technique. These two could teach her a few things.

She sucked in a lungful of air and inched toward Gaetan's brother, right foot in front of the left, suddenly sprinting past him and slashing, catching the katana and nearly wrenching it out of his grip. At the same time, Gaetan jabbed at her, the tip of the saber biting into her side. The air rushed from her lungs and she performed a forward recovery, stepping into the en garde position and unexpectedly throwing them out of their flanking roles.

She feinted successfully toward Gaetan, sweeping in and slicing at his protective vest. It didn't hurt him, but it forced him back, and that gave her a chance to attack the other one in earnest. The twin leaped forward and kicked, catching her in the stomach just as she brought her sword around at his leading arm.

"Aïe!" he shouted, which Annja translated as "Ouch!"

Gaetan recovered before she had a chance to come at the other one again. He shot forward with a dropkick, his heel connecting waist high and sending her back into the metal door. Her head hit hard and she nearly lost her grip on the sword. He'd used enough force that she was woozy. She tried to shake it off, but her vision blurred and she began to wonder if indeed she might lose this fight.

Annja bounded to her right just as both of them stabbed forward. She whipped around the side of the structure, hearing at least one blade connect with the door. The rooftop was still out of focus, but she charged forward, feet flying across the slick surface, water splashing up behind her. She had to put distance between them. She could probably beat either man one-on-one. But together? Together they were actually better than her, and that realization settled in her stomach like wet cement.

If she could separate them, she could take them. Separate… That's when it came to her. She'd seen them before, in an Olympic fencing match she'd attended in China. They'd competed separately, but the local news had run a brief segment on them because they were quirky—black men raised by white parents, twins who excelled at the same sport. A sportswriter compared them to the American Williams tennis sisters. She couldn't recall the last name of the fencers. She ran faster, knowing they were right behind her. She reached the edge of the roof and without pause leaped off, dismissing the sword and stretching her arms forward. The buildings were close together in this section of the city, and she cleared the gap and fell a full two stories to the neighboring structure. She tucked and rolled, landing with her knees bent and a painful jarring sensation shooting into her spine.

Would they be daring enough to follow her?

She sprang up, her pounding head still making her dizzy, and risked a glance over her shoulder in time to see both brothers flying toward her over the gap, Gaetan with his sword out. The other twin had sheathed both of his. They would clear the distance; she didn't need to watch. They were in superb condition and their legs were long. They might hurt themselves in the drop. If not, they'd be on her again in a heartbeat.

Annja continued to run, calling the sword to her again. This rooftop was covered with a gritty mixture that gave her better purchase. She idly remembered from her walk that this building had a café and a music store on the ground floor, and professional offices higher up. Would some businessman hear the pounding of feet overhead?

She couldn't just keep running. They were going to catch her.

Little needles of pain flickered through her legs and up her back. She'd jarred herself worse than she'd first thought. If she made it through this brutal encounter, she was going to look for a chiropractor. She shot past the access door to this building, rusted and not sitting straight in its frame. But by the time she stopped to open it—if she could open it—the men would be on her.

God, what am I doing? She was soaring again, propelling herself off the roof and onto another, this time only a one-story drop. She'd kept the sword out this time and landed better, but the pain shooting up her legs was worse. She caught her breath and twisted around to see both brothers leaping, too. But one was a beat ahead of the other.

A chance…

She stepped to the edge of the roof and swung with all her strength, catching Gaetan across the stomach. The vest protected him from the edge of her blade, but not from the force she'd used. For a heartbeat he hung suspended, horror on his face, eyes so wide they threatened to pop out. Then he fell, hands flailing for any kind of purchase, but coming up with nothing. She'd managed to knock him far enough out that he couldn't grab the edge of the building.

His scream was like fingernails raking a chalkboard, and Annja clamped her teeth shut at the sound of it. A dull thud against something metal followed.

"No!" his twin shouted, landing on the roof within an

arm's length of her. He looked over the side. "Gaetan! Gaetan, no!"

Annja used the precious moment to gain some distance, darting toward the center of the roof and another access door. She heard shouts in Spanish from below.

Across the street a window of a taller building flew open and a woman stuck her head out, shouting. Annja didn't even try to understand what she said, but could tell the woman wasn't looking at the ground where Gaetan had fallen. She was gazing at her and at the man charging her with both swords swinging.

Annja put her back against the access door, dropped a hand to the roof and caught her breath as both his swords passed through where she'd stood a breath ago.

"Murderer!" he shouted.

Annja didn't answer, but slipped under his next swings, changing position with him so that now he had his back to the door.

"My brother! You killed him!" His rage was saving her, his attack uneven and his attempt at footwork off.

Annja parried each blow and then took the offensive, lunging and recovering, then lunging again, an unanticipated move that let her land a blow. But it was against his chest, her blade scraping the Kevlar and not hurting him.

"I don't want to kill you," she repeated.

His face twisted into a grotesque mask. "You'll be joining my brother, bitch. You'll be the one to die." He extended his left arm with the saber and then swept at her with the katana.

She skittered back a few steps. Finally her wooziness had passed, but her head throbbed, her side ached from where she'd been slashed, and with each step it felt as if she was walking barefoot on glass. Annja had thought separating them would let her win. She'd thought she could take either one of them alone.

But this man was better than her, and he didn't have her injuries.

"Why does Lawton want all these swords?" Annja's words came out in a rush, revealing that she was winded. She needed this chance to catch her breath.

Her opponent leveled a sharp, controlled blow against her sword, not managing to knock it aside, but loosening her grip. She clamped both hands around the pommel in response and held tight as he followed through with the saber, bringing it down hard at an angle, as if chopping a piece of wood.

The woman across the street continued to shout, and other voices joined hers. Out of the corner of her eye, Annja saw several windows open and faces appear, some of the watchers waving frantically.

"Policía!" She heard this repeatedly until the shouts were drowned out by the sound of approaching sirens.

Annja jockeyed for a better angle, thrusting low and trying to catch her opponent beneath his protective vest. She feinted and tried again, cutting his saber arm instead, when he brought it in for a failed parry.

Blood sprayed in an arc from his wound, and he cried out. But he didn't drop either sword.

"Murderer! Bitch!" he raged. Then he struck with a compound attack, twin feints designed to catch her off guard. He hit her sword, nearly wresting it from her, and scored a second hit with the katana deep into her leg.

Annja dropped to her knees and slammed her teeth together to keep from screaming.

"Murderer!" he shouted, as he came at her once more, aiming for her throat this time.

She couldn't ignore the pain, so she used it as fuel, driving her sword up like a spear, finding a seam in the Kevlar and pushing in.

He gasped and stepped away from her blade, dropping the saber and pressing his hand to the wound, all the while slashing at her with the katana, keeping her from stabbing him a second time.

The sirens wailed louder, and she heard the screech of tires. Car doors slam. He continued to swing at her with the weapon, but he was distracted, and his gaze flashed between Annja and the edge of the roof.

"They'll come up here, the cops," she said.

"Salope meurtre!" he hissed, retreating to French. *"Je vais vous tuer!"*

Maybe he didn't know she was fluent in French, or maybe he was just railing at her in his native language.

"Vous allez mourir!"

"Everyone dies," she replied. "I just don't intend to today." Despite the agony, she forced herself to stand, meeting his next blow, feinting and sliding her sword against the edge of the katana, catching one of the deeper nicks. She beat her sword against his, stepping in and standing on his dropped saber.

"How about you?" she asked. "Are you ready to die today?" She was ready to kill him. A part of her wanted to.

He swung the katana back, the tip touching the access door behind him. Before he could bring it forward, Annja moved lightning-fast, kicking high at his head, then kicking lower and ramming him in the stomach.

The air left his lungs, but he didn't go down. He held his right leg back, but straightened the left, his heel catching her across the kneecap of her already wounded leg. Annja dropped again. Dizziness crashed over her, and she watched as he raised the katana once more.

He looked like an executioner.

She tried to bring her sword up to counter, tried to roll away.

Her sword…Joan's sword. Would she die before she learned its name?

"Fichu!" he cursed.

The access door behind him opened.

"Un autre jour!" he called to Annja, as he whipped around, running across the roof, sheathing the katana as he went. Another day.

Annja saw him leap, and then blackness claimed her.

22

"The police have a lot of questions," Roux said. He sat next to her in the hospital room. Her flannel shorts and ripped T-shirt had been replaced by a hospital gown. "I have a lot of questions, too." He stared at her for a moment. "They have an officer outside your room, to question you when you're up to it."

Annja blinked, bringing the old man into focus. She tried to say something, but only a croak came out. Her mouth felt full of cotton, her tongue swollen. He held a cup with a straw in it for her.

"You were in surgery for a while."

Her eyebrows rose.

"You were cut badly, Annja. The doctors thought you might lose your leg."

The wound had been that severe?

"My leg?" The words came out a hoarse whisper. She took another sip of water and tried to prop herself up. Roux held her down.

"You didn't," he said. "It's still there under all the

bandages." He set the cup on the stand. "No doubt your indefatigable constitution saved it."

Annja looked up at an eggshell-white ceiling. Sun streamed in through a window to brighten the already yellow walls. She smelled flowers—a small bouquet on the stand, probably from Roux—and the stringent scent of antiseptic. She had a clamp on her finger, taking her pulse, and a machine next to the bed with a blood-pressure cuff hooked to it and a panel that showed her heart rate.

"How long?"

"Were you in surgery? I didn't ask that. All I know is they brought you in yesterday morning. Someone told me it was before six, so the night-shift doctors stayed on longer to work on you. I didn't get here until last night." He leaned back in the chair and let out a long breath. "You heal remarkably fast, Annja, but you could have died."

"I know." A dull ache permeated her body, despite whatever painkiller they'd given her. "He was good, Roux. Maybe the best I ever fought."

"Who?"

She pictured his face, seeing the face of both of them: Gaetan, whom she had pushed to his death. "I don't know. But his brother—"

"Ah, that would be the man they found on the Dumpster in the alley?"

She nodded. "His name was Gaetan."

"I suppose if I buy a newspaper today, I might find the report and the obituary."

"They were swordsmen, Roux. Good. And the one—"

"Who got away?"

So the other twin had managed to leap to another building and elude the police. But he was wounded; he'd have to get medical help somewhere.

"He was better than me."

Roux shook his head. "I don't know about that, Annja."

"I do." She drank the rest of the cup of water and told him about being rousted out of bed by the two men, forced to climb up to the roof. "I know that he was better than me."

Neither said anything for a while. The sounds of the hospital crept through the gap under the closed door.

"So I know some of it," Roux said. "Indulge an old man and tell him the rest."

She did, about Archard Gihon and Dr. Lawton, about the auction and Tizona, the sword of El Cid, about Honjo Masamune, which was wielded against her, and before that the theft of Durendal from Rocamadour and the Wallace Sword from near Stirling.

"And there might be more," she said. "I'd only started, really, to dig into it."

He scowled. "I warned you, Annja."

Be careful that history's monsters don't come chasing you. "But I have to see what it's all about. This guy is more than just an obsessed collector. He knows something about Joan's sword, too. I need to find out what it is."

Roux stood and worked a kink out of his neck. "And even if you didn't want to pursue it, I fear it would pursue you."

"That man I fought…he'll be back."

"And what about this Dr. Lawton from the auction?"

She propped herself up. This time Roux didn't stop her. "I'm going to get out of here."

"Not today, Annja. You do heal fast, but not that fast. You're impressive, but you're not immortal."

"Like you?"

"You really were close to death."

"I'm going—"

"You're going to stay here at least until tomorrow." His expression was stern. "Promise me. Any other soul who suffered that cut probably would have lost a leg. You had other cuts, too. And any other soul would be laid up a week…or more. You can give it until tomorrow."

She shook her head.

"Promise me."

"Fine."

"Get better. Rest. I've got a feeling we'll have to be at our best."

We?

He stooped and picked something up off the floor. Her laptop. He set it on the nightstand. "I checked you out of your hotel. Your suitcase is over there." He pointed to the small closet. "When you feel better, start pursuing your quarry through the mystical space of the web. Information is strength, Annja. Knowledge indeed is power."

There is also power in names. She'd get the name of Gaetan's twin brother, for starters. That shouldn't be a difficult search by going through reports on Olympic fencing matches. And she had two more: Archard Gihon and Charles Lawton.

"I'll be back to check on you tonight. Then you can tell me where we're headed."

The uncharacteristic "we" again. Annja was at the same time pleased with and dreading the notion that Roux was involving himself in this. She watched him leave, and then opened the laptop and started typing. She didn't start with Gaetan or Archard or Charles Lawton—the men's names would come later. She pulled up the Google search engine and typed in *named swords*.

23

Sarah couldn't pronounce the name of the place she'd slipped into twenty minutes ago. The Kunsthistorisches Museum. It was the biggest building she'd ever set foot in. Enormous and old, looking like a castle and some grand government building at the same time, it stretched across several blocks of Vienna. The sight of it this afternoon had taken her breath away.

"It's too much," she told Ulrich. "The place is simply too huge. I'll get lost inside."

"Your faith will keep you safe," he'd said.

But her faith, and her belief in Dr. Lawton's plan, wasn't keeping her nerves in check. The voices in her head weren't helping; they were only adding to her doubts, questioning if she was up for this. Maybe if someone was with her, if she wasn't prowling the halls and stairwells alone, she wouldn't feel so skittish. Sarah looked at her watch. She had forty minutes left.

One hour. That was all the German was giving her. He was elsewhere in the building, had used his expertise to finesse the security system and reroute monitors and replay loops so guards wouldn't notice her. But he wasn't going to stay long. Ulrich said one hour; longer than that was too risky. He had a car a block away, parked in an alley outside a service entrance. She had to be there in an hour—forty minutes now— or he would leave without her. There was another man with them. He called himself Crescendo, though Sarah knew that wasn't his real name. Pierre DePaul was a thirtysomething graduate student assigned to Dr. Lawton. She didn't know why he called himself Crescendo, and wasn't going to ask; she just went along with it, like everyone else. One of the professor's paladins, Crescendo's specialty was restoration and maintenance. The sword she was tasked with retrieving tonight would be passed along to him for sprucing up.

And then it would be hers.

Dr. Lawton had officially named her one of his paladins before he left for Spain, and said as such it was time to claim her weapon. He'd presented her with a few choices. At the time, she'd thought this would be the easiest to obtain. She didn't tell him that, though. She'd said the history of it entranced her, and she thought her inner spirit most fit that of the man who'd once wielded it.

"I agree," Dr. Lawton had said. "This blade would suit you."

If she could find it.

Thirty-five minutes left.

"Damn, Archard." As much as she railed against

his company and his insistence that he run things, she wished he was here. He would have made her case the museum during the day, exploring the exhibits, reading up on the history, playing the tourist. It's what he'd ordered in Rocamadour and Stirling, and both thefts went off without a hitch. But he was in Spain with Dr. Lawton, getting a sword the legal way, and she'd told them she could handle this mission. The voices in her head told her she should be in charge.

After all, she'd done such a good job on the initial cleansing foray in Rouen, leaving no solid clues for the police with the slain Buddhists and Scientologists. She'd gotten herself and the twins in and out, and then she'd returned to Paris with a triumphant accounting of their bloody activities.

Sarah hadn't wanted to spend the time scouting the place out in person. The voices in her head always chided her for pretending to be a tourist. Besides, she'd looked it up on the internet. Unfortunately, the website didn't reveal just how humongous this place was. She'd seen a picture of the sword and noted which room it was in. She'd borrowed the glass-cutting kit from Ulrich and had a piece of cloth in her pack to wrap the sword in. She'd dressed in tight-fitting black-and-gray clothes so she'd look like a shadow as she skulked through this place, and her shoes were ballet slippers…soundless.

Thirty minutes and she'd looked through every nook and cranny of the room the sword was supposed to be in. She found the case where it had been. Empty.

"Damn. Damn. Damn."

There was a card in the case, and she'd pulled out a small flashlight to read it. God, it was dark in this museum. To conserve electricity, there were lights only in the halls, and they were dim. She started to read the card, and then she heard the sound of footfalls.

"Damn. Damn. Damn." The voices in her head chanted far worse profanity.

The security guard. Noting the curtains in this room, heavy fabric, brocade or velvet, she hid behind one. Sarah was small and knew she wouldn't disturb the folds enough to draw attention. A light came on and the footsteps grew louder. She heard the sound pant legs make when they rub together, and imagined the security guard being on the portly side to cause the material to rub like that. She listened as he made a circuit of the large room. The light flicked off, and she waited a few breaths before looking out. Gone.

She glanced at her watch. Twenty-five minutes left.

Sarah didn't want to run from this empty-handed. If she didn't get this sword, maybe Dr. Lawton would depaladinize her. Maybe it would be months before she could regain his favor. She skittered to the empty case and flicked on her flashlight.

Removed for restoration.

No!

She took a few deep breaths. Fought the icy feeling that had seeped into her arms and legs. If Archard had been here, if they'd visited this museum as tourists, she would have known the sword was gone. Dr. Lawton was going to be seriously pissed.

She slunk from the room and started toward the back staircase, passing through an incredible space with a high, octagonal dome ceiling. The lighting was sparse and the decor dark, but Sarah swore she'd never been in a place so beautiful. Gold leaf and stucco ornamentation were everywhere. She'd like to kick herself for not following Archard's lead and scoping the place out during operating hours. To see everything well lit would be amazing. But to leave without her prize…

Wait a minute. The sword was being restored. Was it being restored here? When she'd been on the museum website, she'd read about their labs in the basement.

The Kunsthistorisches was a fine-arts museum, with staff to do restoration on its paintings. That's what the place was known for—the work of the masters that hung on the seemingly never-ending walls. Paintings had been displayed here for more than a hundred years, the building commissioned originally so the Hapsburgs' art collection could be seen by the public.

Sarah looked at her watch when she hit the lower landing. Fifteen minutes to go. If she left right this minute, she'd have a little time to spare to make it to the alley and the rental car. But the prize… The restoration lab was only one floor down, if she correctly recalled what she'd read on the website. Damn, if only she'd paid more attention, hadn't been so cocky.

She hurried down the rest of the steps and emerged

into a corridor almost as dark as a cave. The only light came from right above her head and the far end, both sporting two words, one in German, the other in English: *Ausfahrt/Exit*. She pressed herself against the wall and listened. Not a single footfall. She'd noted the presence of only three guards since she'd come in here. Sarah had expected more…and maybe there were. It was a big, big place, after all. But maybe they'd grown a little lax with security. It had been a decade since Cellini's *Salt Cellar* had been stolen, recovered a couple years later. At the time it had been the greatest theft of an art treasure in Austria.

If Sarah found the sword, would her theft surpass it?

How many minutes did she have left? She glanced toward her watch and then stopped herself.

"Just do it," she growled.

She inched down the hall, pausing at doors and shining her flashlight in through the windows. On the third stop she found a workroom filled with tables. She almost kept going, but then spotted a shield on one of them.

"Bingo." The door was locked, but there looked to be nothing modern or high-tech about it. She reached into her pack and pulled out a set of picks the German had given her. She knew how to use them. That had been one of the first skills she'd picked up after joining Dr. Lawton's group. She made the sign of the cross over her chest, not that she was Catholic—Methodist born and raised—but the gesture gave her a small measure of confidence. "Dear God, please let Ulrich have knocked out any surveillance down here." A moment later, the tumblers clicked and she was inside.

Hurry, she admonished herself, flashing the light over each table. Spears and more shields, a chunk of breastplate...what were those doing in an art museum, anyway? And one sword.

She drew in a deep breath, discovering that the air was overly cool down here. Maybe important in restoration work. "Be it," she whispered. "Dear God, be it."

Sarah practically floated toward the table. The sword lay on a piece of feltlike material. A study lamp of some sort stretched over it. She flipped the switch.

"Ah, this is mine." She tried to swallow the words, which she'd spoken too loudly. Immediately, she glanced over her shoulder to the door, which she'd forgot to close behind her. Whew, no one there to hear her.

First it had been Attila's, and now it was hers. Her fingers touched the blade.

Attila the Hun had thought he was destined to rule the world. His reputation had earned him the title the Scourge of God. His sword, the Sword of God.

Sarah wrapped her right hand around the pommel and marveled at the decorative gold work. A disc at the handle's base was worn but looked almost globelike, perhaps reflecting the warlord's plan to conquer the world. The delicate designs were worn in places, especially along the guard that curved upward and inward like the sweeping horns of a bull. Was that what they were restoring? Some of the fine details? She would have to ask Crescendo.

Sarah hoped whatever it was that needed restoring was basically finished. She didn't want Crescendo to have this weapon any longer than absolutely necessary.

Her sword.

Hers to help in the cleansing. She couldn't wait to show this to the twins and to gloat over it. Especially as Gaetan didn't have his "named" sword yet.

This one? Sarah's very special sword. The Sword of God, it was called, and Tiew. Attila had named it Tiew after his ancestors' war god.

"Tiew," she said, trying out the sound of it. "Sarah and Tiew."

Attila had ruled the Huns for almost two decades. His empire was vast, from the Urals to the Rhine, from the Baltic Sea to the Danube. He'd plundered the Balkans, invaded Italy, but couldn't capture Rome.

Could she help Dr. Lawton capture Rouen with this?

It felt good in her hand.

Her hand. She turned her arm so she could see her watch.

Time was up.

More than up.

She dashed out of the room, holding Tiew close and knocking one of the shields off a table in her rush. It made a harsh clanging sound that echoed off the walls and followed her out into the hall. For a moment she couldn't recall which way she'd come, with two exit lights offering her ways out. She picked the closest and ran.

Out the door and up the stairs, feet pounding on the steps. Sarah didn't try to be quiet; the possibility of a quiet exit had been dashed with the clanging shield. Lights were coming on upstairs, and she heard the crackle of something. Maybe an alarm or walkie-talkie; maybe some intercom buzzing a warning. Her heart pounded in her throat.

Would Ulrich have left without her? It had been quite a few minutes more than an hour. But he wouldn't have abandoned her, would he? She was one of Dr. Lawton's chosen paladins. He couldn't leave her!

Up another flight of stairs and down a hall she'd been through before... The smug faces painted centuries ago stared down their noses at her, the landscapes a blur of watercolors and oils as her feet slammed across the marble.

Someone shouted, *"Stopp. Halt!"*

Obviously they were shouting at her. Two voices. And obviously she wasn't going to stop. If she did, she'd be arrested, jailed until she was Archard's age.

Sarah ran faster, falling when she rounded a corner, dropping Tiew. She popped up right away, grabbed the sword again and raced for the back exit she'd come in. Her side was on fire, she was running so fast, and it felt as if her kneecap was busted. But she couldn't be running like this if it was broken.

Dear God, she prayed, *don't let the sword be bro-*

ken, either. Had she ruined it when it hit the marble? She couldn't have damaged her sword, her instrument to help Dr. Lawton cleanse his chosen city.

"Faster!" she screamed, as if that word could somehow make her legs pump harder.

Then she was behind the building and across a parking lot, flying into the Vienna night. It wasn't especially chilly, but she was freezing, her teeth chattering. Her clothes were soaked with sweat, her skin dotted with it.

Sarah sprang into a small park and hid behind a tree, taking in great swallows of air as she listened to the sirens. How many? Checking for a number gave her an excuse to stand there and catch her breath. One, two, definitely three. Lights came on outside the museum, and the flashing lights of police cars joined in. The station must not have been far.

She ran again, having gotten her bearings. The alley where the rental car had been parked was less than a block away. Sarah cut toward it, darting from tree to tree and then dashing across an intersection, away from the museum. Lights played across the palatial structure, revealing people milling on the steps. She clung to the buildings on this side of the street, slipping under awnings and pausing in crevices to watch the scene. The sirens had stopped, but there were even more lights, a police van. There were gawkers out on the street, too. Where had they come from? Apartments? Bars? Didn't matter; she had to get out of here before they looked down this block.

In the alley, she felt a little better. It wasn't as dark as when they'd parked here. The lights from the museum stretched to the ends of the alley. Sarah tried to calm down…but failed. She tried to at least breathe slower, and managed that. She stumbled toward the spot where Ulrich had left the car.

It was gone.

Sarah held the sword even tighter against her and wedged herself into a narrow space between buildings. Could a paladin cry?

What was she going to do? Her purse, passport, airline ticket, change of clothes…all that was in the car with Ulrich and Crescendo. What the *hell* was she going to do?

The tears came hard and her shoulders shook. She heard voices, but they were from a good distance away, people calling to one another. Not the voices in her head; they'd gone silent. Listening to the distant voices gave her something to do, something to occupy herself so she wouldn't think about prison. It was police or security guards talking.

"Dieb." Thief.

She admitted she was that…but for a righteous cause.

"Schatz." Treasure. Did they even know what was taken yet? She doubted that. They probably wouldn't figure out just what was gone until the museum staff came in to take a look.

"Frau." Woman. Someone had gotten a look at her.

"Judendiche." Youth. Teenager. They hadn't gotten a good look.

Sarah needed to pee. She clamped her legs together and looked up, hoping for some divine intervention to this crisis.

"Get in."

She yipped in surprise. Ulrich had brought the car back with its lights off, pulling in so quietly that she hadn't heard it coming. *Get in. Get in. Get in.*

Dr. Lawton said Joan of Arc had heard voices. Maybe Sarah could be like Joan. Dr. Lawton was like Charlemagne, Archard like Roland. She could be—

"Get in now," Ulrich snapped.

Sarah slid into the backseat next to Crescendo.

"I found my sword," she told them. "Ulrich, Crescendo, meet Tiew. It never left Attila's side, and now it won't leave mine."

"Oh, yes, it will," Ulrich said as he exited the alley and pointed the car away from the museum and the assembly of police cars. "Tiew will be carefully packed away in the belly of our chartered plane before midnight." He said something else, but Sarah wasn't listening. She was thinking about what outfit she would wear when Dr. Lawton presented her and Tiew to the other paladins. Maybe she'd go out and buy something new. Her take from the cash box of the Buddhist bookstore was burning a hole in her pocket. Maybe the voices in her head would help her pick something appropriate.

"My sword," she said, patting the pommel.

Crescendo leaned close and rested his chin on her shoulder. "And now we're going to get mine, sweet Sarah."

Her eyes grew large.

"We've got another stop in Vienna," he explained. "One of Charlemagne's swords is on display at the Imperial Treasury. It's not far, and with the police distracted at the Kunsthistorisches Museum, it should be easy."

Ulrich looked into the rearview mirror, turned on the car's lights and sped up. "And, Sarah, this time if you're not out in an hour, we really will leave you behind."

24

The pain medication made her head fuzzy, and when it started to wear off and the nurse came in to offer her more, Annja declined.

"The police officer outside would like to talk to you," the woman said. She was polite and smiled sweetly, a practiced expression that Annja thought was only half-genuine.

"I'm so tired, I think I'll sleep for a while. Tell him I'll talk to him later."

"Her."

"Tell her, then."

The nurse shut the door on her way out and Annja kept surfing.

Angurvadal was the first one she came to, a sword whose name meant "Stream of Anguish," Frithiof's weapon. But Frithiof the Bold was a mythical Norse character, and so Annja skipped on to the next.

Ar'ondight, the sword of Lancelot. Another skip.

Balisarda, sword of Rogero and supposedly crafted by a sorcerer...another piece of fiction.

Colada. Annja stopped at that one. It was another of El Cid's swords. She bookmarked it. A real sword, it might be a legitimate target of Dr. Lawton's. She'd get back to it, figure out where Colada was and if it could be obtained, legally or otherwise.

Corrougue, sword of Otuel, another possibility that she bookmarked. Otuel had been a Saracen ambassador to Charlemagne, and history claimed he was rude and imperious. He'd challenged Roland to a duel, fighting first on horseback. Both horses died in the fight, and the two men continued their brawl. At Charlemagne's urging, all the spectators prayed for Roland to survive and for Otuel to convert to Christianity. Scholars record the incident as a miracle: a snow-white bird had appeared and perched on Otuel's shoulder. The Saracen ended the fight that very moment, called Roland his brother and became a Christian.

Curtana, the Sword of Mercy, Edward the Confessor's blunted sword. She saved this one, too. She remembered actually seeing this sword somewhere, probably a few years ago in a museum. Could it also be a target?

Annja heard the door handle turn, and she closed the laptop and feigned slumber. "Sorry, regulations," the nurse said, waking her out of her pretend sleep to take her blood pressure. "It's a little high. You should rest. Relax."

After she left, Annja resumed her search.

Flamberge, or Floberge, another of Charlemagne's swords, was pictured in its display case in a museum in Vienna. It was reported stolen less than a day ago. The sword had also been used by Rinaldo, one of Charlemagne's twelve peers.

"Damn him. Just how many swords does the man need?"

She concentrated on "sifting," ignoring Excalibur as fiction, along with Merveilleuse, Mimung, Nagelring, Quern-biter, Azoth and Schrit.

Durendal was linked to a website with a picture of precisely where it had hung, as well as another picture of the piece that had been imbedded in the cliff. There was another link to the story of its theft, in which Brother Maynard, whom she'd spoken with earlier, was quoted as saying, "A loss for all of France."

She found Tizona in a link to a story about the auction and how much money the sword went for. Lured by other links off the page, Annja searched for upcoming auctions, but didn't find anything about swords.

"Too bad he couldn't collect comic books for a hobby. Or baseball cards or those little Hummel figurines." She closed the link and moved to another that referenced a weaponsmith, Munifican, who supposedly forged Durendal along with Sauvagine and Courtain for a fellow named Ogier the Dane. One of Charlemagne's peers. The swords each took three years to make…and were said to have a spark of the divine. Since Durendal was already stolen, she suspected the other two were on Lawton's list. She added them to her own list.

So many named swords…

What was hers called?

The blacksmith Wieland had forged Flamberge for Charlemagne and Balmung for Siegfried.

Crocea Mors—Yellow Death—was Caesar's sword.

Haute Claire, Very Bright, was fashioned by a Gailas for some fellow called Oliver. She made a note to look a little closer at that one. Gailas had also made Joyeuse for Charlemagne.

Joyeuse.

Annja stopped cold, something percolating in her brain. She highlighted the reference. If Durendal was taken, Joyeuse must also be on the list. Both were said to be God-touched swords. Joyeuse was one of history's most famous weapons. In the Louvre. Likely safe there, with all the security. She'd seen it in passing years ago when she was looking at an Old Masters exhibit.

Next...

Philippan was the sword of Antony.

Caliburn was another name for Excalibur. She passed by this entry.

If Annja couldn't dig in the dirt, her passion, she'd dig through the various websites hosted by museums and history buffs around the world. She skimmed over replica-weapons pages, which were good for finding more important links and for getting a look at copies of various swords. She had to admit the replica of Honjo Masamune looked in much better shape than the real one wielded by the twin who had almost killed her.

Lobera had belonged to King Saint Ferdinand III of Castile.

Napoleon's sword had been sold at an auction years ago for six and a half million. Lawton perhaps? Did he have that much money? She couldn't find a record of the sword having a name, though, and moved on.

Kusanagi, also called Grasscutter, was the Sword of the Gathering Clouds of Heaven. "Huh, more fiction."

Legbiter. That sounded fictitious, too, but after reading further, she put it on her list. It was a Gaddhjalt sword belonging to the Viking king Magnus Barelegs, killed in County Down in 1109.

Szczerbiec, the coronation blade of Polish kings.

A sword at West Point was said to be the personal weapon of Tomoyuki Yamashita, a general of the Japanese Imperial Army in World War II. Too recent.

Zulfiqar. She noted this one, too, an ancient sword of Ali, an Islamic leader related to Mohammed.

Grus, wielded by the Polish prince Boleslaw III Wrymouth.

The Sword from Heaven, wielded by Joan of Arc, once belonging to Charlemagne, lost to history. "The Sword from Heaven." Annja felt it with her mind. Was it true? Did the sword actually have a name? *The Sword from Heaven*... She let it roll around in her head for a moment.

The Wallace Sword, with an onion-shaped pommel of gilded iron, the original scabbard, hilt and belt supposedly made from the skin of Hugh Cressingham, an

English commander. "Lovely," she said. "And also gone, no doubt to Dr. Lawton."

What made some of these swords divine, God-touched? That they were wielded by devout men for holy causes?

"In the forging, I think," she mused. The finest swords were forged without flaws and impurities in the metal that would cause the blades to break. But even the finest blades had some minor imperfections that caused them to crack and fracture during battles. In centuries past there wasn't a precise recipe, making the crafting a little mysterious...which was why some legendary blades were believed to be laced with mystical properties and purposes.

Poor tempering made a sword less flexible, weak and brittle. Using the precise amount of carbon, manganese and chromium smacked of alchemy and sorcery.

If it had taken three years to make Joyeuse and Durendal, how long had it taken to make the Sword from Heaven?

She found a link for "Swordplay in France" and followed it to the headline Swordsman Slays Buddhists. The article wasn't from centuries ago; it was from earlier this week.

"Oh, dear God in heaven," Annja said as she read. Some Buddhists were shot, others were killed by what forensic examiners claim were sword slashes. One survivor, a toddler, said two black men did it.

Gaetan and Luc.

"What the hell? Why go after Buddhists in a book-store?" Annja's eyes grew wider. Did the bookstore have a famous, named sword? According to the article, the only thing missing was the cash box, reported taken. Maybe there had been some sacred sword hanging on the wall the police didn't know about, Annja mused.

Then she found another article. That same night six Rouen businessmen had been killed in their homes, four of them shot in the head, two slashed with a sword. Police said the only thing the men had in common was that they were confirmed Scientologists.

Buddhists, Scientologists and swords.

Annja closed the laptop and set it on the floor beside the bed. She wanted out of here...now. Get back to France, find Dr. Lawton and figure out what the hell was going on. But she'd made a promise to Roux. She looked at the clock on the medical monitor. It read 10:59.

After midnight would be the next day.

She closed her eyes and settled back into the pillow. An hour's nap.

THE WARM SUN ON HER FACE woke her. Roux was at the window, leaning against the sill, his face pressed to the glass.

"I thought you said you were coming by last night," she said, stretching. "I waited up for you."

"I came by," he said. "But I stayed in the lobby." His eyes were fixed on a point that seemed far beyond the street below. "Do you feel up to leaving?"

"I wanted to leave yesterday."

He didn't move from the window. "So have you decided where we are going?"

Annja slipped out of bed and disconnected her finger from the heart-rate monitor, flipping off the dial so the machine wouldn't beep. She tested her leg. Sore but serviceable; a throbbing pulsed in her hip. She padded to the closet and got her suitcase. "Give me a few minutes to wash up."

He didn't reply, still staring at…something.

She went into the tiny bathroom and was delighted to find a shower. Holding her hand under the spray until the temperature was as hot as she could stand it, then gingerly stepping in. Roux was right; she healed remarkably fast. But her leg was going to ache for a while, and where she'd been cut on her side still stung. She'd try to take things easy.

When she was finished, she rooted through her suitcase for something comfortable and then put on her tennis shoes. Annja was pleased to note the care Roux had taken to fold her new dress.

"Have you decided?" he repeated when she emerged.

"Back to France. I don't know. Let's start with Paris. That's where Dr. Lawton lives."

"And what is your plan for Paris?"

"The Louvre is on the list."

"I've been to that museum one too many times," he grunted.

"You don't need to come with me. I work better alone."

He shrugged. "I could see it again."

"First, though, I need to go back to school. You don't need to accompany me there, either."

"One should never stop learning," he said.

25

The lecture hall was about two-thirds full, holding roughly two hundred people, most of them students. Annja and Roux sat in the middle toward the back. She guessed some of the older members of the audience were teachers. A few had briefcases at their feet.

The buzz of conversation surrounded her, all in French. A man, maybe twenty, chatted with his companion about an art major he'd had a horrible date with. "He was so cheap I had to pay for my own latte, and he was going to stiff the waiter for a tip. Never again."

A girl showed off her engagement ring to the people she was sitting near. "We haven't picked a date yet, but it has to be in winter because we're going skiing on our honeymoon."

Annja had done a little digging into Dr. Lawton's credentials, discovering that he'd inherited money from more than one source, some of it "old money," and that had put him in a position where he'd never have to work again. She was surprised he even bothered to teach. Maybe he was like her and just had a passion for his work. Unfortunately, he also had a passion for thievery and was likely connected to the murders of the Buddhists and Scientologists, and who knew what else.

"He hasn't had a lecture like this for a while?" Roux asked the student sitting to his left. Annja, on his right, leaned slightly forward to get a look at the fellow Roux was talking to.

He was in his twenties, nerdy-looking with a sweater vest, thick glasses and short, slicked-down hair. He had a clipboard on his lap with a legal-size pad on it, and he played with a marker, twirling it in his fingers. Despite his scholarly appearance, he appeared to be fit and muscular—and old-fashioned. Most of the other students had iPads and netbooks.

"Usually only once a quarter, though last year he had one of these talks every few weeks. Don't think he gets paid any extra for them. They're not part of the regular curriculum."

"Then why—?" Roux prompted.

The nerd shrugged. "I dunno. Some of his students— I'm one of his seniors—become very interested in a specific area and there isn't class time to cover it. So he hosts a special lecture. Like this one—Charlemagne, the Second Coming."

"So tonight is entirely on Charlemagne?" Roux smiled warmly. "A fascinating man."

"The professor? Yes, definitely." The nerd's head bobbed.

Annja knew Roux had meant Charlemagne.

"The professor is probably the most fascinating man I've ever known. I've decided to write my master's thesis on Charlemagne's lasting influence on modern-day France. If it hadn't been for Dr. Lawton, I'd be picking up a teacher's certificate and be stuck at a high school in Nice, where my parents live. He opened my eyes."

A dozen more students trickled in, finding places to the far right and left of the lecture hall. A custodian came in and changed the plastic liner of a large waste can at the back of the room, then went to a panel on the wall and dimmed the lights.

"Did you know that Dr. Lawton is a descendant of Charlemagne?" Roux's new friend asked. "It's not published in the university listing, but if you study with him long enough…"

Dr. Lawton, a descendant of Charlemagne? Annja hadn't come across that in her internet research. That could well explain the professor's fixation on the emperor…but on the swords? Charlemagne's swords, maybe, but on the Wallace Sword, Durendal, Honjo Masamune? Unless… She swallowed hard. Unless he was trying to equip more than just himself. The twin brothers she'd fought on the rooftops were armed with swords, and they were used in the murders of the Buddhists.

The professor entered, attention riveted on him and the conversations died.

Annja had to admit he had presence—the way he made an entrance, the way he walked, his whole appearance. He wore a gray suit with a four-button jacket, well tailored but a decade or so out of fashion. His hair was pulled back, and the features of his face seemed so pronounced that she guessed he wore makeup.

When he spoke, his voice was as smooth as honey in the silence of the large auditorium. It carried easily to the back of the room. He had a stage voice to go with his presence.

Annja touched Roux's knee. *He is charismatic,* she signed. *Frighteningly so.*

Roux made a fist and moved it up and down. *Yes.*

Annja was more interested in watching the professor's effect on his audience than listening to what he had to say. People continued to drift in. Only the professor's lined face struck a chord with her. From the auction in Spain.

"Charles the Great, or Charlemagne, is perhaps the most important historical figure…certainly in France, but also throughout all of Europe. King of the Franks, he inherited the crown with his brother, becoming sole king some years later at his brother's death. He inherited more than a title, however. With it came the moral obligation to protect the rights of the Holy See. He warred against the pagan Saxons in Germany, insurgents and the Moors of Spain. In 800 the pope crowned him emperor of the Western Empire. Charles brought order during one of history's most tumultuous times. He left behind an indelible and unforgettable history, much like the mark Christ made on the world."

Annja shifted in her seat and looked at Roux. He was intently studying the professor.

"Simply put, Charlemagne was Christ come to earth again." Now Dr. Lawton had definitely said something to pique Annja's curiosity. Like the best television evangelist, he still held everyone captive, but his demeanor had suddenly changed. He thumped the podium like a fire-and-brimstone preacher might thump a Bible.

"Christ had his twelve apostles. Charlemagne had his twelve peers." The professor stepped away from the podium and paced the stage, all eyes following him. "Their goals were the same. Christ sought to save humanity through his death. Charlemagne sought to save humanity through the dissemination of Christianity." Lawton spread his arms wide, feet together, his body a cross. "The goals are the same for the man who is the Third Coming, who is among you even now."

Annja shivered.

The twelve apostles of Christ.

The twelve peers of Charlemagne.

The twelve paladins of Charles Lawton?

The professor switched back and forth from fire and brimstone to scholar. An extraordinary actor. She shivered again. It wasn't an act, was it? Dr. Lawton bought into everything he preached…taught.

"Charlemagne, the Second Coming, gathered twelve men and equipped them with God-touched weapons. Roland's Durendal, Oliver's Haute Claire and Otuel's Corrougue, among others."

Annja's eyes widened. In the hospital she'd skimmed over an item about the sword Corrougue missing from an exhibit.

"Charlemagne made religious reforms and was given the titles of Augustus and emperor," Lawton went on. "Christ was King of the Jews. Charlemagne was the father of the Holy Roman Empire. Christ was the son of the ultimate father. Charlemagne and Christ, and the one who is the Third Coming, stand out from all others as personifications of selflessness, nobility, and as conquerors of pagans and heretics. They set out to build a City of God." Several students chanted the next line with him: "One God, one emperor, one pope, one City of God."

"Drive out the nonbelievers!" the nerd next to Roux shouted, startling her companion. "Only Christians should live in the City of God."

"Only Christians!" a woman in front of them called.

Annja balled her fists, her fingernails pressing into her palms. She'd attended voodoo ceremonies in New Orleans, where participants shouted with a fervor like this. It was unsettling, to say the least.

"Christians unite!" This came from somewhere down front.

"Build the City of God!" another said.

Dr. Lawton returned to his podium, and the room became dead quiet again. "Charlemagne the scholar read extensively and treasured the works of Augustine of Hippo, who espoused the creation of such a city and championed any war considered just. The church was Saint Augustine's City of God, but Charlemagne knew the church wasn't enough, that one city on the map wasn't enough. Charlemagne sought to make all of France…and beyond…his City of God. Unfortunately, he died before he could realize his goal. He succeeded in driving Muslims out of the Christian world, but not all of them." The professor rocked back on his heels and gazed from one attendee to the next. "Perhaps in the Third Coming Charlemagne's plan will be realized."

There was wild applause, and some people in the audience stood.

Annja slipped out of the auditorium during the excessive adoration, Roux following. Behind them, she heard the applause die down and the professor continue his lecture.

"I've heard enough." She had goose bumps on her arms, and the hair on the back of her neck had risen.

"Quite," he said. "More than enough as far as I'm concerned."

In the hall, watching them like a sentry, stood Archard Gihon.

26

It had been raining outside. Annja could tell because Archard wore a raincoat, and the shoulders and sleeves were drenched, his hair slick with water. A little puddle had formed around his feet.

"Is the lecture done already?"

Annja looked around Roux to where the girl who had spoken leaned against the hallway wall, with two others diagonally across from Archard.

"I said, is the lecture over already?" she repeated.

They had the look of freshmen, and wore jeans riding low on their hips, and tight, plunging sweaters. The one who had spoken had dark brown hair, irregularly cut. Her earrings dangled below her shoulders.

She blew a bubble, popped it and sucked it back into her mouth. "I said, is the lecture—"

"The lecture hasn't finished," Roux said.

The other two giggled, one of them twisting a red-blond curl around her finger. "We're waiting for our boyfriends." She sighed, her stretched sweater protesting. "They're *so* caught up in all that historical religious crap."

Out of the corner of her eye, Annja saw Archard open his mouth as if to say something. He drew his lips tight and his gaze drifted from the three girls to Annja. Odd, she thought, that he looked so unemotional. Interested and detached at the same time. Distant, yet observant. He reminded her of Mr. Spock in *Star Trek*.

"We left early," Roux said.

"Wish John would leave early." She twisted her curl tighter. "You a professor?"

Roux shook his head. "I've had enough of this," he said softly to Annja.

She headed toward Archard, then pivoted on the ball of her foot and started down the long hallway to the parking lot. She heard Roux's footfalls behind her.

"Would you like to see Durendal?"

Archard's question stopped them in their tracks.

"Miss Creed?"

"Yes." She turned, a second behind Roux.

"I will give you that courtesy. I think you appreciate fine swords."

"It doesn't belong to you," Annja said.

"Ah, Miss Creed, it does. I was destined to have it, Roland reborn."

This had to be a trap. But it was a tempting one.

"No," Roux said.

"I didn't ask you, old man."

"Yes," Annja said. "I would like to see Durendal."

"Who's Durendal?" the girl with red-blond hair asked. "Is he some celebrity?"

"A rocker?" the other two asked almost simultaneously.

Archard gave the girls a withering look—the first hint of real emotion he'd displayed. He looked at Annja. "In my car, in the faculty parking lot." He took a step down the hall in the opposite direction, then stopped and looked over his shoulder. "I'll not repeat the invitation, Miss Creed."

Annja brushed by Roux and hurried after Archard.

It was still raining. It had rained most of the time she'd spent in France, weather that matched her dark mood. The faculty parking lot was nested in the center of a U the building formed. A few lampposts illuminated about a dozen cars, with shadows from the brick walls around the lot making the place look desperate... like a scene in a noir film. The rain made the blacktop appear liquid.

"Won't Dr. Lawton disapprove of this?" Annja paused just outside the back door. "You showing me this sword?"

Archard turned and looked at her, more emotion on his face. Was it anger? It melted back behind the stoic mask. "God-touched sword, Miss Creed. My mistake. I thought you'd truly want to see it, your connection to the divine and all." He shrugged and shook some strands of hair out of his eyes. "I rescind my offer."

"Dr. Lawton—"

"I do not always agree with him, Miss Creed. I believe in him, and I trust him completely. But I do not always agree." He started to turn. "And the invitation was only for you, not your companion."

Annja hadn't heard Roux come out the back door, but she had picked up the scent of his cologne.

Archard waved. "Good night, Miss Creed." He turned and threaded his way through the cars.

"Wait!" Annja called. "Stay here, Roux," she added under her breath. "Keep an eye out. I don't like this."

"I don't like it, either."

She hurried after Archard, splashing through puddles. "I'm sorry. I didn't mean to—"

He raised a hand dismissively and kept walking.

She watched him, fit but not an athlete. He didn't strike her as someone who would have been able to scale the wall and reach the sword in Rocamadour. Luc or his dead brother were athletic enough.

"Who got Durendal for you?" Annja was practically at his shoulder now. "In Rocamadour? Who stole it?"

She reached out and caught him by the arm. At the same time she felt for her sword, sensing it was poised, ready to appear. "Who stole it?"

He wrenched his arm free and glared at her. Once more the anger quickly disappeared behind the implacable mask. "The sword is mine by right. It's not theft to retrieve something belonging to me." He let out a sigh bordering on exasperation and raised his gaze skyward. Rain pattered against his face. "Your sword. Did you steal it?"

Annja didn't bother to hide her surprise.

"Did you steal it? Or is it yours because of some divine right?" He lowered his head and blinked the water from his eyes. "What does it matter how we come by something that we are meant to have?"

He walked around a four-door navy Renault Koleos, a family man's car. He reached into his pocket and pulled out a key ring, pressing the button and popping the trunk. The trunk light was dim and revealed a piece of dark material. Archard leaned in and pulled the fabric back.

"Beautiful," Annja said. She sought her sword in the otherwhere, grasping the hilt… *Wait,* she told herself.

"To call it beautiful is to insult it," he replied. "Such a word isn't adequate."

The sword had been reforged, the broken point rejoined with the piece that had hung in the cloister in Rocamadour. It had been cleaned, too. The tempered steel blade gleamed, even in the feeble light. The pommel was leaf shaped, covered in gold and decorated with figures in relief. The quillons were lion heads, mouths opened and curved toward the blade.

"Beautiful" *was* inadequate.

"It once belonged to Hector of Troy." Archard's voice had changed, becoming reverent. "It came to Roland by Malagigi. Would you say Malagigi stole it? Did Roland steal it? Does it matter if I stole it? It was meant to be mine."

Annja leaned closer to get a better look. Her breath fogged part of the blade.

"It's not yours."

"God-touched. Did you know that there is a tooth of Saint Peter in the hilt? A saint. God-touched. And though it has bloodied many men, it also has blood in it. Drops of Saint Basil's blood are in the hilt and were put in the steel as it was forged. Blood of a saint. Doubly touched by God."

"Archard—"

"The Blessed Virgin Mary herself, Mother of Christ. A piece of her raiment, her cloak, is in the pommel." He extended his hand and let his fingers play across one of the lions' heads. "Do you know *The Song of Roland,* Miss Creed?"

Annja didn't answer.

"Lords my barons, whom send we, then
To Saragossa, the Saracen den?
'I,' said Roland, 'will blithely go.'"

"And you are Dr. Lawton's Roland?"

Archard continued to quote the poem, caressing the sword, his expression softening his features. Annja wrapped her jacket around her, very aware of her own sword.

"I got the impression you follow Dr. Lawton like a

puppy. But who follows you, Archard Gihon?" She was trying to provoke him. She intended to take Durendal, call for Roux and get out of the rain. Brother Maynard would be pleased to get the sword back, though perhaps disappointed it had been reforged.

Archard persisted in reciting his poem.

"You're nuts, too," Annja said, so quietly she barely heard herself.

She reached for Durendal with her left hand. With her right she grasped her own sword.

At the same moment, Archard grabbed the trunk hood and slammed it down hard on Annja's shoulder blades.

If it looks like a trap, she thought, a lance of misery pressing against her back....

"'Distraught was Roland with wrath and pain,'" Archard recited.

27

She felt like a mouse that had gone after a piece of cheese in a spring-loaded trap. She wasn't broken by it, though, just hurt and upset with herself. She pushed the hood up, whirled, kicked out and connected with Archard to send him reeling. She called for her sword.

"Thief!" she spat. "Worse than a thief!"

He kept himself from falling, stepped back, hands raised defensively, his expression unreadable.

"Roux!" Annja shouted. "Trap!"

A car door opened and slammed, followed by a second and a third.

Annja pointed the sword at Archard's belly. "We're going back inside." She held her blade with her right hand and with her left reached behind her to the trunk, feeling for Durendal. "And we're calling the authorities. You might think you've got a right to this sword, but you're not Roland."

There was a spitting sound and a bullet whizzed by her head. She spun to put herself fully behind the trunk, using it as a shield and keeping an eye on Archard. A second shot spat by…from a gun with a silencer.

"Roux, look out! There are more of them!"

On her right she heard the sibilant hiss of a metal sword being drawn. A heartbeat later she heard it on her left.

"Put the gun away, Sarah!" someone called from a distance. "We don't want her dead."

"I would have gotten you out to the parking lot one way or another, Miss Creed," Archard said. "But this way you got to see Durendal first. My gift to you."

"Some gift." She was angry at him—the blood-boiling, furious sort of angry. But she was even more upset with herself for following him out here. He didn't have a weapon, so she couldn't use her sword against him, but…she lunged, bringing her foot up and sweeping his leg forward, catching him off balance. As he tried to recover, she raised her sword and brought the butt of it down hard on his shoulder. He dropped to his knees and she jumped out from behind the car. Luc Niveau advanced on her, a sword in each hand.

She hadn't been able to beat him before, on the rooftops in Spain—though that was when he was with his twin. Could she now? There were two more figures behind him, each with a sword.

"This is great." Annja ground her teeth. She looked toward the back of the building, where the light was brighter. Roux had been standing just outside the door, but he wasn't there now. "Roux?" She crouched, avoiding Luc's swinging blades, then jumped back up, slamming the trunk lid to keep Archard—at least temporarily—from getting Durendal. She spotted another man on the far side of the car.

Four swordsmen and Archard, who'd been reaching for Durendal to make it five swordsmen. Too bad he'd pulled his hands away before the hood came down. She might have broken all his fingers. She skittered back a few feet to put some distance between herself and Luc, and to find a car to set her back against.

Four swordsmen and Archard.

And a woman with a gun.

Tough odds…made worse because of Luc. She knew how very good he was. She hoped the others weren't as skilled. They couldn't be; if they were, she was toast. She wouldn't let them completely surround her. At best they could only come at her from three sides.

Where the hell was Roux? He'd fought on her side before.

Luc was approaching from her left. The one on her right was stocky and had a barrel chest. He was maybe five feet tall, counting his shock of spiky hair. Looked like a dwarf. She couldn't make out many other details in the poor light. If their intent was to rattle her, they were succeeding. Big-time.

Annja could see the weapons clearly enough. Luc was still wielding Honjo Masamune and a saber, the fellow on the right a massive two-handed blade that she knew must be cumbersome to hold. Despite the deepening shadows, she recognized it from the picture she'd seen as the missing Wallace Sword. Lawton's "paladins."

"Annja, take care!" At last she heard Roux, but she still couldn't see him. He called to her again, and then she heard the unmistakable sound of ringing metal. Roux was engaged in a sword fight with a foe she hadn't seen.

Roux was good, a paladin of Joan of Arc and a veteran of battles that stretched back through the centuries. With him on her side, somehow...somehow they just might get out of this.

She rocked back against the car, avoiding Luc's next swing. He was using the flat of the blade against her.

She spotted Archard moving to his car again and popping the trunk.

Damn, she was going to have one more swordsman to fight. Five to one. She'd managed that before, she told herself, but not against trained warriors.

The two men closing in behind Luc wore tight-fitting clothes that wouldn't hamper their movements. Maybe students of Luc. The stocky man with the Wallace Sword swung the two-handed blade around his head, creating a dull whistling noise meant to impress and frighten her. If he connected, it would hurt.

In the next heartbeat, Annja decided to take the offensive. She sprinted at the stout man, ducking beneath his arms, elbowing him in the stomach and cursing when she didn't budge him. It felt as if she'd slammed her arm against a brick wall. Spinning around behind him, she brought her sword about, not using the flat of the blade but the edge, slicing at his side and cutting through his heavy vest. She wasn't sure if she'd reached the flesh beneath, but she swung a second time as he turned to face her, connecting for certain this time, rewarded with a spray of blood when her sword cut through his shirt.

"Brûle en enfer!" he screamed.

"I guess that hurt," Annja said. She leaped, landing on the hood of a nearby car and jumping up to the roof. From here she could see Roux—he was engaged with three swordsmen—and she saw the woman leveling the gun at him, trying to draw a bead.

Go ahead and shoot him, Annja thought. *You can't kill him.* But Annja could be killed.

Eight swordsmen. Where were the other four? she thought wryly. Charlemagne had had twelve peers. Was Lawton not able to get twelve misguided idiots to follow him? Or had she killed one of them when she'd pushed Gaetan off the roof in Spain?

"Come down, Miss Creed," Archard called. The other swordsmen were deferring to him and hadn't swung on her since he'd held up his free hand. "You can see that you're outnumbered. You don't need to suffer injury."

A glance at the man with the Wallace Sword and the line of blood across his stomach told her she'd hurt him, but not badly. His face was twisted in fury.

There were a few lights on in the building overlooking the faculty parking lot. She hoped someone would glance out a window and call the police. Lawton's lecture couldn't go on too much longer. Some of the students would surely come out this back door, to their residences. If she could prolong this until somebody called the cops, she was confident her attackers would scatter at the first siren.

"But not all of you," she whispered. "I don't want all of you to run away." Annja wanted to take some of them down, if for no other reason than to cut the number of Lawton's peers.

At the far end of the lot, Roux was still fighting with the other three swordsmen. If the circumstances had been different, Annja would have enjoyed watching him. He was amazing, keeping the three from landing even a single blow. Medieval knights were trained to fight multiple adversaries. Annja had some of that training…and some tricks she'd picked up along the way from her opponents.

"Your poem ends badly," she told Archard. "Roland dies."

"Heroically, for God and for Charlemagne. I don't consider that a bad ending."

In front of the car, Luc tapped his twin swords on the hood. "Don't make this easy," he said.

"Never." Annja leaped at him, clearing the hood, heel out, and catching the side of his head, bringing her sword down and sliding it along his. She jerked the blade, catching the crosspiece of his saber and sending it spinning out of his hand. She vaulted onto the trunk of the next car and skittered up to the roof. The impact dented it, and she hoped the owner's insurance would cover the damage.

A quick look toward Roux told her only two men were fighting him now.

The five swordsmen surrounded the car she was perched on. This time Luc was the one to hang back, cupping his hand against his stomach before stooping to retrieve his saber. His eyes were bright and his expression mean, and he said something to Archard that Annja didn't catch.

"Hey!" The shout came from above them, from someone finally looking out one of the windows. *"Qu'est-ce qui se passe là-bas?"*

"La police! Appellez la police!" Annja hollered. Rarely did she need the cops, but the odds were bad.

And then two more men with swords ran into the parking lot, and the odds got worse.

That made ten, though one near Roux was down. Eleven with the woman, who'd started firing at Roux. She might have fired earlier and Annja just hadn't heard because of the silencer. Were all of Lawton's peers assembled?

"Truly, Miss Creed, let's end this," Archard pleaded. "No reason for anyone to die here."

"Devons-nous garder en sécurité?" the one with

the Wallace Sword asked. *"Ne pouvons-nous tuer et de prendre l'épée de cette façon?"*

"No, we are not to kill her," Archard said.

"But I have no such constraints," Annja returned. "I can kill you. Now…back off and let my companion and me out of here."

"Get her!" Archard shouted.

"This is going to become bloody." Annja slid down the windshield and landed on the hood, swung at a man who looked vaguely Asian, her blade biting into his neck.

His scream was short and terrible. Blood sprayed in a wide arc from the wound, showering her as she dashed forward, trying to take her fight closer to Roux.

"Crescendo!" Archard hollered.

"Crescendo's down?" the woman with the gun shouted. "Not Crescendo!"

"Stop! Stop! *J'ai appelé la police!*" someone called from above.

"About time," Annja muttered. "I hope they get here quickly."

"Company!" yelled the woman near the back door. Sarah. Again she fired at Roux, and Annja wondered if her aim was good and Roux could ignore bullets, or if she was just a lousy shot.

Two down in any event, Annja thought, one each for her and Roux. That left eight. No sirens yet. But a handful of students spilled out the back of the building. A girl squealed. The rest grabbed for their cell phones, some making calls, some taking pictures. *"La police!"* one of them shouted.

"Miss Creed!"

Annja spun to see Archard on the car, drawing Durendal back and sweeping it at her. It caught the yellow light and looked for a heartbeat like liquid gold. Beautiful. The flat of the blade caught her in the midsection, just enough to put her off balance.

Someone else landed beside her on the car, which rocked on its shocks. She crouched to steady herself and stepped sideways so she could keep an eye on Archard and on the other...Luc.

Damn, she didn't want to face the expert fencer with these odds.

"La police est là! La police est là!" one of the students hollered.

"Finish this. Wrap it up." Archard waved to his men and took another swipe at Annja, the tip of Durendal catching her jacket and ripping it, momentarily tangling her in the fabric.

She heard sirens coming along the street on the front side of the building. Three distinct sirens. Tires squealing.

More students were edging out into the parking lot. A campus security officer was shouting at them to keep back as he pulled his gun.

"Don't!" Annja called, but in the cacophony he didn't hear her. She dodged another lunge from Luc. It wouldn't be the flat of the blades connecting anymore.

She easily sidestepped Archard's attack; he wasn't in Luc's league. Out of the corner of her eye, she saw Roux clock one of his attackers on the side of the head, dropping him.

And she saw Sarah turn and fire on the security guard. Annja didn't hear the gun, but she saw the result. The man tottered and Sarah fired again.

Students started screaming.

Then the rest of hell broke loose. Three police officers rushed out the back door, Sarah firing on them and taking two down before the third spotted her and raised his weapon. One of the students knocked him down and cheered her on. Sarah fired repeatedly on the downed cop, catching one of the onlookers, too. In the next breath the students scattered, some retreating into the building, the rest madly running in all directions like disrupted ants.

That the swordsmen hadn't scattered with the arrival of the first policemen was surprising. They were either that cocky or that loyal and driven.

A siren screamed louder, announcing a police van pulling into the faculty lot. Annja tried to stay focused on the swordsmen around her, but she was distracted by the students and the police...and Sarah, whom she considered perhaps the greatest threat.

Luc's saber dug into her calf at the same time as Archard landed a blow against her back. The muscles of Annja's legs bunched, and she leaped back toward two cars to use them as shields. But the man with the Wallace Sword grabbed her ankle, pulling her down and reaching up to grasp her sword. She struggled out of his grip. Her freedom was brief.

Luc pursued her, slamming her against the asphalt and driving the heel of his shoe onto her left hand. She felt the bones break, and ground her teeth together to keep from crying out.

Flat on her stomach, she managed to swing at the stocky man, connecting. The sirens continued, the blue lights bouncing against the buildings and the puddles on the asphalt. Police officers shouted for order as the students continued to scream and run in panic.

"A gun!" one of the cops shouted. "The woman has a gun! She—" His words were cut off; Sarah must have shot him, too.

Annja rolled over. On her back and cramped by the confined space, she tried to sweep her blade up, but hit nothing. She struggled to right herself, almost succeeding, but Luc jumped on her arm and drove his heel down on it again. She felt more bones break.

"Stop it!" Archard said. He squatted and held Annja's sword arm down. The three men, squeezed in between the cars, barely managed to keep her immobile. Annja was strong, but they were heavy, and Luc landed his heel hard against her arm one more time. The pain was awful, and she concentrated on staying conscious. "Stop," Archard commanded.

"She killed Gaetan."

"Alive," Archard spat. "We need her alive." He

reached for Annja's sword, but his fingers closed on nothing.

"You can't have it," she told him. "You can't…"

Annja didn't hear the sirens anymore.

28

She registered stiffness, and when she tried to rotate her shoulders to work it out, she discovered she couldn't move.

It was worse than not being able to move; she twitched and pain racked her. A martial-arts instructor once told her that pain is the body telling you that you are still alive.

Annja opened her eyes and saw only shadows. She was tied to an uncomfortable chair, secured so well that her attempts to wriggle free met with failure and only made her feel worse. In fact, she wanted to get the license-plate number of the pickup truck she was certain had run over her.

There'd been too many of them, and they were too good. Annja had fought against swordsmen before, some individuals better than the ones she and Roux had gone against…how long ago? Minutes? Hours? How long had she been out? But there had been too many for her and Roux.

Her fault. She was the one who'd obligingly marched into Archard's trap.

Annja tested her jaw. It was sore, but it moved. Her mouth was dry. She'd been out for quite some time. Was there a part of her that didn't hurt? Her eyelids maybe. *Pain is the body telling you that you are still alive.* Annja felt very alive.

Her leg, which had been healing, was hurting again, and bleeding, though not a lot. She felt the congealed stickiness of drying blood against her leg, essentially gluing the fabric of her pants to her skin. Her neck ached from the way they had tied her to the chair. Her hands were behind her, and she cringed when she tried to wriggle free of the knot again. The cords were tied in such a fashion that even if she called for her sword she wouldn't be able to hold it. It felt as if biting ants were crawling all over her left hand, and she could barely twitch her fingers. At least some of them were broken. She could tell that her left arm was broken, too. How badly? It had happened when she went against the man with the Wallace Sword, and Luc. She'd seen the viciousness etched on his face when he mashed her arm.

Her ribs? A few of them might be broken, too. She should be on a stretcher in some E.R., not tied upright to a chair. She should be anywhere but wherever here was. It had been a while since she'd been beaten like this. Twice now, in a handful of days, she'd been battered to a pulp. Twice Lawton's men had brought her close to death.

Wherever they were holding her felt cavernous. She couldn't see any walls, but it had that big feel to it, reminding her of times she'd spent in caves. The air was still, with no hint of a breeze. She concentrated to pick through the scents. Old wood, oil, dried sweat—hers. A hint of exhaust. She was still in the city.

Was Roux nearby? Had they captured him as well or had he escaped?

Listening, Annja couldn't hear anything at first, and then sounds crept in. The whisper of traffic from a nearby street, a muted car horn, creaking from somewhere overhead. She squeezed her eyes shut, counted to ten and slowly opened them again. More accustomed to the dark, she sorted through the shadows. Blocky shapes, boxes…no, crates. The place was indeed big and cavernous, and given the smells of old wood, oil and now the crates, she figured she was in a garage or warehouse. The creaking was footsteps, but they sounded high overhead, as if someone was walking across a floor or rafters. She tried to crane her neck, but that wasn't happening. Once more she attempted to worry at the rope holding her wrists; whatever held her legs and ankles was even more secure.

Hot needles of pain laced through her hand, and she gave up.

"Annja?" Roux's voice. "Annja!"

"Roux?" She talked in a stage whisper that carried, but hopefully not far enough to alert whoever was upstairs.

"Are you all right?"

No, she wasn't. She hurt terribly, and she was tied up, things were broken. "Fine. You?"

"I am—"

Lights came on, bathing the warehouse in a dull mustard glow. The bulbs hung from inverted tin cones regularly spaced over the assortment of crates, tables and sections of open cement floor. Annja blinked at the suddenness of it and spotted Roux on the floor, tied like a rolled carpet. His face was crusted with dried blood.

Footsteps grew louder, but she couldn't turn to find the source. Three sets, no, four…five…coming down a metal staircase she couldn't see.

"Good morning." She recognized Lawton's smooth voice. "I had expected you to wake up earlier. My paladins must have been a little too rough on you and your friend. Who is he, by the way? He's not willing to speak with us…other than spilling expletives. So rude. Your father? Grandfather?"

Lawton came around to stand in front of her. He'd changed into blue jeans and a long-sleeved turtleneck the color of wet slate. Archard was with him, as well as Luc, his face cut and swollen from the fight with Annja. A third man was new, distinguished looking, but very thin, as if his skin was pulled too tight. The fifth set of footsteps ended behind her. The big man who'd wielded the Wallace Sword?

"Who is he, your companion?"

Annja stared, her eyes daggers aimed at the professor.

"I suppose it doesn't matter," he said. "Now, it is not my desire to kill you. You are not an infidel polluting the purity of France. But you do stand in the way of my City of God, and so I will do what I have to. Unless you cooperate."

"You're mad."

"Touched? Yes, I will give you that. Divinely so. Charged by God and my ancestor with a mission. But not mad. A madman could not be the architect of God's city."

"You don't need my sword to build your city."

"Your sword is mine by birthright, Miss Creed. In effect, you stole it from me, and all I want is my property back. Simple."

"I don't have the sword with me."

He bobbed forward, the move reminding her of one of those glass birds eternally dipping its beak into a vessel.

"My men have watched you, sparred with you. They've seen you pull it out of nothing."

"Pull it out of nothing now," Archard said. His cheek was scraped, and his nose looked as if it might be broken. He favored his right leg. At least she'd managed to hurt him. "Give us the sword and you can be on your way."

"And if you truly think you need a sword in exchange

for yours," Lawton said, "you can choose from extras I have in my armory."

"Though nothing with a name," Annja guessed.

"Nothing God-touched," he corrected. "I explained to you before, Charlemagne—my ancestor, and I can trace a direct line to him—once owned the sword Joan of Arc wielded. I have a right to it."

"To drive out anyone in France who isn't a Christian?" Annja took a leap there, but it made sick sense. His lecture about the City of God, a place only for Christians, and the news from Rouen about dead Buddhists…

"My paladins and I have a lot of work to do."

"Why not go after Charlemagne's personal sword? Or Edward the Confessor's? Is the security for the crown jewels too much?"

He slapped her hard.

"I will have Charlemagne's sword. But I will assign that one to my friend Ulrich. It is yours I intend to wield."

So she had a name for the gaunt man next to Archard—Ulrich. Not that it would do her a lot of good in her current predicament. Yes, names were power. But she was powerless at the moment.

"Crescendo wielded another of Charlemagne's swords," Lawton said. "Now that will be passed along to the next man."

"I got it for Crescendo in Vienna," someone said from behind Annja, someone female and young, judging from the sound. "It's where I picked up mine, Tiew."

The sword of Attila the Hun. Had Annja read about that theft when she was in the hospital? She'd read so much about swords she had difficulty keeping them straight.

"I will arm my men only with God-touched swords. Now, produce yours."

"And you'll let me go?"

"Of course."

"It would be that easy?"

"Yes," Archard replied.

"Annja, do not—" The gaunt man stuffed something in Roux's mouth.

"Of course I will let you go," Lawton said. He had that reptilian look that made her stomach churn.

"Go to hell," she said, bracing herself for the slap she knew was coming.

"Ulrich, please set the stage. She needs a little more persuasion."

"My pleasure." The gaunt man retreated into the depths of the warehouse. Annja heard him talking, his accent hard to place. German? American? He spoke in French to someone, but he wasn't a native. So there must be more people here.

Testing her bonds again, she felt only pain. She suspected all the fingers of her left hand were broken, likely her wrist, too.

The gaunt man returned with two men behind him carrying split boards. She noticed they all wore swords. All except Lawton.

She felt chilled when they arranged the wood around the base of her chair and retreated into the darkness again.

"Sarah, she needs something more suitable to wear."

"Yes, Dr. Lawton."

Annja heard the swish of fabric behind her, and then something was dropped over her and tugged down so her head came through the neck hole. It was an oversize white choir robe, the sleeves empty at her sides. *No.*

"Continue," Lawton said.

"Let me." Luc produced a plastic bottle of lighter fluid and squirted the wood. The gaunt man and his two buddies returned with more wood and stacked it around the chair.

"Maybe we should have a trial first," the woman behind Annja said. "Joan of Arc had a trial, so Annja Creed should…you know…if we want to keep it authentic and all."

"For you, Sarah, we'll have a trial." Lawton propped his fingertips together in front of his chin. "The court of Dr. Lawton and his paladins is called to order. Miss Annja Creed, you are charged with…" His eyes narrowed in thought. "You are charged with theft of my property. My priceless property. How do you plead?"

"Go to hell." She wasn't about to play along with this farce. Besides, she knew he wouldn't kill her. If he wanted the sword so badly, he'd have to keep her alive.

"Guilty," Archard said. "Annja Creed is guilty."

"I pronounce sentence, and that sentence is death. It

shall be meted out immediately." Lawton dropped his hands. "Luc…"

The swordsman lit a match. "For my brother," he said, tossing it on the planks.

Annja's throat tightened as the sound of flames followed. She heard Roux speaking around his gag and thrashing, heard the crackle of the fire. She was in the worst of her nightmares, the chill replaced by a heat that made her heart pound furiously. The wood started to smoke. Old and dry, it was going up quickly.

"Your sword?" The professor gestured, and the woman behind Annja stepped around to the front. She had a fire extinguisher in her hand and a sword strapped to her hip. "Sarah can put the fire out if you'll produce it."

Everyone dies, Annja thought, though she'd expected to have more years on this earth.

The flames grew higher, the heat increasing.

Her choir robe caught fire at the hem.

Through the smoke she saw the men and the woman raise their swords, like she'd seen the crowd do in one of her nightmares. It wasn't a City of God; it was a city of swords Lawton was building.

Annja cried out when the flames touched her legs. She'd only imagined the agony Joan of Arc must have felt when she'd been burned at the stake, and now some nutjob was doing the same thing to her. She tried to rock the chair backward. Maybe if she could get the fire to spread to the cords around her wrists, she could break free.

And then what? Face all these people in another sword fight? She thought of Rembert back in New York, of her producer, Doug, of Garin and Roux. Roux, tied on the floor. He'd survived for centuries. He'd survive this…somehow. And for the second time in his very long life, he would have failed in preventing a woman he was charged with protecting from being put to death by fire.

Annja's throat burned as the fire spread farther up the robe and reached her pants beneath it. She sucked in a smoky breath, hot tears streaming down her face. Then she was coughing uncontrollably as the chemicals from the fire extinguisher hit her and the wood.

The woman Lawton had called Sarah emptied the contents of the fire extinguisher and tossed the empty canister against the concrete.

"She won't give up the sword," Sarah said. "So what do we do next?"

"Luc, Ulrich, put her in a cell downstairs," Lawton growled. "Archard, Sarah, get rid of her companion."

The young woman screwed up her face. "Kill him, right?"

"As painlessly as possible," Lawton said. "Shoot him in the head. Drown him. Your choice, Sarah. As for Miss Creed, maybe she'll have a change of heart with a change of scenery. We'll let her stew for a few hours, and then we'll bring her back. Let's make a more suitable pyre in the meantime."

Annja was carried through a manhole at the back of the warehouse and then bounced down a crumbling set of stone steps. She was in the Paris underground, the tunnels that had brought her to the city in the first place. To shoot episodes for *Chasing History's Monsters*.

Luc pushed her into a cell and slammed an iron door shut behind her, turning a key to lock her in. There was an oil lamp hanging from a peg in the hall, turned so low she couldn't see much of her surroundings.

"Bring your sword out now, Miss Creed," Luc taunted. "I'll take it away from you properly…in honor of my brother, whom you murdered." He spat at her and gripped the bars, his face contorted in anger. "Bring it out!"

Annja was still so tightly tied that she couldn't even manage a sitting position. They'd bound her like a pig to be hauled to market.

"Bring it out!"

She felt for it, at the edge of her mind in the otherwhere. But she still couldn't move her fingers to grasp it. But maybe…

Luc pushed away from the bars. "It is you who will be going to a fiery hell, unless you give the professor your sword. I hope you don't give in. I really hope you don't. I want to see you burn, bitch." He grabbed the lantern off the peg, carried it with him for several feet and then smashed it on the floor.

Then there was nothing but blackness and his retreating footsteps.

29

Roux couldn't be killed, could he? Annja lay on her side in the darkness, wondering what had become of the old man and how Lawton's crew might have disposed of him. He couldn't be killed...he'd lived this long. But could they bury him so deep, or put him somewhere so remote, that he couldn't possibly return? She wouldn't look for him to save her. Annja had learned in her childhood at the orphanage to depend solely on herself. But would she need to save *him*—provided she could save herself?

She summoned the sword, her fingertips touching the pommel behind her. She couldn't hold it, but if she kept in contact with it, the sword wouldn't disappear into the otherwhere. Pain jolted through her limbs as she maneuvered herself so the cords touched the blade. She started working on them, moving back and forth. The steel cut into her flesh. Despite the added misery, she didn't stop.

While she sawed, she listened to water drip and the squeal of rats. No human sounds, no footsteps. Summoning the sword was just what Lawton wanted and was the last thing Annja wished to do. But without the sword, she wouldn't get out of here.

Maybe even with the sword she couldn't. Annja hadn't gotten a good look at the cell she'd been tossed in; she might not have the tools to effect an escape. They'd taken everything from her except her singed and shredded clothes.

It took more than a few minutes, but she finally cut through the cords and freed her hands. New pain pulsed through her, like a rhythmic drum coming up from the fingers of her left hand, thrumming into her shoulder, then her neck. *Pain is the body telling you you're alive,* she reminded herself. Now to free her feet. She sat up, clasping the sword with her right hand; her left was next to useless, feeling as if an elephant had stepped on it. At least she had some sensation in it, even if it was agony.

Her ankles had been bound with rope thick enough to tie a good-size ship to a dock. Part of it was singed, but not enough to make a difference; there would be no wiggling out of it. Annja wondered which one of the "paladins" had managed the knots.

"Be careful that history's monsters don't come chasing you," she mumbled as she put the sword to them and started to cut. "Well, they did more than chase me. They caught me."

She sawed in time to the dripping water, meanwhile straining to hear other things…footsteps, maybe a car or siren…something to indicate how far she was beneath the warehouse. She heard nothing above or below.

The rope finally cut, she released the sword back to the otherwhere. She rubbed at her legs with her good hand, then wriggled around to pull the choir robe off. She waited a moment, breathing evenly and deeply, then stood, gritting her teeth as pain exploded through her left arm.

Damn, but she hurt. This trip to Paris had been largely one misery after another. Annja bent her knees, rolled her head and fought a bout of dizziness.

No matter how intently she stared into the darkness, she couldn't see anything. It was like being in a cave without any source of light. She picked a direction and shuffled forward, bumping into a damp wall. She touched it with the back of her right hand and turned, keeping the wall to her right and inching along. Another wall, and she repeated the process, and then another before she found the bars. Annja pressed her face into a gap between them and inhaled. She smelled the oil from the lantern Luc had broken and the fustiness of this place, rats and their waste, spoiled things she didn't want to think about. She wondered if she'd been near here when she and Rembert and the rest of the crew were filming.

With the fingers of her good hand, she explored the bars. Rusting iron, but strong. After a few moments, she found the lock.

Suddenly, out of the darkness, she saw a hazy glow.

A flashlight beam. Sounded like only one person, in a hurry. She stepped back from the door and pulled out the sword, holding it in her right hand.

Archard appeared in front of the cell, keys in one hand, flashlight in the other. He peered at her through the bars. Saw the sword before she quickly let it go. His eyes widened, but he didn't say anything for a moment. "You are in pain," he finally managed to murmur.

"You think?" Annja's hair was in her eyes. Looking at him was like trying to spot something through tall grass.

"'Distraught was Roland with wrath and pain; Distraught were the twelve of Charlemagne.'"

"Great, your poem again."

"You are more a student of history than myself, Miss Creed. My interest is narrower than yours. Studies did not come easy to me, so I concentrated on one area." He watched her for a moment, as if he expected her to say something. "I've patterned myself after one of my favorite historical figures. Roland, favored paladin of Charlemagne. Did you know that some historians think he might have been Charlemagne's nephew? Roland was a Frankish count, glorified in French epics as well as in Italian stories, where the tellers called him Orlando. Roland sounds better, don't you think? Durendal was his sword, Veillantif his horse, Olivant a horn he blew before going into battle. He was the only man who openly opposed Charlemagne's plans to make peace with the king of the Saracens. He was the last of the twelve peers to die."

Annja remained silent.

"He has decided to kill you. Dr. Lawton," Archard said. "He's going to burn you to death, not just torture you like he did earlier. I am to bring you to him." Her visitor paused. "And he said it would be my honor and responsibility to light the match."

Annja studied him.

"But I cannot abide by that. You are not a heretic or an infidel, and perhaps you have as much right to that sword as Dr. Lawton believes he has."

"I have far more right," she stated.

Archard looked surprised at her comment. "I pray you keep it, then." He put the key to the lock, holding his eyes on hers. "You cannot go upstairs, Miss Creed. You cannot take eleven people armed with swords and guns."

"So the twelve paladins of Dr. Lawton are fully assembled."

"Anew. You killed two last night, between you and the old man. But there were others in his service... waiting in the wings, I guess you would say. And they're assembled to witness your demise."

"If Lawton wants the sword, doesn't he know that killing me—"

"He's decided that with you dead, God will send the sword to another, and that he is the only logical other. He believes it is the only way he can come by your weapon."

"And what do you believe?"

"I believe in him and what he hopes to accomplish. I follow him, as Roland followed Charlemagne." Archard turned the key. "But I do not believe that killing you is what God intended. You cannot take the eleven upstairs, but there is another way out. Through the tunnels." He gestured to his left. "I would hurry. Dr. Lawton will send someone to check on you and me."

Archard opened the door and stepped aside, and Annja rushed him, turning the sword so that the flat of it struck him across the stomach. The air rushed from him and she hit him again. He dropped the flashlight and doubled over, went to reach for his own sword, but she stopped him, raising her leg and kicking at his knee with all the power she could summon. She heard the crack and saw in the dimness the astonishment on his face. He dropped to the stone floor and she dropped with him, rapping the butt of her sword against the side of his head. His leg was twisted at a painful, awkward angle.

She felt for a pulse, relieved when she found it. Dismissing her sword, she fumbled at his waist, freeing his sword belt. Annja had trouble fitting it on, with only one good hand to work with, but finally managed. "I'll make sure Durendal gets back to where it belongs." Next, she pulled the belt out of his pants, fastening it around her chest and cinching it tight to hold her broken hand and arm immobile. Finally, she scooped up the flashlight and shone it down the passage in each direction.

"Let's buy me a little more time." Using just her feet, she pushed Archard into the cell and closed the door, then locked it. She thought about taking the keys with her, but instead tossed them down the hall. It would make it easier for someone to let him out.

One way would take her back up into the warehouse, and that's where she wanted to go. Annja wanted to confront Lawton with her weapon in hand. But Archard said there were eleven with him, certainly all with swords…how many of them stolen? For a madman's insane plan.

She picked the other direction, trusting that Archard was right and that there was another way out through the tunnels. The corridor narrowed and curved, angled down and split like a snake's tongue. The air was still, with nothing stirring to give her a clue. She chose to go right, moving faster now and barely stopping in time to avoid a break in the stone beneath her feet. Annja shone the flashlight into the hole. There was a chamber beneath, a stack of small crates against the wall, and to make life easy for her, there was a rope ladder dangling down.

"Convenient." Maybe too convenient. *If it looks like a trap…* But she had a bum arm, and she needed to put distance between herself and Lawton and his paladins.

It would be the way to go, deeper under Paris. The

tunnels wound their way throughout the city and would eventually take her to freedom.

Then she would go looking for Roux.

30

They'd taken her watch and her cell phone, so she had
no clue what time it was, how many hours had passed.
And she had no way to call for help. She was tired, but
her fatigue wasn't an accurate measure of the passage of
time. It could be noon, for all she knew. She didn't know
where she was, either, other than somewhere under a
warehouse that was somewhere in Paris. And that it
was cold here.

Annja would have to confront Lawton again, but
when the odds were better, when she had help.

A tunnel led away from the chamber and she directed the flashlight down it. She had no choice. It was
the only path available to her without having to go back
up a level and try a different route. But she knew there
would be others; the tunnels beneath the city were a
maze of passages and caverns.

Something made her pause.

The crates.

They were wood, each about a foot square. Nothing
stamped on them. Why not keep them in the warehouse

upstairs? They would be harder to get at down here…
but also harder to find. Wine that someone wanted kept
chilled? She set the flashlight on one and reached for
her sword, using it to pry the top off another—not an
easy task with one hand. This could waste a few precious minutes, but might be important. It was the archaeologist in her, Annja thought, always looking to
unearth some treasure or clue, even though she should
be hightailing it out of here so she could call the police.

"What the…"

The crate held two silver metal canisters, each the
size of a vending-machine soda can, carefully nested
in packing material. A piece of masking tape served
as a label, written in a Cyrillic scrawl. Annja held
the flashlight closer. She could read Cyrillic—to an
extent—but these words were difficult for her to figure
out. She worked on them like a tot in first grade sound-
ing out syllables.

Tabun. Soman. "What the hell does that mean?"

She set the lid back on and worried another crate
open, while her common sense told her to move along.
Get to the police.

Two more cylinders, marked the same.

A third crate revealed something different. Instead
of cylinders, she found some sort of Mylar container
filled with liquid and labeled with more of the hand-
scrawled Cyrillic on masking tape: *sarin.* The word
froze her. *Cyclosarin* on the other container.

"Oh, hell."

She knew what sarin and cyclosarin were, and tabun and soman were likely of a similar nature. Liquid nerve gas. They were called G-series chemical warfare agents, developed by German scientists, hence the *G* attached to them. Hideously nasty stuff. And that's why they were down here, where it was cool. At room temperature they became volatile. Odorless, colorless and lethal. Enough of it could wipe out entire communities, especially if the wind was blowing...or used surgically, in small indoor places. There were nine crates, and if each held two canisters, that would be eighteen containers of liquid nerve gas.

Why weren't they all the same? Annja almost immediately answered her own question. Lawton likely hadn't been able to get as much as he wanted from one source, hence the different varieties in different packages.

This cleansing Lawton intended...the liquid nerve gas had to be part of it.

Murdering Buddhists and Scientologists with swords had been shocking, attention grabbing. But it had been just a prelude. Annja felt as if she'd just been dropped in ice water.

She really had to get to the authorities now. Right now.

She wished she could take one of the canisters with her as evidence, but no. If she dropped it she'd be dead, and there'd be no way to report her grisly find. And if she dropped it within range of innocent people, she'd be killing more than just herself.

Annja relegated the sword to the otherwhere, grabbed the flashlight and hurried down the passage. She paused when she spotted a discarded miner's helmet, but soon saw that its light was broken, useless to her. Maybe she would come across another in better shape, one that might give her a little more light, so she could see better and move faster and have her good hand free for her sword. Miners' helmets were standard gear for utility workers, tour guides and the cataphiles who delighted in exploring the dark web of tunnels.

She moved on at an almost reckless pace, hoping wandering cataphiles wouldn't come across the crates. Unless they were Russian or Ukrainian, they wouldn't have a clue what the stuff was.

Annja hoped she'd come across a ladder that would lead up to the street. She would call out, hoping there was a cataphile within range of her voice, or some city worker down below, checking the stability of the tunnel she was in...but after she was farther away from the warehouse and the nerve gas. Had Lawton discovered Archard in the cell? Had he sent men looking for her? What had triggered Archard's inexplicable turnaround? As if she'd believed it.

The next time the tunnel split, Annja took the wider route, where she could move faster. But after a hundred yards, she came to a mound of rubble where a section of wall had collapsed. Retracing her steps, she took the other branch, its tight corridor slowing her. She had to turn sideways and squeeze through. Maybe Lawton had caused the collapse in the other tunnel, to keep people from discovering his nerve-gas cache. Annja had to inch her way through now and twist to avoid hurting her broken hand. She wasn't entirely successful, scraping the back of it and ripping her already tattered shirt. She thought of Roux, to keep her mind off her own predicament. Somewhere, he was all right, she hoped. Or working himself toward being all right.

The tunnel became so tight that the rock dug into her chest, stomach and even her face, adding to the pain that pulsed from her broken arm and hand. She was certain she'd have to abandon Durendal—the long sword wasn't helping her in this tight fit. Just when she thought she'd get stuck and suffocate here, she managed to scrape through. The tunnel widened on the other side, and she stopped to catch her breath and aim the flashlight ahead. Nobody in Lawton's cadre was small enough to come this way, even Sarah. Relief washed through Annja. She checked to make sure the rescued sword in the belt at her hip was undamaged.

"Safe," she pronounced. Or as safe as she was going to find herself until she could reconnect with Roux and alert the authorities to all of this. Annja pressed on, training the beam right and left, up and down, looking for other corridors and praying for some form of escape.

"Where the hell am I?" She blew out a breath in frustration. She was thoroughly lost in the arteries of

Paris, one of the oldest subway and sewer systems in the world.

She hollered now, until she was hoarse, but got no response. She picked up her pace and let the worries about the liquid nerve gas and Lawton's prospective targets tumble through her head. Rouen had a Muslim community. In fact, Muslims were found in sizable numbers throughout France. More Buddhists. More Scientologists. More of anything that wasn't Christian…and just how Christian was that?

Two years ago she'd searched some of the limestone quarries located below a cluster of posh boutiques. Annja could picture those old caverns in her mind. Was she near one of them? So far, there was nothing familiar here…. If she could find something she recognized, she could make her way out.

In the early 1100s, when Philippe Auguste was king, he'd ordered extensive quarrying to provide limestone for building ramparts to protect Paris. And who would protect Paris now from Lawton?

The corridor narrowed again and rose, then almost immediately descended again and turned in a serpentine course, doubling back and going ever deeper. After a few minutes Annja found the slope became steeper and slick with water that oozed through a crack in the wall. She had to creep along to keep from falling.

She shivered, not just from the fear of what Lawton had planned with the nerve gas. It was even colder here and certainly quite a bit deeper than when she'd first come below. Her teeth were chattering. The flashlight beam bounced off water droplets clinging to the ceiling. More rivulets ran down the wall ahead. The air smelled of mold, damp earth and old stone.

Annja forced herself on, skidding to a stop when she finally came to a chamber lined with bones. The dead were stacked like cordwood to her right and left. On a shelf that ran around the entire chamber, skulls were perched, staring at her with empty eyes. More than six million bodies were supposedly buried in various catacombs beneath Paris.

Some bodies had been buried down here even before the 1800s, when cemeteries became overcrowded and city officials ordered skeletons to be dug up and dumped into the old quarry tunnels. Archaeologists dated some of the oldest to Merovingian times, others to the French Revolution.

The bones in this chamber were the shade of eggshells and old parchment. Femurs were stacked like logs reaching waist height, and between the puddles that dotted the floor were chips of bone. All of it had a patina that on pottery or art would be considered striking and beautiful.

Annja walked softly, tiptoeing around bone fragments out of respect.

The tunnel continued beyond this place, and Annja had just stepped into it when she heard something—an echo? Laughter? She turned to face the bone chamber again and focused on the sound—of voices seeming to come from the skulls. She caught the gist of a conversation. About nearly getting caught on the way in here.

"Where are you?" Annja whispered. "Who are you?" She cocked her head. The voices weren't coming from either tunnel entrance. Above her? Taking a chance it wasn't Lawson, she yelled for help in French, English and German, repeating the cycle, then stopping and listening again.

She heard laughter, then voices again. She finally realized they were coming from a level or more higher. The skulls were acting as speakers to funnel the sound. Whoever was talking probably didn't hear her, but she tried again, anyway.

Nothing.

"Dammit." She shivered. It was as cold as a wine cellar down here.

Annja's stolen flashlight died. And now it was pitch-dark.

31

"Dammit," Annja repeated.

She needed to get out and report the liquid nerve gas. "Hey!" she screamed. "Help!"

She dropped the useless flashlight and groped behind her, running her fingers over smooth bones and broken bones, getting momentarily tangled in a rib cage, then finding stone. She traced it—the lip of the passage that would lead who knew where. Running her hand along the wall, she tentatively moved forward. At first she stepped cautiously. Exploring the Paris underground was more dangerous than caving. So many sections had collapsed, and gaps had opened in floors leading to still deeper chambers. One misstep could send her into oblivion...and then no one would learn about the nerve gas until it was too late.

The passage narrowed, so much that Annja scraped her shoulders. She went about a dozen steps before it widened and she couldn't touch both walls at the same time. Another chamber. "Hello?" Her voice didn't echo back. She chose to go right, walking that way until she encountered something. Stone, then more bones. Her fingers fluttered up and down; the bones reached from floor to ceiling, feeling as if they were stacked in order, with the largest on the bottom, the skulls at the top. Some were small and fragile, including the skull of an infant.

She continued cautiously, probing ahead with her fingers and feet, finding a mound of…something on the floor and working her way around it. A crunching sound signaled that she'd walked across small bones. They stretched for a few yards, then her feet found stone again.

"Hello!" she called out. *"Bonjour! Allô!"*

Nothing.

"Anyone here?" A pause.

She listened and tried again.

"I need help! *Au secours!*"

There was no answer.

Though it was difficult to guess the passing of time, Annja was certain she'd been down here at least an hour. Her teeth continued to chatter, and she'd touched a spot of wall that had frost on it. She was undoubtedly missing other passages, but she alternated going left and right, feeling bones here and there and then nothing but stone for what felt like another hour. She tripped in a depression, picked herself up and felt large, deep scratches on the wall. Initials: JM & BR. The edges were sharp and stone dust flaked away; they'd been carved fairly recently, by cataphiles, most likely.

"Hello! *Bonjour! Allô!* Anyone here?"

She kicked another helmet with a broken light, a canvas sack. In frustration, she stopped and leaned against the stone.

The cold had seeped into every pore, and Annja's toes were starting to go numb. It wasn't in her nature to give up or give in, so she counted to nine, the number of crates filled with liquid nerve gas, and struck out again.

After another dozen yards or so, she hit a dead end. She turned around and followed the other wall back to where she'd been, finding with her feet the discarded helmet and canvas sack. She stretched her right arm out, shuffling forward until she found another wall, then worked her way along it. More carvings. She traced them and read "Jesse, be my wife."

Annja felt a measure of relief at the evidence that someone had been here. That meant there was a way in and a way out, or at least there had been once. She just had to keep hunting.

Two hours, maybe three. She had to have been stumbling around down here at least that long. Her thoughts drifted to Roux once more and then to Rembert safely back in New York. Had he gotten to hold his grandchild yet?

Her fingers brushed against wood. A ladder! It was old, felt rickety, but it was propped against the wall and would take her to a level higher. She stepped on the first rung and then squeezed her eyes shut as a bright light pierced the darkness, coming from behind her.

Annja turned, cupped her good hand over her eyes and opened them. The person held a high-powered camping lantern in front of him. It cast a blue-white glare against the stone and turned the rivulets of water into molten silver.

"I am so glad to see you," Annja said.

"The happiness is mine, Annja Creed. Dr. Lawton will be so pleased with me." The speaker set the lantern down and stepped to the side.

Annja let out a groan.

It was the young woman in Lawton's service, Sarah something or other. Her face and hands were scraped and her clothes filthy and torn. She'd apparently squeezed through the same impossible tunnel that Annja had forced herself through. So Annja had been wrong; there was one in Dr. Lawton's company who could fit.

Sarah smiled and drew a sword from a scabbard at her waist, Tiew, once wielded by Attila the Hun. That must've been as hard to navigate through the narrowest tunnel as Durendal had been.

"Are you going to come back with me?" she asked.

Annja reached for her own sword, wrapping her right hand around its welcome pommel. Carefully, she lowered Durendal to the ground so she could defend herself unhampered.

"I guess that's an answer," Sarah said. "A bad answer. Now I'm going to have to drag your corpse back to the warehouse. Luc taught me everything I know, and if you don't give up, I'm going to kick your sorry ass." She made a gesture with her free hand and then stood en garde. "Dr. Lawton made me leave my gun topside, so I'll just have to cut you up."

Annja studied their surroundings. The ladder, on her left now, was an old one that must have belonged to a painter, spotted as it was with different colored paint. Dirt was caked on some of the rungs, and a scarf was tied to an upper one. And at the top was an opening… where she wanted to be.

The chamber she and Sarah stood in was small, and graffiti had been painted along one wall, a mix of English, French and something that looked Scandinavian. A dozen half-crushed beer cans were strewn under a quasi-Egyptian symbol—someone had tried to spray paint the Eye of Horus but had gotten it wrong.

"What are you waiting for?" Sarah asked. "Afraid? Just hand over your sword and I'll let you leave."

"You'd be a hero, right?" Annja said. She was using these few moments to size up Sarah. The girl had been in the fight earlier, but with a gun. Annja didn't have a good measure of her skill.

Sarah shook her head, her breath like mist. "The only reward I need is to be one of his paladins."

"Christ's disciples, Charlemagne's peers and Lawton's band of idiots."

Annja's insult worked. Sarah charged her, face red with anger and lips working.

32

Annja parried her first blow easily. Sarah was using two hands on her weapon, putting as much power behind the swing as possible. She was pretty strong, and Annja was at a disadvantage, still injured, exhausted and able to use only one hand in the fight. But Sarah wasn't as skilled as the other swordsmen Annja had faced. Her moves were classic but clumsy in comparison to Luc Niveau.

"You should have studied a little more," Annja said. She deflected the next three blows and then attacked, trying unsuccessfully to disarm Sarah. The girl clearly wasn't an expert, but Lawton probably figured Annja an easy target, given how injured she was. He likely thought there wasn't any fight left in her. "Luc apparently isn't a great instructor...or maybe you're just a poor student, Sarah. You couldn't win a match against a five-year-old."

Spittle flew from the young woman's lips and she beat her blade against Annja's faster, with no skill behind the moves now, just anger. Annja parried each

time and then traded a few blows back, always trying
to knock the sword from her opponent's fingers.

"I know what you're doing," Sarah sputtered. "You're
just trying to piss me off."

Annja spun to the girl's side, angling the flat of the
blade against her waist and swinging hard. The way
Sarah screamed made Annja think she might have broken a few ribs. But better that than killing her. Sarah
was young and might find redemption in a prison cell
in Paris.

"How about you just give up?" Annja offered. "I really don't want to hurt you."

"Pig!" Sarah spat. She tried to vary her swings now,
shifting back and forth on her feet, trying to catch Annja
off guard.

"What's Lawton going to do with the nerve gas?"
she asked, continuing to knock away Sarah's blows.
The girl was growing tired, and Annja started to press,
putting her on the defensive. "What are his targets?"

"Nerve gas?"

Was it possible Sarah didn't know about it? Maybe
Lawton kept some—or all—of his paladins out of the
loop.

"The nerve gas under the warehouse." Annja evaded
a few more lunges, then tried to disarm her again. "I
found crates of it."

"I don't know anything about that."

"The cleansing, you know."

"Rouen is for Christians." Sarah was slowing, and

she tried a feint that didn't work. "France is for Christians. It's what Charlemagne wanted, and Dr. Lawton is going to build the City of God that Charlemagne couldn't."

Annja kept her talking, wearing her down, swatting at her already-injured side.

"The cleansing, Sarah. He's going to use nerve gas to kill people. Some Christians might get caught in that. Nerve gas is dangerous."

"Dr. Lawton didn't say anything about nerve gas. And the voices didn't tell me anything, either."

"Voices?" Annja asked, lunging forward and then back. The other woman didn't reply. Too busy trying to catch her breath and fend off Annja's swings.

"But you know about the cleansing."

"Sure." She shuffled to her right. It was like a dance, but she was having trouble keeping up with Annja's footwork. "I've been cleansing. Good at it. No regrets."

"You don't mind killing for Lawton?"

"Buddhists. They die pretty easily. Scientologists. Muslims—"

"All that blood on your hands, Sarah."

"Even got a transgender. No worries, it all washes off."

Annja had had enough. She obviously wasn't going to get more information out of Sarah this way, and maybe the girl really didn't know anything about the nerve gas. But she did know where the warehouse was.

Annja would get that out of her, climb the ladder, make her way out of the tunnels and find the police.

"It never washes off, Sarah. The blood never washes off." She could still see the faces of everyone she'd killed and the image of Gaetan falling off the roof.

"It washes off *me!*" Sarah gritted her teeth, and the muscles in her arms bunched beneath her thin shirt. She stepped back and swept the sword forward, connecting hard with Annja's blade. She swung again, her breath ragged and her shoulders heaving. Another failed feint, another missed swing, and then she jumped back, dropped the sword and pulled a SIG Sauer from the back of her waistband. She leveled it at Annja.

Panting, she walked backward until she was even with the lantern. "Now, I'd ask you nicely to drop the sword, but you made it abundantly clear that isn't going to happen. Your blood will wash off just fine."

Sarah pulled the trigger. Annja leaped and the bullet hit the wall behind her. She dropped and somersaulted toward the girl, daggers of hot pain shooting through her broken arm and down her back. Jumping up, she swung her sword at the gun. But Sarah had shifted and fired again, the bullet whizzing by Annja's head and hitting stone. A third shot and Annja felt her hair move and pain tear at her temple. The bullet had grazed her.

She adjusted her grip on the sword, pulled back and swung again, slicing open her opponent's stomach. The girl's look of horror lasted only a heartbeat, and then she fell dead.

Annja stood over her. "Didn't leave me a choice." She couldn't risk dueling with Sarah any longer. The nerve gas had to be reported.

She stared at the body for a few moments, catching her breath. Dismissing her sword, she retrieved the one Sarah had dropped. She managed to wedge Tiew under her sword belt and did the same with Durendal. Picking up the lantern with her good hand, Annja returned to the ladder and looked up. She held the lantern handle in her teeth, gripped the first rung and started to climb.

The tunnel above was so low she had to hunch over and waddle down its length. She went left at the first intersection, following a trail of food wrappers, an unfortunate sign that people had been this way. Fossils dotted the floor on one side of the passage, while the other was slick mud. The lantern, back in her hand again, revealed a rusty pick stuck in the muddy side, and several feet later, an even rustier horseshoe. A hundred years ago, animals had labored under the streets, hauling stone. Some archaeologists believed that even the Romans brought horses down here to help them haul limestone they'd used to build arenas and bathhouses.

The air was musty now, but Annja imagined that it must have been so filled with dust in centuries past that workers would have choked on it.

Another few yards and she reached a seriously porous section, a length of wall clearly close to collapsing. She knew that very few Parisians living above realized how dicey the foundations of their city had become in places. She'd read about various collapses, one shortly before America had declared its independence from England. Houses and businesses along Avenue Denfert-Rochereau had fallen. Years later there were more collapses, and King Louis XVI ordered crews down to shore up the quarries. They'd started dumping bones there shortly thereafter.

Work continued to this day to bolster the walls of the catacombs. The most recent collapse of note was sometime in the 1960s, when an entire Parisian neighborhood had disappeared into a big hole.

The corridor branched and Annja looked for more garbage, like a bird following bread crumbs.

She barely avoided falling into a dark hole the lantern light hadn't penetrated. Annja caught her foot at the edge of it and tumbled, rolling to keep the lantern from breaking. Then she held it over the hole and looked down. The light didn't stretch to the bottom; it would have been quite a drop. But there were scratch marks along the lip, hinting that somebody had ventured up it. Would have been a tight fit.

Annja picked herself up and continued to follow the passage, seeing more graffiti on the left wall but not taking the time to read it. Soon she came to a pit. It was big, and she had to press herself against the wall and inch around it, shale giving way beneath her toes as she went. Probably what was left of an old well; she saw black water, with an oily residue floating on it.

There was another chamber with bones, this one ar-

ranged like an actual crypt, more orderly and with chalk
notations near some of the remains. Annja resisted the
temptation to read them.

She stopped cold when her lantern revealed a body
facedown in the center of the passage.

"Shoo!" The rats didn't move away until she stamped
her feet. A closer look showed him to be a young man,
probably dead only a day or two, his head crushed by
a rock. Murdered? There was rubble around him, and
Annja glanced at the ceiling. No, part of the tunnel had
collapsed on him. She'd tell the police about this, too.

There was still no way up, but she saw evidence
people had been here in a crushed cigarette pack and a
discarded Coke can. The corridor widened and Annja
blinked to make sure she was seeing correctly. Limestone blocks had been carefully arranged like benches,
with cushions on them, a lawn chair to one side. A
sleeping bag was stretched out across other blocks, with
two pillows. On the wall behind was a mural, something abstract like Picasso painted in his late years, all
in blues. The smell was different here. The fustiness
remained, but with a hint of apples and cinnamon. She
saw air fresheners spaced throughout the room.

"Home, sweet home." There were niches in the wall,
recently carved, from the look of the sharp edges. Thick
candles sat in them. Another niche contained a big
camping lantern. "And why couldn't the occupant be
home now?" He—or she—would know the quickest
route out of here. A good sign, though, despite Annja

taking issue with the underground being disturbed. She looked for more bread crumbs to follow, taking the middle of three exit tunnels from the unknown cataphile's quarters.

The tunnel finally started to climb, branched again, and Annja trusted her instincts and picked the left one. She was rewarded more than a dozen yards later when it turned and she was struck by a horrible stench. Wastewater coursed through a channel at her feet, and to the side ran a thick pipe that probably carried water for cleaning streets, watering city properties and supplying fire hydrants.

"Yes!" Her light played on a blue-and-yellow sign that dangled from the ceiling: Rue des Rosier. She tromped through the wastewater and headed toward it. A handful of yards ahead, a ladder led up to a manhole cover. Annja knew the street ran roughly parallel to Rue Rambuteau, a large thoroughfare. She had no idea where she'd traveled, not with all the twisting, turning, doubling back, rising and falling. But she knew where she was coming out. Rue des Rosier wasn't very long, and there was a police station nearby. "Yes. Yes. Yes."

The wastewater rose higher over Annja's feet. She was in desperate need of the police, Roux and a hot bath.... Her heart pounded. A good *cleansing*.

She dropped the lantern at the base of the ladder and started to climb.

33

"I'd prefer not to make a habit of this, Annja. Visiting you in the hospital."

Roux stood by the curtained partition to Annja's E.R. bed. She sat on the edge, staring at the cast on her arm the nurse was hooking a sling to. Annja's face was covered in small bandages, as was her right hand. There were more beneath the gray sweatpants and navy sweatshirt a policewoman had loaned her after Annja had stumbled into the station and told the story about the warehouse, the swordsmen and the liquid nerve gas.

They'd believed her. She looked as if she'd been through a war, and had two stolen swords as evidence. More than that, her celebrity gave her credibility; the commander on duty was a regular viewer of *Chasing History's Monsters*. At her insistence, they'd let Annja clean the stink of the underground off in their locker-room shower before driving her to the hospital.

"I'd prefer not to see you battered and bloodied so often."

"You don't look so good, either," she replied, with

a warm smile. Roux's face was scraped and his hands crisscrossed with scabs. She suspected he had worse wounds under his ragged clothes. "Glad you're all right."

He shrugged, looking older to her than ever. Tired. She wanted to ask him if Lawton's men had really tried to kill him, thought they'd killed him. Did they pitch him in a river? Bury him? How had he survived it?

"I'm getting out of here in a few minutes," she said. "I'm not waiting for the doctor. I'm not wait—"

"No arguments."

The nurse looked at her. "You should wait, miss. The doctor will be back in a little while to give you instructions and prescriptions for antibiotics."

Annja didn't say anything.

"Here's a pamphlet about managing your cast. You said you're American? Your doctor will have to take this off in three to six weeks. It's all there in the pamphlet." She pressed it into Annja's hand.

When the nurse left, Annja slid off the bed, slipped into a pair of tennis shoes—provided by a second policewoman with her size feet—and dropped the paper in the wastebasket.

"I'm not waiting for the doctor."

"No argument," Roux repeated. He followed her to the parking lot.

"The police, you told them about the warehouse," Annja said. She didn't ask it as a question.

Roux nodded. "It was one of four warehouses in the area. When I…"

"Recovered?"

"I went back to the area. I wasn't awake when they moved me." He paused again, and Annja filled in the gap. Roux must have come to nearby and found the warehouse district. "Only four buildings were large enough for it to be where we were held. I contacted the police—"

"I didn't see you at the station I went to. I—"

"I didn't go there in person, Annja. But I learned later that you had." His brow was creased in concern.

Had Roux thought they'd killed her? Had he worried that he'd lost two women he'd sworn to protect?

"I didn't know about the nerve chemicals at the time," he told her. "I didn't know anything about what was in the warehouse."

"It was under the warehouse." And how did he know about it now? She hadn't mentioned it to him, only to the police. He obviously had contacts in the department hierarchy that were willing to spill secrets.

"The nerve gas is real. I saw it. Maybe I should have brought a canister with me, I don't know. Lord, but I hope they get it all. Nine crates. What the hell was he going to do with them? What if there were more? What if he had more someplace else? What if—"

Roux turned to face her. "Annja, while you were in the hospital, the police found the warehouse."

She held her breath.

"They didn't find any liquid nerve gas in the tunnel below. Just empty crates."

Annja's knees started to buckle and her mouth worked. "Dear God."

"The police are still there. A sergeant I know will let us in." Roux pointed to a car, small and sleek. Annja wondered if it was his or a rental. "They're still searching."

She hurried toward the vehicle, her mind churning with ugly possibilities. Were Lawton and his paladins going to wipe out every non-Christian in Rouen? If she had her laptop…cell phone…anything, she could search the internet to find temples and gathering places, Muslim and Buddhist leaders, people she could alert. Hopefully, the police officials were already looking into that.

"Rouen…"

"That does seem to be where he plans to create his City of God," Roux said.

"Why Rouen?"

Her question went unanswered.

A pair of officers on duty outside the warehouse demanded Annja and Roux stay back. There was a barricade on the street, an assortment of police cars and SUVs, and a large van that a man in a white hazmat body suit stood beside. There were dogs, too, a trio of German shepherds sitting dutifully by a police car, unleashed.

At Roux's insistence, one of the officers retreated inside the warehouse, returning a few minutes later with a sulky look on his face and waving the two in. "Just don't touch anything," he said. "We're dusting. Understand?"

"Clear like crystal," Roux replied.

The place sent shivers through Annja. In the center sat the pile of wood where they'd started to burn her. A dozen officers moved slowly through the cavernous room. Some took pictures. Others were dusting surfaces for fingerprints. One was in the rafters. A woman who had some authority, judging by her uniform and the patch on her sleeve, came down the spiral staircase, her footsteps echoing. She looked to be in her late thirties or early forties, prim, pressed and all business.

"You can go up," she told Roux, her eyes twinkling.

Annja detected a comfortable familiarity between the two. Perhaps this was Roux's source on the Paris police department…perhaps something more. She decided not to ask as she passed by, detecting the scent of Calvin Klein's Euphoria. She took the stairs two at a time.

"Look, but don't touch anything," the policewoman called after her.

An icy feeling settled in Annja's stomach as she reached the top. The door was not what one would expect to find in a warehouse, not when everything below was cement, corrugated steel and aluminum. It was a black door that looked like the lid of a coffin, with a wreath of dead flowers hanging on it.

"The place of a madman," she whispered. "Don't touch anything, huh?" Well, she had to touch the black doorknob to go in. Her fingers closed on it and she waited a beat. Roux wasn't coming up the stairs. A glance over the rail showed him still talking to the policewoman.

Annja took in a deep breath and went inside.

The room looked like a small art gallery, the furnishings scant but opulent. Brocade cushions padded high-backed chairs carved out of bleached wood; candelabras were filled with fresh candles. Annja stepped onto a thick rug that was shot through with metallic threads. A velvet rope stretched across one section of wall, perhaps to keep Lawton's visitors from getting too close to the paintings. The walls were dark maroon, which helped show off the portraits that hung everywhere. The place was completely incongruous with the warehouse under it.

The largest painting, directly opposite the door she'd entered and lit from above in an ornate gilded frame, was of a well-dressed, middle-aged man with black curly hair past his shoulders. There was a hint of white at his temples and lines around his eyes.

All the dark pictures looked as if they'd been rendered by Old Masters, reminding Annja of Rembrandt's self-portrait. The men and women were dressed expensively—from the 1300s through perhaps 1500. But the large portrait of the black-haired man clearly held the place of honor in the room. She went behind the velvet rope for a closer look.

"Charles Lawton." The portrait was supposed to be of Charlemagne, according to the words imbedded in the frame, but the resemblance to Lawton was unmistakable. It wasn't the same man she'd seen in Paris, in the lecture hall or ordering her burned—Lawton didn't have someone paint Charlemagne with his own face on it—but it was close. The painting looked authentic, and Annja searched her memory for other portraits of Charlemagne she'd seen.

"Dear God. Oh, dear God."

34

That's what had been niggling at the back of her brain when she'd first seen Lawton at the auction in Spain, a sense of familiarity. She *had* seen him before…an echo of him in any event, in images of Charlemagne.

So unless Lawton had hired a plastic surgeon to make himself look like Charlemagne, he could pass for the historic figure's son or brother. Descendant, definitely.

Descendant of Charlemagne, student of Charlemagne and scholar of the man, too. Lawton had apparently built his life around his ancestor. But why try to build his City of God now? Why not a decade ago or a decade in the future? Was there something important about this timing? Or had he been laying the groundwork for a long while? And why was Annja's sword so damn important to his collection?

She turned away from the portrait, but the image of Charlemagne still burned in her brain, except that he had Lawton's white hair. She grabbed her head in frustration and stared at the opposite wall. By the door she'd entered was another striking portrait, this nearly as big as Charlemagne's, but in a less ornate frame. In fact, it looked as if the weathered wood could crumble at any moment.

"Not possible." But somehow she knew it was indeed possible.

Annja had seen images of Joan of Arc. She'd once stood inches from a statue of Joan rendered by the French sculptor François Rude.

But this version of Joan she stood staring at had been in many of Annja's dreams and nightmares, sometimes dressed just as she was in this painting. According to historians, only one portrait was painted of Joan with her sword, and it was lost, likely destroyed in a fire. But it hadn't been destroyed. Annja knew that this was it. A little brass plaque affixed to the frame read Jeanne d'Arc, Maid of Orleans.

Charles Lawton, who had the money to buy ancient swords, finance this warehouse operation and who knew what else, had the lost painting hanging on his wall. It was beautiful, Joan was beautiful, and Annja found herself drawn to the face. Annja looked nothing like her, though Roux had thought she must be related somehow.

The Joan in the painting wore a boy's white shirt, open to midway down her chest, showing off a scar. Through the ages, white had served as an emblem of purity, and here it stood in stark contrast to the dark pants she had on, frayed around the cuffs. She wore men's boots of an old military style. On the ground in front of her was a white banner, again symbolizing her purity. A fleur-de-lis, the French emblem, could be seen on a fold of it.

Her hair was cut short and she could have passed for a boy…probably did on the battlefield.

The sword was in her lap, her right hand holding the pommel. It was Annja's sword—exactly the same. Annja let out a breath she didn't know she'd been holding. A cross, likely bronze from the color of the old oils, rested in Joan's lap as well, partially obscured by the sword. There was an engraving on the cross, but Annja couldn't make it out. The paint had spiderweb-fine cracks in it.

The signature of the artist was also obscured. Would restoration reveal the engraving and the artist? Behind Joan, the image of Saint Catherine's Church in Rouen was hazy, as if a fog lay across the land. What Annja at first had thought were a collection of sticklike trees were actually French soldiers.

She knew the story of Joan of Arc by heart. What she hadn't learned in history classes in school and college she'd gained through her own studies. The patron saint of France had brought the nation together at a critical time and swung the Hundred Years' War in her country's favor.

After a moment, Annja crossed to a display case that contained an ink-drawn map on a piece of parchment. A pencil notation at the bottom read Circa 1400.

Annja had to lean close to make out the details. It was of a village called Domremy. Joan was raised there by her parents—historians think she was twelve or thirteen when she claimed to have heard celestial voices. Sometimes they came with visions of saints: Margaret of Antioch, Michael the Archangel and Catherine of Alexandria. These voices persisted, urging her to help the dauphin to become king of France. She managed to convince him of her divine mission to save the country and was handed troops to command. Later, however, when the dauphin became king, he refused to support her military operations against the English.

Bourguignon soldiers captured her and sold her to their English allies, who in turn gave her to an ecclesiastical court in Rouen. Another map in the case revealed that city in 1400. Joan was held there for more than a year, tried for heresy and finally condemned to death. The sentence was commuted, but later reinstated by a secular court. Joan was burned at the stake in the Old Market Square of Rouen, highlighted on the map by a pen drawing of a campfire.

Annja remembered the feel of the fire licking against her and seeing Lawton's determination through the smoke. Mostly she remembered her terror.

There were other items in the glass case, an old, old book opened to a page of text: "Twenty-five years after the inconceivable slaying of the Maid of Orleans, the church retried her case. This time, they pronounced her innocent." It would be hundreds of years later, in 1920, that she was canonized by Pope Benedict XV.

Under a short sword on display, a plaque read Charlemagne's First Weapon. Not God-touched, Annja suspected, else it would have been in the hands of one of Lawton's paladins. There was a mounting for another sword, however, and it was empty. Was it meant for hers? Annja understood why the professor wished to have her sword. It didn't contain the tooth or blood of some saint, or a piece of the Virgin Mary's robe. But it had been wielded by a saint, Joan of Arc. And more than that, it had once belonged to Charlemagne, Lawton's ancestor.

Annja moved on, noting a few places where the residue from fingerprinting powder remained. She doubted the police knew how valuable some of the pieces in the warehouse were. Maybe they'd find more than Lawton's prints. Maybe some of his followers were terrorists. If the police had found other clues here, they'd likely already gathered the evidence.

Where was Roux? Still talking to the woman officer? Annja hoped he was trying to learn what the police had discovered. She continued her tour of the room, trying to take in everything, to place the people in the portraits on the walls, some of whom bore a resemblance to Charlemagne and Lawton... Relatives?

She'd nearly passed by it, but her eye for detail was sharp. There was a place in the carpet that was rubbed, as if something had sat on it or been moved across it. She squatted and ran her fingers over the weave.

"Don't touch anything," the police had told her. But they wouldn't mind her messing with the carpet, wouldn't even know it; they'd left her up here alone. She smiled. Roux was talking to the policewoman to buy Annja time to explore the place.

"Interesting." She traced the carpet depression back to the wall. "Really interesting." Annja stood and studied it. There was an almost imperceptible break in the paint, at the edge of one of the unidentified portraits. She pushed on the wall, heard a click and smiled when it popped open. "A secret door. How utterly original, Dr. Lawton." It would have been left open had the police found it, and the edges of the panel would have been dusted for fingerprints, leaving some residue left behind. She'd tell them about it on her way out—after she was done exploring.

Annja slipped inside. The size of a large closet, the space had two file cabinets, a toilet and a sink. There were cleansers on the floor and feather dusters, probably used for keeping the gallery clean, and even a portable vacuum that looked to be battery operated.

She started with the cabinets, pulling the bottom door out slowly, cringing when the metal made scraping sounds. For all the money he'd spent on the room and on the swords, Annja thought he could have afforded better file cabinets. She worked quickly. Roux wouldn't be able to engage the policewoman in conversation indefinitely.

Scanning documents, she found little of interest. Term papers mostly, which she would have thought Lawton would have kept in his office at the university. But maybe these were from particularly bright students, ones he could groom into followers. She selected one at random and stuck it behind her back in the waistband of the sweatpants, pulling the sweatshirt over it. In the top drawer she found nothing of note—records on the warehouse, taxes and the like…things the police might have an interest in, however. The second cabinet yielded more student papers. But a middle drawer caught her attention. The first few folders were filled with newspaper clippings and printouts from internet sites about famous swords, where they were being auctioned or exhibited. There were articles on Honjo Masamune, the Wallace Sword, El Cid's Tizona and more. Behind these were blueprints. Annja tugged them out. The first was of the Wallace Monument near Stirling. Another of West Point in New York. A street map of Avignon was wedged between them and fluttered to the floor. The Louvre. Annja bit her lip. Charlemagne's Joyeuse was on display in the Louvre.

How did Lawton get such detailed blueprints? How did he come by anything? she mentally chastised herself. Blueprints for the Tower of London, with handwritten notes about monitors.

"Son of a—" He was going after Joyeuse and the

swords kept with the crown jewels. She knew he would—this was no great revelation, just a confirmation. Obsessed with Charlemagne, and with swords, the professor would insist on having his ancestor's famous weapon. That he hadn't gone after it earlier surprised her. Why not make that his first target? He'd managed break-ins at the Wallace Monument and other museums. Security at the Louvre and the Tower of London would be tenfold compared to what his paladins had previously tackled. Maybe it was the high-level security that had kept him away.

Annja tried to tell herself the Louvre could not be robbed. But she did worry. It had been robbed before.

She looked through the contents of more folders, going faster now. News clippings. She passed by the first batch, but then gave them a quick study. A paragraph in one of the articles was circled. Dated November 7, 2005, it quoted a Muslim rioter talking about revenge for the deaths of two fellow Muslims who were electrocuted while trespassing at a power station: "It won't end until two policemen are dead." The paper clipped to it was a handwritten note with a dozen addresses. Where Muslims were living in Rouen? France had a sizable Muslim population, estimated to be between five and six million.

Another clipping was an article about Jewish communities throughout the world, citing that France had the largest population of Jews in all of Europe. Census estimates put the number at about five hundred thousand, most of them in metropolitan areas…including Rouen.

Folded behind it were a photograph and an article about a Jewish archaeological find in Rouen that experts believed was a yeshiva, a school for Jewish religious studies. The site was uncovered in the 1970s during a restoration project on one of Rouen's court buildings. The site suggested that at one time the city was a Jewish center, and cemented the image of France as a melting pot. The address and tour information were circled; the monument was open to the public. Annja cringed.

There were other clippings, small ones, on a Hindu speed-dating gathering scheduled for next week in a hotel ballroom in Rouen; an upcoming Wiccan gathering in a meeting room at the public library; an approaching lecture by a local Rastafarian. There was a scrawled note about Sikhism and a partial address, but something had been spilled on it, and Annja couldn't make it out.

She could spend hours in here going through every folder, losing herself in the collection of clippings and papers and trying to ferret out Lawton's list of priorities. That would be for the police, though. They were resourceful and could throw enough people at the project to sift through it quickly…if they realized how much of a threat Lawton was.

That he had liquid nerve gas.

The police knew just how serious this was. They weren't stupid.

But she wouldn't leave it all on them. Annja caught sight of herself in the mirror over the sink. She looked like hell. Strands of her hair hung in clumps around her face. She reached up with her right hand and tucked them behind her ears, then picked off bandages the nurse had put on her cheeks; already she was healing underneath. Her broken arm would take a little while, though.

She dropped the bandages in the wastebasket. *Wait.* The police didn't need to think they were clues to anything regarding Lawton. As she bent to pluck them out, she saw an empty pill vial in the basket.

She stared at the mirror, which served as the door to a medicine cabinet. Opening it, she took a quick inventory of the contents. It revealed the usual stuff: aspirin, antacids, Band-Aids, rubbing alcohol and two prescription bottles reading temozolomide and isotretinoin. With no idea what they treated, she pocketed them, to look it up later. Tampering with police evidence, she realized. She'd have to clue them in if this led to anything concrete.

She heard footsteps on the stairs. Poking her head out of the secret closet, she found them growing louder. Annja scampered into the room, gesturing toward the panel door when the policewoman and Roux came in.

The officer's surprise quickly melted into anger. She looked from Annja to Roux. "I think you two should be on your way."

"Certainly," Annja replied. She walked past Roux

and took the stairs two at a time, weighing destinations in her head. The Louvre, the Tower of London, back to Rouen… Where was Lawton going next?

35

"Thank you," she told Roux as she slid into the car beside him.

"Not a problem," he replied. "I always enjoy talking to Beatrice."

Maybe Annja would ask him later about this Beatrice. "Learn anything?"

"Only that the police are taking this dead serious. They believe you about the liquid nerve gas. The description you gave matched other cylinders recovered from terrorist groups in the Middle East. Interpol is sending agents."

"He didn't have a computer." Annja was talking more to herself than Roux, who pulled away from the warehouse and headed north. "Not upstairs, anyway. Paper, though, lots of it. Old-fashioned." She was disappointed in the lack of something she could have searched easily and taken with her...*maybe* taken with her. "Did the police say if they found a computer upstairs?" Perhaps they'd already taken it back to their headquarters.

Roux shrugged. "They carried out boxes."

"Evidence of something."

"This reliance you have on computers, Annja…" He had to brake as a car turned in front of him, the passenger inside bobbing her head and singing to something playing on the radio.

"They make things easy, that's all." She paused. "Do you have one with you? A netbook? An iPad? A—"

He made a tsking sound. "Whatever for?"

"I want to look something up." She stretched back her good arm, pulling the student paper out and dropping it behind the seat to look at later. Then she dug in her pocket for the prescription bottles. "I should have left them for the police. But they've still got an empty one to work with in the trash. I just—"

Roux leaned close, keeping one eye on traffic as he turned into a retail district. Sale signs were plastered across a few of the store windows, garish and bright and meant to attract customers like a fish to a shiny, spinning lure. It was working; shoppers were streaming into the largest place. Left hand on the wheel, he took the bottles from her with his right.

"'Temozolomide,'" Roux read, then sat straight and gave the traffic his full attention. "What's the other one?" He turned the bottle so he could read it.

Annja couldn't make out the dosing information as she tried to read around his fingers.

"They're both prescribed for Charles Lawton," he said. "This one is isotretinoin."

"I want a computer to look them up and—"

"They're cancer drugs, Annja."

Roux's response startled her. "How would you know…"

"I have lost friends through these years," he said. "Not just to sword fights."

Or burning at the stake, Annja thought.

"Temozolomide—Temodar—is prescribed to slow the growth of certain cancers. The other, the same thing. Since he has prescriptions for both, I'd say he has a brain tumor."

"I don't follow your logic." Annja pressed her back against the seat. Her first thoughts were of Roux, that he knew about the drugs. He must have been very close to someone taking them to know their names and exactly what they were for. His personal life was largely a mystery to her, and though she loved to find her way through a mystery…this was one she would leave alone.

"It would explain quite a bit," he said.

"The way he's acting. The obsession," Annja suggested. "The driven single-mindedness and—"

"No." Roux's expression was sorrowful. The sadness was deeply etched in the lines on his face. "It could explain why he's moving so quickly. He's running out of time. But I think the plan was there a long while ago. I don't think a brain tumor has triggered his plan for a City of God."

Annja nodded. "All right, I'll give you that. If he thought he was dying, he would be desperate to build it in whatever time he had left. Charlemagne, after all, died before he could see it happen."

Roux turned left and pulled over to the curb.

"But why Rouen? Why build his city there and not here in Paris?"

He looked at her. "Because the Christians in Rouen got it wrong, Annja, and in the process of building his City of God, he's going to show them how to get it right." Roux paused and pocketed the medicine. "At least, that's why I think he selected that city. A good place to start, eh?"

She pressed herself even deeper into the seat. Roux was talking about Joan of Arc, the trial that had branded her a heretic and had had her burned at the stake. It was the Church—Christians—who had tried her and killed her. Burned her body three times so there was nothing left to bury. They'd taken it back later, a "do over" as it were, and then named her a saint. But they'd gotten it wrong the first time.

"Lawton is getting it wrong, too," she said. "Killing Buddhists and—"

"Scientologists."

She told him about the clippings mentioning upcoming events for Jews, Rastafarians and Wiccans in Rouen.

"Killing everyone who isn't Christian doesn't seem very Christian to me."

"Wars in the name of God haven't always been…" Roux searched for a word and came up lacking. "In any event, that is why I suspect Rouen."

"But we're not going there first."

He raised an eyebrow.

A pair of teenagers strolled by and tapped on Annja's side of the car, asking for directions.

"I've not been to that restaurant before," she said. "Sorry."

They meandered on and stopped someone on the corner, who, judging by his gestures, proved more helpful.

"We're going to Rouen. Well, I am." Annja frowned. "Lawton and his…paladins…will be heading there, and that's probably where they'll release the nerve gas."

"Beatrice said the police in Rouen have been put on alert."

"But I think he's got another stop or two planned first."

Roux scratched at a spot behind his ear. His cuts and scabs from the fight in the parking lot last night had all healed. "The Louvre."

"Yeah, it has to be on his list. He wants Charlemagne's sword."

"La Joyeuse."

"There are others on his shopping list, but from what I've gathered, they're with the crown jewels in the Tower of London."

"No more formidable than the Louvre."

"But farther away. He'll go for Joyeuse first. We didn't leave him a choice, did we, Roux? The police are swarming his place. He's got to speed up his timetable."

"Then why not just—"

"Go to Rouen right away and start cleansing it?" Annja dropped her chin to her chest. "Because he doesn't have a sword. He wanted mine, said Charlemagne had it first. That it should be his. Archard had Durendal. Luc, Honjo Masamune. A big dwarf was swinging the Wallace Sword at me. There were some other blades out in the parking lot last night that looked like they could have come from a museum."

"Tizona."

"It might have been out there, too. It was pretty dark."

"And there was a lot going on."

"Controlled chaos," she said. "I don't think Lawton bought Tizona for himself. For one of his paladins, certainly, but he'd want something with a Charlemagne angle. Whether because he's obsessed with his Charlemagne ancestry or the brain tumor is to blame, he's going after a sword his ancestor used."

Roux pulled out into traffic and turned north at the next intersection. "To the Louvre, then."

"You don't have to go with me," Annja reminded him.

He stepped on the gas pedal. "One never gets tired of seeing that museum."

The Louvre had had its share of thefts. In 1998 *Sevres Road* by Camille Corot was taken from an exhibit room that didn't have video surveillance. Police believed a collector of nineteenth-century Impressionist paintings likely hired someone to make off with the $1.3 million work. In 1911 an Italian worker stole the *Mona Lisa,* which helped make the painting one of the most famous in the world. Only a decade ago officials at the Louvre had acknowledged that a pair of eighteenth-century candlesticks had been stolen, worth about $60,000. They'd been reported missing earlier, but the museum had managed to keep the fact quiet for some time. Auditors discovered that the museum had poor records of just how many pieces of art and artifacts it owned, and that it had been plagued by more thefts than it reported. Word had crept out that even a marble statue had been taken from one of the galleries.

So Annja knew that while the museum's security had improved, it was not infallible, and certainly not what it should be considering the treasures it contained. In its defense, museum staff continued to cite a small budget. Reporters from time to time printed stories about insufficient guards and employees that took coffee breaks stretching into hours.

More than six million people visited the Louvre each year. One of them was going to be Lawton.

Built on the bank of the Seine, the Louvre wasn't a museum originally. It was first intended as a fortress, then a palace and later as a repository for Henry VI's works of art. But it was opened to the public as a museum more than two hundred years ago.

Annja had seen Charlemagne's sword there in passing—twice—but had never stopped to really look at it. She'd been more caught up in the various collections of

European paintings and sculptures. On one visit she'd spent hours in the rooms devoted to Roman, Egyptian and Greek art.

She sat quietly now, watching the pedestrians and traffic, as Roux drove. Her thoughts drifted to Rembert and his grandchild, and to her producer, whom she hadn't contacted for a few days. There was a story here for *Chasing History's Monsters*—about Charlemagne and his descendant Charles Lawton, the collection of God-touched swords and his plans to build a City of God. But it wasn't a story she wanted to film.

It was a story she'd been forced to take a starring role in, and she wanted no part of it.

At the end of the street, she could see a section of the Louvre. Traffic was heavy in this area, with many people heading home from work. The museum would be open for only another hour.

The wing along the Seine, where she would find Charlemagne's sword, was built during the sixteenth century. To get there they would go through the Richelieu wing, which had been added three hundred years later. The most recent addition was the glass pyramid, a controversial project constructed in 1989 by the American architect I. M. Pei. Annja didn't like it. While the pyramid let sunlight shine down into an underground floor, she felt it incongruous to the old, classic feel of the rest of the place.

"…one of the key figures in European history," Roux was saying. "King of the Franks, warred against the pagans and Lombards and Saxons, the Moors. Crowned the emperor of the Western Empire, he was more than a figurehead. Law, agriculture, trade…it all flourished under him."

Annja's right thumb rubbed across the seat belt as if it were a worry stone. "I don't need the history lesson, Roux. I know all about Charlemagne."

Her companion fell silent and found a place to park. They walked the few blocks and paid to get in.

"You've only got an hour," the attendant told them.

"That should be enough," Roux said.

Enough for what? Annja thought. Lawton and his crew only struck at night. But enough time to see the sword…really look at it…figure out how he might approach the theft.

"Watch me be wrong," she said.

Roux cocked his head in question.

"Watch my guess be the wrong one. Watch him go after the swords in the Tower of London or after innocent people in Rouen."

"So you're changing your mind. Women do that."

"No, I'm not. I'm just hoping he doesn't outthink me here and do something else." Annja glanced at her reflection in the highly polished floor. She looked wretched. Hair mussed, no makeup, left arm in a sling and wearing the borrowed workout clothes of a generous policewoman. She looked like someone who had either just finished a jog or was about to start in on some serious housecleaning. No wonder the attendant stared at her.

She started toward the wing where she remembered seeing the sword a few years ago. "First floor, Richelieu wing. Hope they haven't moved it. Should've asked, I guess."

"The French police are good," Roux said. "They have their best people on the nerve-gas hunt."

"Interpol is good, too," she admitted. She didn't have to save the world—or Rouen or Paris, for that matter—all on her own. Annja picked up the pace, the soles of her borrowed shoes squeaking against the floor. They were just a hair too big and her feet slid in them. She felt a couple of blisters coming on, but blisters were nothing next to the aches she couldn't shake.

She passed people who were clearly weary, their rounded shoulders and slow gait indicators that they'd spent hours here. One tall man rubbed his eyes with one hand and the back of his neck with the other. A solid day of museuming, as Annja called it, was hard work.

The sculptures and Old Masters she passed were a blur of colors, the chatter of the other visitors a buzz that she shoved to the back of her mind. Eyes darting everywhere, she tried to find a familiar face—one of Lawton's "paladins." She could have sworn she'd spotted Luc, but a second look showed the black man as tall, but not tall enough. She realized she was huffing and drawing looks from the tourists, so she slowed down, but only a little, never glancing over her shoulder. She knew Roux was there.

Finally, she came to the second room in the Richelieu wing, filled with collections of decorative arts from the Middle Ages to the nineteenth century. Relics from Napoleon glittered for her attention.

"There. Joyeuse."

Annja was struck by the magnificence of the sword.

36

A dozen people milled here. One woman, squat-looking and on the arm of a young man, gave her a passing glance. The rest were men of various ages, enjoying the artistic weapons on display. These weren't simply old military pieces the Louvre put in cases for the public to see. These were ones that glittered and gleamed, as much works of art as the paintings by Picasso, Michelangelo and Renoir.

Why hadn't she paid attention to the sword on her previous trips? It truly was a work of art.

"Belle," the squat woman said as she admired it. Indeed, Joyeuse was beautiful. *"Magnifique."*

A pair of Italian gentlemen stood as close to the exhibit as they could, so Annja had to wait behind them, peering through the gap between them. "The sword of a king," one said.

Indeed, Annja thought.

It was displayed tip down in a thick case, probably some type of plastic.

Joyeuse was one of the most famous swords in the

world. The traditional coronation sword of France, it had been reproduced by weapons makers everywhere and hung across fireplaces.

"He already has the saber, you know. Charlemagne's." Annja kept her voice low. Roux was at her shoulder. "When I was in the hospital—"

"Which time?"

She scowled. "I researched missing swords. Charlemagne's saber was stolen from the Imperial Treasury in Vienna, the same night—"

"The Hun's sword was taken." Roux looked at her. "I can use the internet, too, you know."

He scanned the dozen people in the display area, none seeming to catch his attention. "This sword is very much a mystery."

"There's some debate if it was actually Charlemagne's," Annja said. "Some say the proportions are wrong to have come from Charlemagne's time, and they argue that after twelve hundred years, the original wouldn't have survived. But the parts…" She trailed off as an announcement came over a hidden speaker, reporting that the museum would be closing soon. A half dozen of the people slowly made their way out.

"Some of the parts are said to come from eight hundred or thereabout," Annja continued. "Others say pieces are from the early thirteenth century. One antiquarian even thought there was Western craftsmanship involved. Another put it at mid-seventh century. I remember reading an article, back when I was studying sword making, that a sword of this proportion would be no earlier than the eleven hundreds."

"So, a mystery." Roux studied the six remaining visitors. "But there is another explanation for the anachronisms, yes?" He asked as if he already knew the answer.

"Yes. Alterations were made to it through the years."

"Very good."

Annja wrinkled her nose. She didn't like it when Roux played the role of teacher. The plaque beneath the exhibit said the sword had been used to crown Philip the Bold in 1270. She stared at the hilt and listened to the Italian men read from a pamphlet.

"'The hilt was heavily sculpted of gold and had been made in two halves resembling a bulky Oakeshott'… whatever that is. 'The grip, decorated with fleurs-de-lis and diamonds, was removed for Napoleon's coronation in 1804. The gold cross bears twin winged dragons with lapis lazuli eyes.'"

The blade glistened in the light of the display case. The scabbard behind it…Annja doubted there was anything left of the original except perhaps bits of gilded silver and the gems. The velvet and gold-embroidered fleurs-de-lis were added in 1824, according to the pamphlet she read over the shoulder of the Italians, for the coronation of Charles X.

Roux was right calling it anachronistic—bits of this year, bits of that decade. But at the sword's heart, its blade…the blade had been dated to medieval times, the ninth century or earlier. It could certainly have been wielded by Charlemagne. Legend said its pommel contained the tip of the Lance of Longinus, which was said to have Christ's blood on it.

"Forged from the same stuff as Ogier's Curtana and Roland's Durendal," said a man standing in the doorway between this room and the next exhibit.

"The museum is closing," a voice over the speaker announced. "Proceed to the exit."

The man in the doorway was the gaunt German Annja remembered from the warehouse. Ulrich. She thought he'd been in the sword fight in the parking lot, too, but it had been so dark she couldn't be certain.

"It is good advice." His voice was clipped. The pair of Italians walked past him, still talking about the sword. "You should be leaving the museum, too." The other four tourists left. Annja and Roux were alone with him.

Annja reached for her sword, feeling the weight of it in her hand. There were surveillance cameras in this room—she'd spotted them when she entered. Whether they worked was another matter; not all the ones in the Louvre did, though the general public didn't know that.

Roux started toward him, but Annja put a hand on his sleeve. "He's mine," she said.

In that same instant, Ulrich reached into his pocket. He was wearing gloves, and he pulled out a mask and held it to his face.

Annja felt the color drain from her cheeks. She tugged on Roux's arm. "You've got to alert security, help get people out of here."

"Annja—"

"Don't argue. Hurry!"

Ulrich stepped to the side as Roux rushed past him, fast for an old man. He hadn't argued with her, though she'd expected it. Maybe by now he knew what was futile.

"The liquid nerve gas," Annja said. "He has some here, doesn't he?" Her heart hammered in her chest. She'd figured he'd be using it in Rouen. But he had enough—eighteen canisters—to use some of it here.

She could see Ulrich smile through the mask, which Annja realized also served as a respirator. His clothes were tight fitting, his shirt a turtleneck with long sleeves, and with the mask, every inch of his skin appeared to be covered. He reached behind his back and drew El Cid's Tizona.

Annja blinked, her eyes watering. They'd gotten the nerve gas into the air ducts. A rotten way to neutralize the museum's security. "Damn Lawton."

"Perhaps." The word was muffled. Ulrich came forward slowly, arms out and the tip of the sword scraping one of the exhibits. "Perhaps Charles will be damned to hell. But you'll be dying first, Miss Creed."

He said something else, but the pounding of her heart drowned him out. Her eyes were watering fiercely, and she found her lungs tightening, the gas seeping inside her. Had Roux gotten out? Warned security? Did he get straggling tourists out, as well?

Nerve gas was among the vicious chemical mixes

considered weapons of mass destruction, outlawed by countries throughout the world.

Annja went on the offensive, lunging and batting away his parry. He could fence, though he wasn't as good as Luc. But he didn't need to be. All he had to do was keep her here long enough. Annja slashed at his leg, slicing through his pants and drawing blood. He was still safe, she realized; this gas probably had to be inhaled to do harm. And it was doing significant harm to her. Already hobbled with a broken arm, she was going down fast. Her vision was failing, no doubt her pupils contracting… She was salivating profusely, lines of drool spilling over her lower lip and stretching to the polished floor. Annja started shaking.

Minutes left, she thought, her chest tight, as if caught in a vise, and every breath painful. Roux was going to lose his second charge, after all. And her sword? It wouldn't be going to Lawton.

She drove the blade forward, catching her opponent's arm. She felt the blade connect with his bone, he was so skinny, and through the mask, she saw surprise. He hadn't hoped to best her with his fencing, but he'd thought she'd fall to the gas. And she was falling, but she was going to make sure he fell with her.

He made a feeble attempt to strike her, Tizona glancing off her cast, cutting only the sling that held it close to her body. Hot pain pulsed from the broken arm, but the sensation gave her the impetus she needed. Falling, she shoved the blade up at an odd angle, sliding the steel between his ribs and finding his lungs. Ulrich's mask filled with blood and he dropped. Annja scrambled over him, releasing her sword and reaching for his mask, shaking uncontrollably and somehow finding the strength to tug it off him. Nausea struck her and she vomited. When it passed, she continued to shake, but was able to press the mask to her face and breathe. She sprawled there, awkwardly strapping the mask around her head with her good arm. *Deep. Breathe deep,* she told herself. Over and over and over.

Annja could hardly see out the mask for the blood, but she couldn't risk taking it off to clean it. She stayed still another minute, two, the shaking stopping for the most part, but her fingers quivering as if they'd been electrified.

She needed a hospital, a decontamination center... Anyone caught in the museum needed one. Had Roux alerted people? He had to have, she told herself as she struggled to her feet. Unsteady, she leaned against the wall, trying to see through the blood-splattered mask. *Decontamination center, drugs...*

She'd been shot, hit by a car, thrown through windows. This was a first for her—being exposed to nerve gas—and not something she ever wanted to experience again. She glanced toward Charlemagne's sword, in its case. It was safe. Lawton wouldn't be— She was driven to the floor by a vicious kick to her back.

She heard a muffled voice, but couldn't make out what was being said. Annja rolled and rolled, putting distance between herself and her new assailant, catching a glimpse of him through gaps in the blood and still not able to make him out. Darkly dressed, every inch of him covered, with a mask similar to the one she was wearing... The sword, though, she recognized: Honjo Masamune.

Annja sprang to her feet, meeting him sideways so her broken arm was away from him. The sword was in her hand. She hadn't recalled drawing it, but it was there nonetheless, and she knocked away his blow. Luc wasn't using two swords today, perhaps pressing his luck getting the one in through security, or because he'd needed to bring other things with him, such as his respirator. Whatever the reason, Annja was thankful she had only one weapon to worry about.

He was quick, and he darted around her, his eyes flitting past her to Joyeuse's case. His leaps and thrusts were perfectly executed, but Annja parried each one. They were designed to wear her down. She was already worn down, as far as she could be and still manage to stay on her feet. Where he stepped lively, she shuffled. Where his posture was perfect, her shoulders were rounded and her back hunched. It was all she could do to keep from throwing up again. A tremor struck her and she gripped her sword tighter, brought it up and knocked Honjo Masamune away once more.

He was saying something, but muffled as it was by his mask and hers, she couldn't understand. She heard only a pounding in her ears and the rasp of her own breath. If he wanted to wear her down, let him try. She had every confidence that Roux made it out. The police would be here soon, with whatever medical force they could bring with them. She would outlast Luc. She would see him locked away in a Paris prison.

More muffled words, probably curses at her for killing his twin. He wasn't merely trying to capture her now, as per his orders in the faculty parking lot at the university. He was trying to kill her. His strokes were stronger and more vicious, and she had to work harder to keep his blade at bay. Annja kept looking for an opening, but he wasn't giving her one. And with her vision impaired because of the mask, matters were grim. She was guessing, and she was moving back, tangling herself in a velvet rope that circled an exhibit, then working herself free. Spinning, she saw him bring Honjo Masamune down on the rope, slicing it like a laser beam would.

Something squawked over the speaker, and she heard sirens. Multiple sirens. Maybe someone outside was using some device to talk through the museum speaker system.

Luc heard it, too, and he moved even faster. There was nothing flashy in his moves; that stuff was for exhibits. A good swordsman worked quickly, with simple actions designed to kill, not entertain. And a good swordsman—or swordswoman—didn't let a match go on any longer than necessary.

It was just long enough. Annja couldn't see clearly,

and she was still racked with tremors, but she'd been able to detect a rhythm in Luc's footwork. He was predictable, after all. Another few minutes to make sure she was right...

He landed a blow against her sword arm. She'd turned, but not fast enough, and Tizona sliced through the sweatshirt. One more pain to master...

He drew back and she fell to her knees, jamming her sword up with as much force as she could find. The blade sank into his stomach and she pushed until it was in up to the hilt. He fell on her, struggling for a moment before she was able to crawl out from under him. She released the pommel of her sword and it vanished, leaving him flat on the marble, with blood pooling around his jerking fingers.

She started to leave, then stopped, turned and peered at Joyeuse through her blood-splattered mask. It was safe. Annja returned to Luc's body and picked up Honjo Masamune, holding it under her arm. She managed to grab Tizona, too. These swords would have to be returned to their rightful owners as well, she thought, as she stumbled out of the room.

She didn't see a soul in the halls. Annja prayed everyone had managed to make it out, though she suspected some museum staff members must have fallen to the gas. Lawton would have considered them collateral damage.

She should make her way to the bowels of the complex and figure out where the nerve gas was released and how many canisters were used. See if she could find a way to shut it down…if there was any of it left to shut down.

She should…but she lurched toward the exit instead, self-preservation kicking in. She made it out of the pyramid to the sidewalk, taking in the police cars and ambulances, the crowd of people kept back by hastily erected barriers, the news crews that were arriving, before two men in hazmat gear took her by the arms. Which was awkward, considering one of her arms was in a cast… and she was carrying two *swords*.

37

They stripped her and put her in a makeshift shower that had been set up in a white tent on the street. About three dozen other museum visitors had been given the same treatment and whisked off to one of Paris's hospitals. Annja didn't have the strength or the voice to put up more than a feeble protest when they loaded her on a stretcher and sent her on her way.

She had a second shower at the hospital, lathered with a sweet-smelling, oily solution, then was dressed in a faded green, drafty gown and assigned a bed in the maternity ward. It was the only empty private room available, and she'd heard someone demand that she get special attention.

A nurse told her they'd thrown away her clothes and shoes. Annja made a mental note to find the policewomen and reimburse them for the loss. A doctor explained that the antidotes they shot her full of were designed to do the opposite of what the nerve gas did. She was no longer salivating, her eyes had dilated and the tremors had stopped. She felt hungry—famished.

There was no sign of long-lasting or permanent damage, the doctor said, though after questioning he revealed that eighteen of the museum staff had died and that more than a dozen of those treated were left with irreversible nerve and brain damage.

Damn Lawton to hell, she fumed. There was little consolation that he'd waited until the museum was closed to unleash the gas. If he'd released it even a few minutes earlier, hundreds could have died.

"The police want to talk to you when you are feeling better," the doctor said.

"In a while," Annja replied. She closed her eyes and waited for Roux. She knew he'd come to visit…and to complain one more time about how tired he was of visiting her in the hospital.

"Three canisters," Roux told her, "in the ventilation system. They covered all the wings of the museum and the lower levels, too." He explained that the body count was higher than originally thought. They'd found more museum staff members in the underground areas… along with one of Lawton's paladins. His respirator hadn't worked.

"Which one?"

Roux shrugged. "He was a short, stocky man."

The one who'd wielded the Wallace Sword.

"He didn't have a sword with him," Roux said.

She suspected he hadn't brought it into the museum, certainly could not have sneaked that by a security guard.

"I recovered Tizona and Honjo Masamune." She wouldn't even begin to wonder how the other two got their swords past security.

"Now recover yourself, Annja. I truly am done with visiting you in hospitals. Depressing places." He turned to leave, but stopped in the doorway. "I wasn't going to tell you this—not until they released you. But…" She waited. In the silence she heard a cart rolling down the hallway outside, the soft squeak of a nurse's shoes and someone saying, "We have a boy." Roux shut his eyes for a moment. "Joyeuse. In the commotion of clearing out the building…someone got away with it."

Damn him all to hell. "So, he won."

"I wouldn't say so, Annja. You cut his forces. He doesn't have the people left to carry out his plan. I'd say that is some measure of victory."

"A small victory," she admitted. "Maybe we've stopped Lawton's unholy war. Maybe he'll just get more swords and paladins."

"And the police recovered a dozen canisters of nerve gas."

"So three more are missing?"

Roux shrugged. "Perhaps. But maybe that's all there was." He pulled the two prescription bottles out of his pocket. "I doubt very much that he has the time to pursue his…unholy war. Now sleep."

She started to argue.

"Promise me you'll spend the night."

Annja made a face. Nerve gas was serious, not like

cuts and broken arms. She felt as if a dozen trucks had run over her, and her stomach was a cauldron being constantly stirred. "At least the night," she said. *I'm not stupid,* she almost added.

"At least."

"I have very good insurance, Roux."

He gave her a faint smile and closed the door behind him.

She groaned, her head foggy. She'd forgotten to ask him to get her laptop, cell phone, something so she could do some digging. The archaeologist in her could never stop digging…even if it was electronic. He'd be back to check on her, she told herself. When he came, she'd have him get her…

A nurse hovered over her, with pills in a paper cup. Annja swallowed them without protest. "More antidote?"

The woman shook her head, and Annja repeated her question in French.

"To help you sleep," the nurse replied.

That was the one thing Annja didn't want to do; she had too many things to think about.

Her dream was dark, the worst yet since coming to France. In it she was Joan again…or rather herself in Joan's place. She was being led through the streets of Rouen, staring at the featureless faces that peered out windows and from street corners. The clanking armor of her escort and the conversations of all those who watched made a blur of sound in which nothing was decipherable, as if a swarm of angry insects was dancing in her ears. The buzz grew painful, punctuated by a thrumming that she realized was her heart beating.

This time she didn't wear shoes. Her feet felt ice-cold, and the ache intensified with each step, as bits of gravel cut into her heels. Then she felt something soft and warm, heard laughter.... She must have walked through animal dung. She couldn't smell anything this time.

Her terror rose the closer she came to the stake driven into the crossroads. It loomed taller than ever before, and as she neared it, she made out features that her mind must have put there...barbed wire wrapped around, jagged pieces of glass sticking out at odd angles. She was thrust up against it, all the hurtful things digging into her arms and back and adding to the agony. She stood on wood planks and watched as twigs, sticks and boards were stacked around her.

In the audience she saw Gaetan and Luc, dressed in fencing outfits. They bowed to her and fitted fencing masks over their faces. Behind them, on crutches, was Archard, whose knee she had broken in the tunnels under the warehouse. His face wore its familiar stoic expression. Sarah was several feet away, rubbing shoulders with a vaguely Asian-looking man. Crescendo. The German... Annja looked this way and that as someone put a barbed-wire necklace around her to keep her from wiggling. There he was, standing next to the stocky man who'd wielded the Wallace Sword.

Where was Lawton?

The conversations continued to buzz. In previous dreams she'd heard people shout at her to repent, yell at the guards to let her go, pray to God for mercy. Where was the cross? Someone was supposed to press a crude wooden cross into her hands, weren't they? And where was her white gown? Or her boy's clothes? She was dressed in the faded green hospital gown. Shouldn't her arm be in a sling? Hadn't she broken it?

Where was Lawton?

The conversational buzz turned into a sustained scream; the faces took on a horrific aspect, looking melted and deformed like the agonized one in Edvard Munch's famous painting *The Scream,* bloodred sky in the background. But the background was not the Oslofjord; it was of the center in Rouen. Annja could see Saint Catherine's church.

Where was Lawton?

Archard stumbled forward, awkward in his use of the crutches, his leg in a cast covered with hundreds of signatures she couldn't read. An unlit torch appeared in his hand; he blew on it like a boy puffing on a birthday candle. It caught fire, and despite the cacophony that raged around her, Annja heard the flames.

Archard set the torch to the wood, and the world became a wall of red-orange, the colors writhing and spinning and changing, as if they couldn't settle on any particular shade. Finally they turned white…which through the ages was a symbol of purity.

Annja poured with sweat.

The fire grew larger and louder and…

"Good. Your fever broke." Roux stood over her, dabbing her forehead with a handkerchief. She felt a surge of relief ease her tense muscles. "I think they want to keep you for several more days."

"One more," Annja said. She healed quickly.

"I brought you some things to read." He pointed to a few newspapers on her bed tray.

"My laptop."

His sigh was dry and long. "Of course, on my next visit."

Annja groaned and settled deep into the pillow.

She'd thank him for that beautiful bouquet of flowers on the stand, too…when he brought her laptop. She waited until he was gone before picking up the first paper.

It was the *Guardian,* and the lead story was about a terrorist attack foiled at the Tower of London. "Police recovered three canisters of cyclosarin," the story read. "Two men were taken into custody in a failed plot to steal arms from the crown jewels exhibit." She skimmed the rest of it, and moved on to the next paper and the next. That morning's edition of the *Parisien* carried a small notice inside about a university professor who had committed suicide last night—Archard Gihon. Indeed, Lawton's paladins had been removed from the equation, Annja thought. Pity, Archard seemed to have a few redeeming qualities, and perhaps he could have made good in prison.

"Lovely flowers," a nurse said when she came in to give Annja her last dose of antidote. "Rather expensive, I'd say. Your admirer has excellent taste."

Annja took a closer look at the arrangement. It was large, filled with Casablanca lilies, gardenias, hydrangeas, lisianthus blooms and a few stems of stephanotis. A very expensive arrangement, it wouldn't have come from Roux....

"May I see the card?"

The nurse handed it to her and left.

"Meet me Thursday, if you are able."

Thursday was the thirtieth of May.

SHE WAITED NEARLY THREE hours in the Old Market Square in Rouen, pacing, sitting on a bench. Annja had decided she would wait all day if necessary.

Scents from the open-air market were thick and pleasant. The old buildings along the street looked somewhat incongruous with the Sainte Jeanne d'Arc Church looming behind her. A nearby memorial marked the spot where Joan had been burned at the stake.

"Did you know, Miss Creed, that in the final moments of her life, Joan prayed for the souls of her executioners?"

"And that her final words were 'Jesus, Jesus'? Yes, I know." Annja had heard him walk up behind her, his feet crunching over the gravel between the bricks.

"Do you ever hear voices, Miss Creed?"

"Like Joan claimed she did?" Annja shook her head. "Not really."

"It would have been marvelous, my City of God."

Annja and Lawton stood for several minutes without speaking, the sounds of Rouen drifting past them. The air was sweet, if tinged with car exhaust. Not a hint of rain. It had rained for so much of Annja's stay in France.

She finally broke the quiet. "Where is Joyeuse?"

"Where Joan found her sword," he said. "I figured that would be apt." He turned so he could look into Annja's eyes. She was nearly his height. "I got to hold it for a while, feel the history and the divinity of it. The blade…it really was Charlemagne's. And it really was mine for a few days."

"Why are you surrendering it?"

He shrugged his big shoulders. Annja could see a difference in the man from when she'd first spotted him in Spain. His color was sallow, his cheeks a little sunken. "I am defeated, Miss Creed—time and my health are my foes, just as they were my ancestor's. The City of God goes unfinished. Perhaps some other descendant will take up the banner."

"I hope not." Her voice was flat.

* * * * *